The Seedlist Handbook

(Second Edition)

Published by:

KASHONG PUBLICATIONS

Box 90

BELLONA, NEW YORK 14415

—

FIVE DOLLARS - SURFACE MAILING INCLUDED

THE SEEDLIST HANDBOOK

The purpose of this second edition of the Seedlist Handbook is to
continue to provide a quick reference to the recent seed listings of
the three plant societies listed below. Four year's seedlists are re-
presented: 1972 through 1975. The new lists added about 2000 names;
those not listed since 1971 are dropped. This unparalleled resource
is open to members of these three organizations whose secretaries are:

> American Rock Garden Society
> Milton S. Mulloy
> 90 Pierpont Road
> Waterbury, Conn. 06705
>
> Alpine Garden Society
> E. M. Upward
> Lye End Link
> St. John's, Woking
> Surrey, England
>
> Scottish Rock Garden Club
> R. H. D. Orr
> 70 High Street
> Haddington, East Lothian
> Scotland

A reference to its family for each genus has been added. An
accepted breakdown of Saxifraga into Sections has been used. Several
new references are added but the total number has been reduced to under
100. Names that could not be identified by a printed reference that
was easily obtainable are omitted. This is not to dismiss them as
erroneous. Any clarification sent to me will be gratefully received.

Those familiar with the current flux in botanical categories sub-
dividing variations below the species level will find no consistency in
the listings in this handbook. Even my effort to conform to the pre-
ference of the author of the cited reference has been upset at times.
One botanist's variety is another's sub-species. Until Hortus Third
is published, no standard cultivar reference is available.

Some short-cuts are necessary to have the maximum of information in a single line description. The first section indicates the habit of the plant according to the following abbreviations:

A - Annual   Gr - Ornamental Grass

B - Biennial   HH - half-hardy

Bb - Bulb   lvs - leaves

C - Corm   P - Perennial

Cl - Climbing Vine   P gr. as A - Tender perennial
                                          flowering in first year
F - Fern   R - Rock Garden Plant
                                  (mostly under 12")
fls - flowers   Sh - Shrub

frs - fruits   T - Tree

Gh - Greenhouse Plant   Tu - Tuber

Additional abbreviations - '_____' - a cultivar

                           X - a known hybrid

                           * - obviously identified or determined by
                               garden trial by B.H.

In the second space approximate height of mature plant is given.

In the third space the outstanding ornamental and distinguishing characteristic is given, most frequently flower color.

In the fourth space the country or area of its origin is given.

The end-of-the line figures are keys to the references, pages 3 to 7; printed materials that give additional botanical or horticultural data. The tracing of names from early in the last century sometimes leads one into a maze and several names found no later than Don, (29), only to re-surface in a Seed List, must indeed have an intriguing horticultural history.

Bernard Harkness

INDEX TO REFERENCES, as keyed.

1. AHRENDT, L. W. A. - Berberis and Mahonia: A Taxonomic Revision.
1961

2. ALLAN, H. H. - Flora of New Zealand. Vol. 1.
1961

3. Alpenglow Gardens, Catalog #47
n.d.

4. ANDERSON, E. B. - Hardy Bulbs.
1964

5. ANDERSON, E. B. - Rock Gardens.
1959

6. BACON, L. - Alpines.
1973

7. BAILEY, L. H. - Garden of Larkspurs.
1939

8. BAILEY, L. H. - Garden of Pinks.
1938

9. BAILEY, L. H. ed. - The Standard Cyclopedia of Horticulture.
1914-17

10. BAILEY, L. H. & E. Z. - Hortus II
1941

11. BAILEY, L. H. & LAWRENCE, G. H. M. - The Garden of Bellflowers.
1953

12. BAIRD, V. B. - Wild Violets of North America.
1942

13. BEAN, W. J. - Trees and Shrubs Hardy in the British Isles, 8th ed.
1970, 73

14. BENNETT, R. - Penstemon Nomenclature.
1960

15. BENNETT, R. - Studies in Penstemon I, 2nd ed.
1959

16. BLOMBERY, A. M. - What Wildflower is That?
1973

17. BLOOM, A. - Alpines for Trouble-free Gardening.
1961

18. BOWLES, E. A. - A Handbook of Crocus and Colchium for Gardens.
1952

19. BUDD, A. C. - Wild Plants of the Canadian Prairie.
1957

20. CHITTENDEN, F. J., ed. - Dictionary of Gardening. 3 vol.
    1956

21. CLAY, S. - The Present-day Rock Garden.
    1954

22. CLEMENTS, F. E. & E. S. - Rocky Mountain Flowers, 3rd ed.
    1945

23. CORRELL, D. S. - Native Orchids of North America
    1950

24. COWAN, J. M., ed. - George Forrest: Journeys & Plant Introductions.
    1952

25. CROOK, C. - Campanulas and Bellflowers in Cultivation.
    1959

26. DAVIS, P. H., ed. - Flora of Turkey. Vol. 1, 2, 4
    1965, 67, 72

27. DAYTON, W. M. - Notes on Western Range Forbs.
    1960

28. DEN OUDEN, P. - Manual of Cultivated Conifers.
    1965

29. DON, G. - A General System of Gardening and Botany. 4 vol.
    1831-8

30. DUPERREX, A. - Orchids of Europe. A. J. Huxley, trans.
    1961

31. ELLIOTT, R. C. - The Genus Lewisia.
    n.d.

32. ENCKE, F. ed. - Parey's Blumengartneri.
    1960

33. FARRER, R. - The English Rock Garden. 2 vol.
    1928

34. FERNALD, M. L. ed. - Gray's Manual of Botany, 8th ed.
    1950

35. FOSTER, H. L. - Rock Gardening.
    1968

36. GENDERS, R. - Bulbs: A Complete Handbook.
    1973

37. GREY, C. H. - Hardy Bulbs. 3 vol.
    1938

38. GRIFFITH, A. M. - Collins Guide to Alpines.
    1964

39. HARDING, W. - Saxifrages.
    1970

40. HARRISON, S. G. - A Handbook of Coniferae & Ginkgoaceae, 4th ed.
    1966

41. HAY, McQUOWN & BECKETT - The Dictionary of House Plants.
    1974

42. HAY, R. & SYNGE, P. M. - The Color Dictionary of Flowers and Plants
    1969   for Home and Garden.

43. HEATH, R. E. - Collector's Alpines.
    1964

44. HEBB, R. S. - Low Maintenance Perennials.
    1975

45. HEREMAN, S. - Paxton's Botanical Dictionary.
    1868

46. Hillier's Manual of Trees and Shrubs.
    1972

47. HITCHCOCK & CRONQUIST - Flora of the Pacific Northwest.
    1974

48. HYLANDER, N. - The Genus Hosta in Swedish Gardens.
    1954

49. INGWERSEN, W. - The Dianthus.
    1949

50. KAYE, R. - Hardy Ferns.
    1968

51. Kew Handlist of Herbaceous Plants, 2nd ed.
    1955

52. KITAMURA & MURATA - Colored Illustrations of Herbaceous Plants
    1964   of Japan.   (Japanese text)

53. KLABER, D. - Gentians for your Garden.
    1964

54. KOMAROV, V. L., ed. - Flora of the USSR.   Vol. 4
    1936 (1968, trans.)

55. MAIRE, R. - Flore de l'Afrique du Nord.   Vol. 5
    1958

56. MATHEW, B. - Dwarf Bulbs.
    1973

57. Mayfair Nursery.   Pot-grown Rock Plants and Alpines.
    n.d.

58. MORLEY, B. D. - Wild Flowers of the World.
    1970

59. MUNZ, P. - A California Flora.
    1959

60. OHWI, J. - Flora of Japan.
1965

61. Park's Flower Book.
1973, 74

62. PERRY, F. - Collins Guide to Border Plants.
1973

63. POLUNIN, N. - Circumpolar Arctic Flora.
1959

64. POLUNIN, O. & HUXLEY, A. - Flowers of the Mediterranean.
1965

65. POLUNIN, O. & SMYTHIES, B. E. - Flowers of South-west Europe.
1973

66. RANDOLPH, L. F., ed. - Garden Irises.
1959

67. RAUH, W. - Alpenpflanzen, 4 vol.
1951-3

68. REED, C. F. - Selected Weeds of the United States.
1927

69. REHDER, A. - Manual of Cultivated Shrubs and Trees.
1947

70. RICE & COMPTON - Wild Flowers of the Cape of Good Hope.
1950

RICKETT, H. W. - Wils Flowers of the United States.
71. 1966 - Vol. 1 - The Northeastern States.
72. 1967 - Vol. 2 - The Southeastern States.
73. 1969 - Vol. 3 - Texas
74. 1970 - Vol. 4 - The Southwestern States.
75. 1971 - Vol. 5 - The Northwestern States.
76. 1973 - Vol. 6 - The Central Mountains and Plains.

77. RYDBERG, P. A. - Flora of Colorado.
1906

78. SALMON, J. T. - New Zealand Flowers and Plants in Colour.
1967

79. SCHENK, G. - Rock Gardens.
1965

80. SHISHKIN & BOBROV, eds. - Flora of the USSR. Vol. 18
1952 (1967, trans.)

81. Siskiyou Rare Plant Nursery Catalog.
1970

82. STEYERMARK, J. A. - Flora of Missouri.
1963

83. STRASBAUGH, P. D. & CORE, E. L. - Flora of West Virginia, 1st ed.
    1952-64

84. SYNGE, P. M. - Collins Guide to Bulbs.
    1961

85. SYNGE, P. M., ed. - Dictionary of Gardening, 2nd ed. Suppl. 2
    1969

86. TACKHOLM, V. & DRAR, M. - Flora of Egypt. Vol. 3
    1954

87. TAYLOR, A. W. - Wild Flowers of the Pyrenees.
    1971

88. TAYLOR, G. - The Genus Meconopsis.
    1934

89. Thompson & Morgan Seedlist.
    1971

    TUTIN, T. G. ed. - Flora Europaea.
90. 1964 - Volume 1.
91. 1968 - Volume 2.
92. 1972 - Volume 3.

93. VAN DERSAL, W. R. - Native Woody Plants of the United States.
    1938

94. WHERRY, E. T. - The Genus Phlox.
    1955

95. PIZZETTI, I. & COCKER, H. - Flowers: A Guide for Your Garden.
    1975

96. HUXLEY, A. - Mountain Flowers in Color.
    1967

97. CLAUSEN, R. T. - Sedum of North America, North of the Mexican
    1975   Plateau.

- DEDICATION -

To the Seed Exchange Directors, past
and present, whose kind appreciation
of the original effort made a second
edition seem worthwhile.

ABELIA - Caprifoliaceae
  chinensis / HH Sh / 3-5' / white fls, rose tinted / c & e China   46

ABIES - Pinaceae
  koreana / T / 20'+ / cones purplish / s Korea   13
    "   f. prostrata - 5'+, horizontally branched   28
  mariesii / T / 50' / needles white-banded / Japan   46

ABRONIA - Nyctaginaceae
  latifolia / P gr. as A / fls lemon-yellow / coastal Calif. & Mex.   9

ABUTILON - Malvaceae
  darwinii / Gh Sh / dwarf / fls orange-red / Brazil   9
  ochsenii / HH Sh / 12' / fls blue-purplish / Chile   13
  X suntense - HH Sh, 2-3', bright mauve fls   (1)
  theophrasti / A / 2-4' / yellow fls, ornamental pods / India   68
  vitifolium / HH Sh / 15'+ / fls purplish-blue / Chile   13
    "   'Album' - white fls   13

ACACIA - Leguminosae
  armata / Gh Sh / 10' / spiny plant, rich yellow fls / Australia   41
  cavenia / HH Sh / to 20' / deep yellow fls, hedge plant / Chile   9
  cultriformis / Gh Sh / 6' / yellow pompons / N. S. Wales, Austral. 41
  cyanophylla / Gh Sh / 18' / fls golden yellow / Australia   9
  farnesiana / HH Sh / 6-10' / deep yellow fls / Texas, Mexico   9
  leprosa / Gh Sh / 5' / lvs willow-like / Australia   9
  myrtifolia / Gh Sh / 5' / pale yellow fls / Australia   16
  podralyriifolia / Gh Sh / 10' / fls yellow / N.S. Wales, Austral.   41
  polybotria / Gh Sh / 15'+ / lvs pubescent, feathery / Australia   (2)
  spectabilis / Gh Sh / 18'+ / golden ball fls / Australia   (2)

ACAENA - Rosaceae
  adscendens - see A. affinis   (3)
  affinis / R / 8-12" / blue-gray lvs; reddish heads / Antarctica   (3)
  anserinifolia - see A. novae-zelandica   (3)
  argentea / R / ground cover / gray lvs / Chile   33
  buchananii / R / ground cover / pea-green lvs, dense / N. Zealand   17
  caesiiglauca / R / ground cover / blue-gray lvs / New Zealand   85
  glabra / R / 2' spread / green to purplish-red fls / N. Zealand   20
  inermis / R / to 2" / lvs grayish or purplish / New Zealand   (3)
  magellanica / R / 5" / glaucous lvs, red stamens / Patagonia   (3)
  novae-zelandica / R / gr. cover / silky lvs, purplish burrs / NZ   (3)
  ovalifolia / HH R / ground cover / larger lvs / Peru   9
  sanguisorbae - see A. novae-zelandica   (3)
  sericea / HH R / 6" / silky lvs, globose heads / Mexico   29

ACANTHOLIMON - Plumbaginaceae
  androsaceum / R / cushion / fls white / Asia Minor   43
  armenum / R / cushion / fls white / Asia Minor   33
  aulietense / R / subhemispherical / pale pink fls / c Asia   80
  creticum / HH R / 1" / fls white / Crete   43
  diapensoides / R / cushion / pale pink fls / Afghanistan   (4)
  echinus - see A. androsaceum   43

(1) - BRICKELL in Jour. Royal Hort. Soc. June 1971
(2) - JONES in Nat. Hort. Mag. 12:1
(3) - YEO in Plants: Wild and Cultivated. 1973
(4) - GREY-WILSON in Quar. Bull. Alpine Garden Soc. 41:4

ACANTHOLIMON, con.
  glumaceum / R / 4-6" / pale pink fls / Afghanistan   35
  gramineum - see A. aulietense   80
  venustum / R / 6" / fls deep rose / Asia Minor   43

ACANTHOPHYLLUM - Caryophyllaceae
  gypsophilioides - see ARENARIA gypsophilioides   *
  microcephalum / Sh / 6-12" / white fls / Iran, Transcaucasia   26
  spinosum - see DIANTHUS petraeus v. noeanus   35
  verticillatum / Sh / to 10" / fls white / n Iran, Turkey   26

ACARPHA spatulata - error for ACICARPHA spatulata   29

ACER - Aceraceae
  cappadocicum / T / 70' / yellow fls / Caucasus, Asia Minor   13
  circinatum / T / 15-20'+ / lvs have good fall color / w N. Am.   13
  crategifolium / T / to 30' / bark white-striped / Japan   13
  davidii / HH T / 30' / green & white bark / China   13
     "   'Forrest's Form' = 'George Forrest' - open tree in habit   (1)
  dissectum - see A. palmatum 'Dissectum'   46
  ginnala / T / 10'+ / may be shrubby / China, Manchuria, Japan   13
  glabrum v. douglasii - T, 18'+, lvs 3-lobed, w N. Am.   46
  griseum / T / 25-45' / orange peeling bark / c China   46
  japonicum / T / 20' / purplish-red fls / Japan   13
     "   'Aconitifolium' - Sh, 9', cut-leaved form   13
     "   parsonsii - see A. j. 'Aconitifolium'   (2)
     "   'Vitifolium' - large lvs, richly colored in autumn   13
  miyabei / T / 30' / yellow fls / Japan   13
  palmatum / T / to 20' / rounded habit / Japan   13
     "   'Atropurpureum' - 15'+, red lvs   13
     "   'Dissectum' - Sh, 4'+, green lvs, finely cut   46
     "   v. heptalobum 'Osakazuki' - 7-lobed lvs, red in fall   13
     "   'Linearilobum Atropurpureum' - finely toothed purple lvs   13
  platanoides / T / 60' / greenish-yellow fls / Europe   13
     "   'Schwedleri' - lvs purplish in spring   46
  rufinerve / T / 30' / blue-white young shoots / Japan   13
     "   f. albolimbatum - lvs white-spotted   13
  saccharum / T / 100' / Sugar Maple / e North America   13
  spicatum / T / to 25' / often shrubby, red frs / e N. America   13
  syriacum / HH T / 10'+ / leathery lvs, evergreen / Syria, Cyprus   46
  velutinum v. vanvolxemii - large tree with large lvs, Caucasus   69

ACHILLEA - Compositae
  ageratifolia / R / 4" / fls white / n Greece   38
     "   aizoon - superfluous (from Anthemis aizoon)   *
  argentea - see A. clavenae   9
  atrata / R / 4-8" / fls white / Austrian Alps   32
  barrelieri / R / 4-6" / silvery lvs; fls white / Italy   21
  chamaemelifolia / R / 9" / white fls / France   45
  chrysocoma / R / 6-8" / fls deep yellow / Europe   17
  clavenae / R / 6" / white fls; gray lvs / e Alps   38
     "   'King Edward' - see A. X lewisii   38
  clypeolata (of hort.) / P / 2' / fls bright yellow heads / ?   85
  coarctata - see A. compacta   (3)
  colbiana - see A. X kolbiana   *
  compacta / R / 6" / tight head of small fls / Bulgaria   (3)

  (1) - KEENAN in Baileya 5:3
  (2) - MULLIGAN - Maples Cultivated in U.S. & Canada. 1958
  (3) - STOYANOFF & STEFANOFF - Flora of Bulgaria. 1943

ACHILLEA, con.
    X jaborneggi - R, 6", fls white, lvs gray-green   (1)
    X kellereri - R, 6", gray lvs, white fls, Bulgaria   38
    X 'King Edward' - see A. X lewisii   38
    X kolbiana - A. clavenae x A. moschata   32
    X lewisii - R, 6", fls light yellow fading cream   85
    moschata / R / 3-8" / fls white, leaf lobes uncut / Alps   67
    oxyloba / R / 4-10" / fls white / Tyrolean Alps   67
    'Pearl White fl. pl. ' - see A. ptarmica 'The Pearl'   85
    ptarmica 'The Pearl' - P, 2½', pure white double fls   85
    rupestris / R / 4-6" / white daisies / s Italy   38
    schurii / R / 6" / white daisies / e Europe   21, 51
    serbica - see A. ageratifolia   32
    tomentosa / R / 6-12" / fls yellow, lvs whitish / n hemisphere   35
        "   v. aurea - deeper colored fls   6
    umbellata / R / 4-5" / fls white, lvs woolly / Greece   9

ACIDANTHERA - Iridaceae
    bicolor v. murielae - HH C, 2½-3½', white fls, Ethiopia   84
    murielae - see A. bicolor v. murielae   84

ACHLYS - Berberidaceae
    triphylla / P / 16" / aromatic woods-plant / nw North America   27

ACICARPHA - Calyceriaceae
    spatulata / A / procumbent / spatulate lvs / Brazil, Argentina   29

ACINOS - Labiatae
    alpinus / R / 12" / fls violet with white markings / c & s Eu.   92

ACIPHYLLA - Umbelliferae
    aurea / HH P / to 3' / yellow-green tussocks / New Zealand   2
    congesta / HH R / compact / fls on 1" stems / montane N. Zealand   2
    crenulata / HH P / to 2' / rather lax tufts / New Zealand   2
    glacialis / HH P / 18" / spectacular plant / N.S. Wales, Austral.   (2)
    glaucescens / HH P / to 6' / lvs glaucous, grayish-green / N. Z.   2
    hectori / HH P / 2-4' / infloresence taller / New Zealand   (3)
    horrida / HH R / to 1' / thick coriaceous stems / montane N. Z.   2
    monroi / HH R / 10" / yellowish fls / New Zealand   78
    scott-thomsonii / HH R / to 1' / hard pungent points / N.Z. in mts.   2
    similis / HH P / to 28" / fascicled umbels, large bracts / N. Z.   2
    simplex / HH R / 2-4" / cream fls, bronze lvs / New Zealand   (3)
    squarrosa / HH P / 3' / sweet-scented brownish fls / N. Z.   78

ACONITUM - Ranunculaceae
    altaicum / P / ? / fls dark violet / w Siberia   (4)
    anthora / P / 12-24" / fls pale yellow / s Europe   90
    X cammarum 'Bressingham Spire' - 3', fls deep violet   85
    carmichaelii / P / 30-36" / fls deep blue-purple / China   42
        "   v. wilsonii - 6', amethyst-blue fls, e China   85
    columbianum / P / 2-6' / fls deep blue / w North America   27
    delphinifolium / P / 2-3' / fls deep blue / arctic Asia & N. Am.   63
        "   paradoxum - included in the sp.   63
    excelsum - see A. septentrionale   90
    ferox / P / 6" to 6' / fls pale blue / Himalayas   35

    (1) - HECKER in Quar. Bull Alpine Garden Soc. 36:2
    (2) - VALDER in Jour. Royal Hort. Soc. Sept. 1964
    (3) - LeCOMTE in Bull. Am. Rock Garden Soc. 31:3
    (4) - SCHIPCZINSKI in Flora USSR. Vol. 7 (trans. 1970)

ACONITUM, con.
  firmum / P / 3-4' / fls blue to violet / c Europe   90
  fischeri - see A. carmichaelii   32
  grandidentatum - see A. senanense   52
  judenbergensis - see A. variegatum   90
  kusnezoffii / P / 3-5' / bright dark blue or white fls / e Siberia (1)
  lamarckii / P / 3-6' / fls yellowish / s Europe, in mts.   90
  lycoctonum - see A. vulparia   90
  napellus / P / 3-4' / fls purple or blue / Europe, Asia   42
    " judenbergensis - see A. variegatum   90
    " paradoxum - see A. delphinifolium   63
    " tauricum - see A. tauricum   90
  palmatum / HH P / 2-5' / fls large, greenish-blue / Sikkim, Garwh. (2)
  ranunculifolium - see A. lamarckii   90
  senanense / P / 2-4' / fls bluish-purple / Japan in alpine regions 60
  septentrionale / P / 3-6' / fls dark violet / nc Europe   90
  tauricum / P / to 3' / fls blue to violet / e Alps, Roumania   90
  uncinatum / P / 3-5' / fls blue; stem weak / ec United States 83
  variegatum / P / 1-6' / fls blue to white, variegated / c Europe 90
    " v. gracile - 4-5', fls blue to white, Hungary (3)
  volubile / P / 3', trailing / fls bluish-purple / Korea, Manchuria 60
  vulparia / P / to 5' / fls yellow / c Europe   87
  yamazakii - see A. senanense   52

ACORUS - Araceae
  calamus / Aq P / 3' / aromatic rhizome; Sweet Flag / Eurasia   34

ACTAEA - Ranunculaceae
  alba - see A. pachypoda   34
  arguta / P / 16-32" / spherical red frs / nw North America 35
  asiatica / P / 16-28" / white fls; black frs / Far East 60
  pachypoda / P / 12-18" / dull white frs / ne North America 35
    " f. rubrocarpa - frs dull red   34
  rubra / P / 18-24" / shiny red frs / ne North America 35
    " f. neglecta - frs glossy ivory-white   34
  spicata / P / 1-2' / frs black / Europe   90
    " v. nigra - see A. asiatica   60
    " f. rubra - red frs   33

ACTINEA angustifolia - see HYMENOXYS scaposa (4)
  "   grandiflora - see HYMENOXYS grandiflora (4)

ACTINELLA grandiflora - see HYMENOXYS grandiflora (4)

ACTINOTUS - Umbelliferae
  helianthi / HH B / 2' / woolly plant; cream fls / N.S. Wales, Aus. 16

ADENANDRA - Rutaceae
  fragrans / HH Sh / 2-3' / rosy fls / Cape of Good Hope 9
  uniflora / Gh Sh / small / light pink fls; aromatic lvs / S Africa 70

ADENOPHORA - Campanulaceae
  coelestis / P / 4" to 2' / fls white, blue, violet / Yunnan 24
  confusa / P / 3' / fls intense blue / China 11

(1) - SHTEINBERG in Flora USSR Vol. VII 1970(trans.)
(2) - HOOKER - Flora of British India. 1875
(3) - VAJDA - Wild Flowers in Hungary. 1956
(4) - DRESS in Baileya 8:2

ADENOPHORA, con.
  farreri - see A. confusa   11
  forrestii - see A. coelestis   24
  himalayana / R / to 16" / fls blue-lavender / Himalayas 32
  khasiana / P / 2' / fls violet / ne India   (1)
  latifolia / R / 1'+ / blue fls, narrowly bell-shaped / Siberia 11
  lilifolia / P / 2' / fls blue, often pale / Europe, Asia 11
  nikoensis / R / 8-16" / fls blue / alps of Japan   60
     " f. macrocalyx - high mt. form of the sp.   (2)
     " v. stenophylla - alpine variety of the sp.   60
  ornata / P / 2-4' / deep blue fls, open trumpet / se Tibet, w China 11
  polymorpha / P / 2-4' / fls pale blue-violet / ne China 11
  potaninii / P / 2-4' / fls violet-blue / w China, Tibet 11
  remotiflora / P / 28-40" / fls bluish / Japan, Korea, Manchuria 60
  tashiroi / R / 4-12" / fls blue-violet / Kyushu, s Korea 60
  triphylla / P / 16-40" / fls blue / Kyushu, Formosa, China 60
     " v. japonica - as above but corolla not constricted, Japan 60

ADENOSTYLES - Compositae
  glabra / P / 15-18" / fls light purple / s Europe 67
  leucophylla / P / ? / white-hairy lvs; pink-purple fls / c Europe 20

ADIANTUM - Polypodiaceae
  pedatum / F / 1-2' / for shade & moisture / n US, s Canada 38
     " v. aleuticum - 4-5", glaucous, Aleutian Isls., Canada 50
  trapeziforme f. pentdactylon - decurved lower lf. margin, tender 20

ADINA - Rubiaceae
  rubella / HH Sh / small / pinkish-purple fls / se China (3)

ADESMIA - Leguminosae
  glomerata / R / scree plant / hairy lvs; small fls / Andes Mts. 21

ADLUMIA - Fumariaceae
  fungosa / A Cl / high / fls white to purplish / e United States 83

ADONIS - Ranunculaceae
  aestivalis / A / 4-16" / fls red / Europe 90
  amurensis / R / to 1' / fls yellow / Korea, Japan, e Siberia 60
  brevistyla / R / to 1' / fls white, striped blue / Tibet, Yunnan 85
  distorta / R / to 8" / fls yellow / Italy 9
     " tenore - Tenore is the author designation of the sp. *
  pyrenaica / R / 12-16" / fls golden yellow / e Pyrenees 87
  vernalis / R / to 8" / fls yellow / Europe 90

AEONIUM - Crassulaceae
  arboreum / Gh / 2-3' / fls bright yellow / sw Asia 26

AERVA - Amaranthaceae
  tomentosa / Gh Sh / 1' / whole plant white-woolly / Israel (4)

AETHIONEMA - Cruciferae
  arabicum / A / to 6" / white or pink fls / sw Asia 26
  armenum / R / 5" / fls pink / e Anatolia, Transcaucasia 90
     " 'Warley Rose' - 6", deep pink fls 43

(1) - SENIOR in Nat. Hort. Mag. 46:1
(2) - TAKEDA - Alpine Flora of Japan in Colour. 1960
(3) - BLACKBURN - Trees and Shrubs in Eastern North America. 1952
(4) - BENJAMIN in Bull. Am. Rock Garden Soc. 29:1

AETHIONEMA, con.
   cordatum / R / to 8" / fls pink, white or yellow / Anatolia   26
   coridifolium / R / 6-8" / fls pink / Lebanon, Turkey   85
   creticum - see A. saxatile   90
   diastrophis / R / to 10" / pale pink fls / Transcaucasia   85
   graecum - see A. saxatile   85
   grandiflorum / R / 10-18" / fls rose to pink / Russia, Iran   85
   iberideum / R / 6" / fls white / Turkey   85
   oppositifolium / HH R / dwarf cushion / fls pink or lilac / Syria   26
   ovalifolium - see A. saxatile   26
   pulchellum - see A. grandiflorum   85
   recurvum - see A. armenum   26
   saxatile / R / 6" / fls white or pink / e Medit. region   90
   schistosum / R / 5" / fls pink / Cilician Taurus   26
   speciosum / R / 6-10" / fls pink / Iraq, Iran   26
   stylosum / R / 12" / fls pink, white or lilac / w Syria   85
   theodorum - see A. iberideum   85
   thomasianum - differs in frs only from A. saxatile   90
   'Warley Rose' - see A. armenum 'Warley Rose'   43

AGAPANTHUS - Liliaceae
   africanus / Gh P / to 2' / fls deep blue to blue-violet / Cape Prov. 85
   campanulatus / HH P / 18" / fls blue or white / Natal   85
   'Headbourne Hybrids' - 2-3', hardy at Wisley, pale to violet-blue   85
   inapertus / HH P / to 6' / fls deep to violet-blue / Transvaal   85
   orientalis - see A. praecox ssp. orientalis   85
      "   albus - see A. praecox ssp. orientalis 'Albus'   *
   'Peter Pan' - HH P, 18", sky-blue fls   61
   praecox ssp. minimus - HH P, 2', pale blue fls, S. Africa   85
      "   ssp. orientalis - HH P, 4', blue fls, S. Africa   85
      "   "   "   'Albus' - white fls   85

AGASTACHE - Labiatae
   anisata - see A. foeniculum   34
   foeniculum / P / 1-3' / fls blue; lvs anise-scented / nc US   19

AGAVE - Liliaceae
   virginica / P / 3-6' / fls greenish-yellow / s & sc United States   34

AGONIS - Myrtaceae
   flexuosa / HH T / 30' / fls white / Australia   32

AGOSERIS - Compositae
   aurantiaca / P / 4-24" / fls burnt orange / New Mexico to Canada   74

AGROSERIS aurantiaca - error for AGOSERIS aurantiaca   *

AILANTHUS - Simaroubaceae
   altissima / T / 50'+ / Tree of Heaven (or Brooklyn) / n China   46

AJUGA - Labiatae
   pyramidalis / R / to 1' / fls pale violet-blue / Europe   92
   reptans / R / 1' / fls blue, rarely pink or white / Europe   92

ALANGIUM - Alangiaceae
   chinense / HH Sh / 6'+ / small white fls / c China   46

ALBIZIA - Leguminosae
   lophantha / HH Sh or T / to 20' / fls sulphur-yellow / w Australia 46

ALBUCA - Liliaceae
  canadensis / HH Bb / to 3' / fls yellow & green / Cape of G. Hope   70
  cooperi / Gh Bb / 6-18" / green & yellowish fls / Cape Peninsula   (1)
  elwesii / Gh Bb / 12" / pale green fls / e Africa   36
  humilis / HH Bb / 4" / fls white with markings / Basutoland   (2)
  wakefieldii - see A. elwesii   36

ALCHEMILLA - Rosaceae
  alpina / R / 8" / fls greenish; lvs silky / Europe   9
  mollis / P / to 2½' / fls yellowish / e Carpathian Mts.   91
  saxatilis / R / rhizomatous / palmate dark green lvs / s & c Eu.   91
  vulgaris - see A. xanthochlora   91
  xanthochlora / P / 2' / fls yellowish / Europe   91

ALISMA - Alismaceae
  gramineum / Aq / on land, 4" / purplish to white fls / n hemisphere 34
  plantago-aquatica - see A. triviale   34
  triviale / Aq / 1-2' / small white fls / US, Europe, Asia   60

ALKANNA - Boraginaceae
  graeca / R / to 1' / bright yellow fls / Greece   64

ALLIUM - Amaryllidaceae
  acuminatum / R / 6-12" / pink, lilac to purple fls / w N. America   84
  affine - see A. vineale   (3)
  aflatunense / Bb / 3-4' / fls rosy-purple / c Asia   43
  akaka / R / 1-4" / whitish fls; glaucous lvs / Iraq, Iran, Turkey   (4)
  albidum - white fls, sometimes reddish tinged   54
          (some plants in cult. under this name are A. flavescens)   *
  albopilosum - see A. christophii   42
  album / P / 18" / pure white fls, hardier than A. neapol. / Italy   36
  altaicum / P / 1-2' / fls yellowish / c Asia   54
  altissimum / Bb / 2-3½' / fls light violet / c Asia   54
  amabile / R / 4-8" / fls deep rose to magenta-red / w China   84
  amethystinum - see A. ampeloprasum   51
  ampeloprasum / P / 16-32" / fls purple or rose / Europe, Asia   86
  amplectens / P / 8-20" / fls white or pink / w North America   74
  angulosum / P / 10-20" / fls rosy violet / c Europe to Siberia   54
  anisopodium / R / 8-16" / rosy fls / Mongolia, Japan, China   54
  ascalonicum - horticultural variant of A. cepa   85
  atropurpureum / Bb / 15" / fls dark red-purple / Hungary to Iran   32
  atrorubens / R / 3-6" / reddish-purple fls / Nevada, California   74
  atroviolaceum / Bb / 2-3' / fls dark purple-violet / c Asia   54
  azureum - see A. caeruleum   84
  beesianum / R / 9-12" / fls bright blue / w China   42
  bidwelliae - see A. campanulatum   (5)
  brandegei / R / 4" / fls white / n Rocky Mts.   76
  brevistylum / R / 8-24" / fls dark rose / n Rocky Mts.   76
  bucharicum / Bb / 1' / pale brownish fls / Afghanistan   (6)
  bulgaricum / R / to 12" / fls white suffused pink / Balkan Pen.   85
  caeruleum / Bb 1-2' / fls deep sky-blue / Turkestan   84
  caesium / Bb / 6"-2' / fls azure blue / c Asia   54
  campanulatum / R / 8-12" / pale pink fls / California ranges   74

  (1) - KIDD - Wild Flowers of the Cape Peninsula. 1950
  (2) - Anon. in Quar. Bull. Alpine Garden Soc. 39:4
  (3) - de JANKA in Herbertia 11 1944
  (4) - BLANCHARD in Jour. Roy. Hort. Soc. April 1970
  (5) - MORTON in Herbertia 7 1940
  (6) - WENDELBO in RHS Lily Yearbook. 1967

ALLIUM, con.

canadense / Bb / to 2' / fls pinkish, or all bulblets / e&c N. Am. 34
   "   v. mobilense - pink fls, filiform pedicels, US coastal pl.(1)
cardiostemon / P / 18-24" / many small deep purple fls / Iran 37
carinatum / P / 16-20" / fls reddish-violet / Europe 54
caspium / Bb / to 1' / fls greenish-violet / Russia (2)
cernuum / P / 12-18" / fls deep rose to purple / North America 42
   " 'Major' - 18", deep pink selection (3)
   " f. purpureum - several shades deeper in color *
christophii / Bb / 1-2' / fls pale mauve-purple / Turkestan, Afghan. 42
condensatum / Bb 1-2' / fls pale yellow / Siberia, Far East 54
cowanii - see A. album 36
cyaneum / R / 9-12" / fls turquoise-blue / China 84
cyathophorum / P / to 18" / fls blue-violet / w China 37
   "   v. farreri - 12-15", fls reddish-purple, Kansu 84
cyrillii / R / 15" / fls white or rose / Italy, Balkan Pen. 10
derderianum / R / 6" / stellate white fls, violet nerved / Iran 54
decipiens / Bb / to 20" / fls pale rosy-violet / Caucasus, c Asia 54
dichlamydeum / R / 4-12" / fls deep rose / California 85
dioscoridis - see A. siculum 56
douglasii / R / 8-10" / fls rose-pink / Wash., Idaho, Oregon 37
drummondii / R / 6-8" / fls white to red, or yellow / sc US, Mexico 74
elatum / Bb / 2-3' / fls reddish-violet / c Asia 54
falcatum - see A. platyspathum v. falcatum (4)
falcifolium / R / 3" / fls pinkish-purple / w North America 84
farreri - see A. cyathophorum v. farreri 84
fetisowii / Bb / 16"-2' / fls rose / c Asia 54
fistulosum / P / 2-3' / Welsh Onion, fls white / plant of cult. 86
flavescens / R / to 1' / fls pale yellowish / Europe, Asia 54
flavum / R / 9-12" / fls bright yellow / s Europe, Turkey 42
   " 'Minor' - 4", found in s Europe & Caucasus 38
   " v. minus - dwarf form 56
   " 'Pumilum Roseum' - dwarf mt. form of A. pulchellum 56
forrestii / R / 4-16" / fls claret-red to purple / w China, Tibet 24
frigidum / R / 6" / fls whitish, rose-veined / Greece 10
fuscoviolacea / Bb / 12-28" / fls dark purple / Caucasus, Iran 54
galanthum / Bb / 8-20" / fls white / c Asia 54
giganteum / Bb / to 4' / fls lilac / Iran, c Asia 84
haematochiton / R / 4-6" / white or rose fls / s Calif., coastal 74
heldreichii / P / 18" / large bright pink fls / Thessaly, Mt. Olymp. 37
hookeri / P / 9-16" / white to greenish-white fls / India, China 37
hyalinum / R / 6-12" / white or pinkish fls / Sierra Nevadas, Cal. 74
insubricum - similar to A. narcissiflorum but umbels nodding (5)
italicum marmoratum - error for ARUM i. m. *
jajlae / R / 8-16" / fls rosy-violet / Crimea, Caucasus, Asia Minor 54
kansuense / R / 4-12" / fls pale blue / Kansu Prov., China 84
karataviense / R / 6-9" / fls silvery-white / Turkestan 42
kunthii / R / to 1' / white or pink fls / w Texas, se Arizona & s 74
ledebourianum / P / to 2' / fls rose / Siberia, Dahuria 54
leocanthum - see A. leucanthum *
leucanthum / Bb / 2-4' / white fls, green-nerved / Caucasus 54
macranthum / P / to 3' / fls mauve-purple / Sikkim 84
macrostemon / R / 3"+ / fls pink, rose, purple / e Asia (6)
mairei / R / 4-5" / fls pale pink / Yunnan 38

(1) - OWNBEY & AASE - Cytotaxonomic Studies in Allium I. 1955
(2) - BLANCHARD in Jour.Royal Hort. Soc. April 1970
(3) - BECKET in Gardeners Chronicle 166:5
(4) - HERMANN in Herbertia 12 1945
(5) - MOORE in Baileya 4:2
(6) - STEWARD - Vascular Plants of the Lower Yangtze. 1958

ALLIUM, con.
  moly / Bb / 9-12" / fls bright yellow / sw Europe   42
  montanum - see A. senescens   54
  multibulbosum - see A. nigrum v. multibulbosum   55
  murrayanum / R / 1' / fls purplish-pink / w United States   (1)
  mutabile - see A. canadense v. mobilense   (2)
  narcissiflorum / R / 8-12" / fls deep rose / Italian Alps   42
  neapolitanum / HH Bb / 8-12" / fls white / n Italian Alps   84
       "   'Grandiflorum' - 12", fls white, larger   5
  nigrum / P / 1-2' / fls white / se Europe   37
    "   v. multibulbosum - with the bulb producing bulblets   55
  nutans / P / 1-2' / fls rose to rosy-violet / Siberia   54
  obliquum / P / 2-2½' / fls greenish-yellow / Europe, Asia   54
  obtusum / R / 2" / fls greenish-white / Sierra Nevadas, Calif.   74
  ochroleucum / R / 10-12" / fls yellow / s Europe   37
  olympicum / R / ? / fls pink or crimson / Greece   (3)
  oreophilum / Bb / 3" / fls purple / Caucasus, Daghestan   33
       "   v. ostrowskianum - 6-8", light purple fls, Turkestan   42
       "   "   'Zwanenburg' - sel. for carmine-red fls   56
  oreoprasum / Bb / 15-18" / fls rose / c Asia   54
  orientale / Bb / 15-18" / starry white or reddish fls / Asia Minor   37
  ostrowskianum - see A. oreophilum v. ostrowskianum   42
       "   'Zwanenburg' - see A. o. v. o. 'Zwanenburg'   *
  oviflorum - see A. macranthum   21
  oxyphilum / P / 12-18" / fls white / Virginia, West Virginia   83
  paniculatum / P / 12-18" / fls rose / Europe, Asia   54
  paradoxum / R / 8-12" / nodding white fls / Caucasus, n Iran   37
  peninsulare / R / 8-12" / campanulate fls deep purple-rose / Calif.   74
  perdulce / R / dwarf / fragrant rosy-purple fls / Neb. to Texas   (4)
  persimile - see A. tolmiei v. persimile   47
  petraeum / P / 1-2' / fls pale yellow / c Asia   54
  platyphyllum - see A. tolmiei v. platyphyllum   47
  platyspathum v. falcatum - 1'+, globose head, rosy-lilac fls, Tkest(5)
  pleianthum / R / 4-6" / fls white / Oregon, Idaho   37
  plummerae / HH P / 1-2' / fls white or pink / se Arizona, Mexico   74
  polyastrum / Bb / 2' / fls magenta-rose / w China   24
  pseudoampeloprasum / Bb / 2' / fls rosy, purple nerved / Caucasus   54
  pseudoflavum / R / 6-10" / yellow fls / Caucasus, Iran   54
  pulchellum / P / 1-2' / fls reddish-violet / ec Europe to Caucasus   42
       "   'Album' - fls white   (6)
  pyrenaicum / Bb / 3' / fls white, green midrib / e Pyrenees   10
  ramosum / P / 6-20" / fls white / Siberia   37
  rosenbachianum / Bb / 2-3' / fls dark violet / c Asia   54
  roseum / HH Bb / 8-12" / fls bright pink / s Europe, n Africa   65
  rotundum / Bb / to 3' / fls purple to whitish / Eu., Afr., Asia   10
  saxatile / P / 9-20" / fls pale rose / c Europe, c Asia   54
  schoenoprasum / R / 6-9" / fls pale lilac / n hemisphere   42
       "   'Album' - white fls   32
       "   sibiricum - included in the sp.   63
  schubertii / HH Bb / to 1' / fls whitish or rosy / e Medit. region   54

(1) - BECKET in Gardeners Chronicle 166:5
(2) - OWNBEY & AASE - Cytotaxonomic Studies in Allium I. 1955
(3) - WATSON in Quar. Bull. Alpine Garden Soc. 39:4
(4) - HOWARD in Herbertia (Plant Life 16) 1960
(5) - HERMANN in Herbertia 12 1945
(6) - BLANCHARD in Jour. Royal Hort. Soc. April 1970

ALLIUM, con.
  senescens / P / 1-2' / fls rose to violet / w Europe to Manchuria   54
    "   'Altai-Sayan' - 12", fls rosy-violet, c Asia   54
    "   v. glaucum - 10", fls lavender-pink, Far East   35
    "   v. montanum - 18-24", fls light to dark rose, Europe   54
    "   petraeum - see A. petraeum   54
  sibiricum - see A. schoenoprasum   63
  siculum / Bb / to 3' / greenish-blue & maroon fls / s Europe   56
  sikkimense / R / 9-10" / fls purplish-blue / Sikkim   37
  simillimum / R / 3-4" / fls pinkish-white / Idaho, Montana   76
  siskiyouensis / R / 1-3" / fls rose or paler / n Calif., s Oregon   75
  sphaerocephalum / P / 1-2' / fls dark purple / Europe, Asia Minor   84
  stellatum / P / to 18" / fls rose-tinted / nc North America   71
  stipitatum / P / 2-3' / fls lilac / c Asia   54
  suavolens / R / 8" / fls white flushed purple / c & s Europe   37
  subhirsutum / HH Bb / 8-15" / fls white / Medit. region   64
  tanguticum / R / 6-8" / fls bluish-lilac / w China   37
  tel-avivense / HH Bb / 6-10" / fls lilac / Israel, Syria   86
  tibeticum / R / 6" / fls deep blue or purple / Tibet   84
  tolmiei v. persimile - 10", fls pink, longer stamens, Idaho   47
    "   v. platyphyllum - 10", fls pink, Oregon, Idaho   47
  tribracteatum / R / 5" / fls pale rose / California   74
  tricoccum / Bb / to 1' / fls white / e United States   83
  triquetrum / R / 9-12" / fls white or greenish-white / s Europe   42
  tuberosum / P / 12-20" / fls white / China, India   60
  unifolium / P / 8-24" / fls rose, rarely white / US, w Coast Ranges   75
  ursinum / Bb / 6-20" / fls white / n Europe, n Asia   32
  victorialis / P / 1-2' / fls greenish-white / c Europe, c Asia   37
  wallichianum / P / 12-20" / fls purple / w Himalayas   37
  zebdanense / Bb / 1-2' / fls white / Lebanon   84

ALNUS - Betulaceae
  crispa maximowiczii - see A. maximowiczii   69
  maximowiczii / Sh or T / to 30' / fine-toothed lvs / Japan in mts.   13
  sinuata / Sh or T / to 40' / lvs lustrous green beneath / w N. Am.   13

ALOE - Liliaceae
  cryptopoda / Gh / stemless / scarlet fls / Rhodesia, Nyasaland   85
  marlothii / Gh / to 3' / orange fls / Bechuanaland   85

ALONSOA - Scrophulariaceae
  incisifolia / P gr. as A / 2' / scarlet fls / Chile   95
  warscewiczii / P gr. as A / 18-24" / fls br. orange-scarlet / Peru   95

ALOPECURUS - Gramineae
  lanatus / R Gr / 6-8" / silver-gray lvs; of dry areas / c Asia   32
  pratensis 'Aureus' - P Gr, 1-4', lvs yellow, Europe, Asia   85

ALOPHIA - Iridaceae
  drummondii / HH C / 1' / blue fls / prairies, Texas, Louisiana   72,(1)

ALSTROMERIA - Amaryllidaceae
  aurantiaca / P / 3' / fls orange / Chile   42
    "   'Dover Orange' - 3', orange-red fls   42
  brasiliensis / Gh P / 3' / reddish-bronze fls / Brazil   36
  'Dover Orange' - see A. aurantiaca 'D. O.'   42
  haemantha / HH P / to 3' / fls bright red / Chile   9
  hookeri - see A. ligtu   9

  (1) - THIERET - Checklist of Vascular Flora of Louisiana. 1972

ALSTROMERIA, con.
  ligtu / HH P / to 2' / fls lilac or pale red / Chile   9
    " v. pulchra - with narrower and longer lvs   9
  'Ligtu Hybrids' - HH P, 2', fls pink, orange, yellow   85
  patagonica / HH P / ? / fls pale pink / South America   21
  pelegrina / Gr P / 1' / pale lilac fls / Peru   85
    " 'Alba' - white-flowered   *
  pulchella / Gr P / 3' / wine-red fls tipped green / Brazil   36
  pulchra - see A. ligtu v. pulchra   *
  pygmaea - see A. patagonica   21
  violacea / Gh P / 5' / mauve fls, spotted / Chile   (1)

ALTHAEA - Malvaceae
  armeniaca / P / 6'+ / fls lilac-pink; lobed lvs / c & sw Asia   91
  rosea / P / 5-8' / varii-colored fls, Hollyhock / Orient   42

ALYSSOIDES - Cruciferae
  utriculata / R / to 15" / fls yellow / Alps, Balkan Pen.   90

ALYSSUM - Cruciferae
  arduinii - see A. saxatile   90
  argenteum / P / 12-18" / fls golden yellow / s Alps, Italy   90
  atlanticum / R / to 8" / large yellow fls / s & c Spain   90
  borzeanum / R / 4-12" / whitish lvs / Black Sea coast   90
  condensatum / R / to 8" / pale lemon fls / Syria, Lebanon   33
  cuneifolium / R / to 10" / almost white lvs / s Europe, in mts.   90
  'Dudley Neville' - see A. saxatile 'D. N.'   38
  markgrafii / P / 8-20" / lvs green above, gray below / Albania   90
  montanum / R / to 10" / fls bright yellow / e & s Europe   90
  muelleri - close to, or part of A. montanum   21
  murale / P / 9"-2' / fls yellow / se Europe   90
  petraeum / P / to 2' / yellow fls; inflated seed-pod / Balkans   90
  saxatile / P / to 15" / fls yellow / s & se Europe   90
    " 'Citrinum' - pale yellow form of the sp.   42
    " 'Compactum' - 6-9" form of the sp.   17
    " 'Dudley Neville' - light buff fls   38
    " 'Gold Dust' - an English name   *
    " 'Silver Queen' - lemon-yellow fls; silvery lvs   44
    " 'Variegatum' - variegated white, yellow and green lvs   32
  scardicum / R / to 9" / fls pale yellow / Balkan Pen.   90
  serpyllifolium / R / trailing / fls pale yellow / sw Europe   90
  spinosum - see PTILOTRICHUM spinosum   90
  wulfenianum / R / trailing / fls pale yellow / se Alps   90

AMARACUS - Labiatae
  dictamnus / HH Sh / 8-10" / pink fls / Crete   32
  pulchellus / HH Sh / 8-16" / fls rose / se Europe   (2)

AMBROSIA - Compositae
  chamissonis / HH R / mats to 1' / silvery lvs / coastal Cal. to B.C. 47

AMELANCHIER - Rosaceae
  alnifolia v. semiintegrifolia - longer petals, may be tree-like, wUS 47
  canadensis / Sh / to 18' / fls white / e N. America   34
  pumila / Sh / 3' / fls white / Rocky Mts.   93

(1) - GOODSPEED in Herbertia 7 1940
(2) - DeWOLF in Baileya 2:2

AMELLUS - Compositae
  annuus / A / 6" / fls deep purplish-blue / South Africa   89

AMIANTHEMUM - Liliaceae
  muscaetoxicum / P / 3' / fls white / sc United States   71

AMORPHA - Leguminosae
  canadensis - error for A. canescens   *
  canescens / Sh / to 4' / fls dull purplish-blue / e & c N. Am.   13
  nana / Sh / 2' / fls purple, fragrant / e & c North America   13

AMSONIA - Apocynaceae
  illustris / P / 2-3' pale blue fls / sc United States   82
  tabernaemontana / P / 1-3' / fls pale blue / ec & se United States   71
          "   v. salicifolia - lvs glaucous beneath   82

ANACAMPTIS - Orchidaceae
  pyramidalis / P / 9-18" / fls bright rose-pink / Purbeck, Ireland   (1)

ANACAMPSEROS - Portulacaceae
  pyramidalis - error for ANACAMPTIS pyramidalis   *
  rufescens / Gh / 3-4" / succulent / Cape of Good Hope   32

ANACYCLUS - Compositae
  depressus / R / 3-6" / fls white, red reverse / Atlas Mts.   42
  maroccanus / R / 4" / fls white, pink reverse / Morocco   17
  pyrethrum maroccanus - see A. maroccanus   21

ANAGALLIS - Primulaceae
  arvensis / A or B / to 20" / blue, red or paler fls / Europe   92
      "   ssp. caerulea - see A. foemina   92
      "   ssp. phoenicia - included in the sp.   92
  caerulea - see A. foemina   92
  foemina - like A. arvensis, fls blue, s, w & c Europe   92
  linifolia - see A. monelli   92
      "   'Monelli' - see A. monelli, a Linnaean species   92
  monelli / P gr. as A / to 20" / fls blue or red / sw Europe   92

ANAPHALIS - Compositae
  margaritacea / P / 18" / fls pearly-white / N. Am., ne Asia   42
  triplinervis / R / 9-12" / ivory-white fls / Tibet   42

ANCHUSA - Boraginaceae
  angustifolia - see A. officinalis   92
  angustissima / R / 1' / fls true blue / Asia Minor, Armenia   35
  azurea / P / 3-5' / fls blue-purple / Caucasus   42
  officinalis / B or P / 1-2' / fls bright blue, purple / Europe   9

ANDROMEDA - Ericaceae
  polifolia / Sh / to 18" / fls pink / n hemisphere   13
      "   'Grandiflora' - Japanese selection, deeper-colored fls   13
      "   'Grandiflora Compacta' - to 1', coral-pink fls, Japan   13
      "   'Grandiflora Minima' - 2", fls deep rose-pink   43
  nana - see ARCTERICA nana   60

ANDROPOGON - Gramineae
  scoparius / P Gr / to 4' / Prairie Beard Grass / United States   (2)

  (1) - WEBB - An Irish Flora. 1963
  (2) - BRAUN - The Vascular Flora of Ohio I. 1967

ARGS·583

ANDROSACE - Primulaceae

    albana / B / 4-8" / white or pale rose fls / Caucasus   80
    alpina / R / 1" / fls pale pink or darker / European Alps   38
    argentea - see A. vandellii   92
    carnea / R / 1-3" / fls pink or white / European Alps   35
      "   'Alba' - the white form   *
      "   ssp. brigantiaca - 1-3", pale fls, Cottian Alps   38
      "   "   'Alba' - entirely white fls   43
      "   halleri - see A. c. ssp. rosea   92
      "   ssp. laggeri - 2-3", large deep rose fls, Pyrenees   38
      "   ssp. rosea - robust, fls pink, e & sc France   92
    chaixii / A / to 1' / white or pink fls / se France, in mts.   92
    chamaedaphne - probable error for A. chamaejasme   *
    chamaejasme / R / 2" / small white fls / northern hemisphere   38
    chumbyi - see A. primuloides 'Chumbyi'   85
    ciliata / R / 1" / fls deep rose / Pyrenees   38
    cylindrica / R / 2" / milky-white fls / Pyrenees   43
    elongata / A / 2" / white fls with yellow throat / Europe, Asia   80
    foliosa / R / 1½" / flesh-pink fls / Himalayas   9
    hausmannii / R / caespitose / pink fls, yellow throat / e Alps   92
    hedraeantha / R / ½" / fls violet-rose / Balkans   33
    helvetica / R / dense cushion / fls white / Swiss & Austrian Alps   42
    hirtella / R / short / fls white / w Pyrenees   43
    hookeriana / R / creeping / white to purplish fls / Himalayas   21
    imbricata - see A. helvetica   92
    jacquemontii / R / 2-3" / pink fls / Himalayas   38
    lactea / R / 5" / fls white / Eurasia   9
    lactiflora / A / 6-10" / fls white / Asia   35
    lactifolia - probable error for A. lactiflora   *
    lanuginosa / R / 3-4" / fls pale to lavender-pink / Himalayas   42
    mairei / R / somewhat rosetted / white to purplish fls / China   21
    microphylla - of gardens is A. sempervivoides   21
    mucronifolia / R / low lax mass / fragrant white fls / Tibet   32
    muscoidea / HH R / tufted / fls pink, fading white / Kashmir   85
    obtusifolia / R / 2" / fls white / European Alps   38
    occidentalis / A / to 3" / insignificant fls / c North America   82
    X pedemontana - R, 1", white fls, Alps of the Piedmont   33
    'Pink Gin' - cv. of A. carnea X A. pyrenaica   (1)
    primuloides / R / 2-4" / fls flesh-pink / w Himalayas   85
      "   'Chumbyi' - smaller plant, deeper pink fls, silky lvs   85
      "   v. watkinsii - included in the sp.   85
    sempervivoides / R / 3" / fls bright pink / Kashmir, Tibet   35
    septentrionalis / A / 6-10" / fls white / circumboreal   35
    spinulifera / R / 5-6" / fls pale pink, red reverse / w China   38
    strigillosa / R / 6" / fls lilac-mauve / China   33
    vandellii / R / 2" / white fls, honey-scented / Pyrenees   87
    villosa / R / 2-3" / fls white or pale pink / Europe   65
      "   v. arachnoidea - 2", rounder & hairier, Carpathians   42
    wulfeniana / R / 1" / fls pink / e Alps   43

ANDROSTEPHIUM - Liliaceae

    caeruleum / Bb / 6-10" / blue fls / sw & c United States   73

ANDRYALA - Compositae

    agardhii / HH R / 5-6" / fls lemon-yellow / Spain   38
    lanata - see HIERACEUM lanata   33

    (1) - MATHEW in Quar. Bull. of the Alpine Garden Soc. 49.4

ANEMONE - Ranunculaceae
```
  alpina - see PULSATILLA alpina                                      90
  apennina / R / 4-9" / fls sky-blue / Italy                          9
  altaica / T / to 1' / fls white veined blue / n Asia                90
  aurea - see PULSATILLA aurea                                        (1)
  baicalensis / R / 6-9" / white fls / e Asia                         32
  baissunensis / R / to 1' / yellow fls / wc Asia                     (1)
  baldensis / R / 4-5" / fls white / Alps, Jugoslavia                 90
  barbulata / R / 2-3" / fls white / China                           33
  biflora / R / 8" / red fls / Kashmir                                33
  blanda / Tu / to 10" / blue fls / se Europe                         90
     "    'Atrocoerulea' - fls deep violet-blue                       36
     "    'Radar' - fls bright purplish-red                           56
     "    'Rosea' - bright pink fls                                   43
     "    'White Splendour' - large white fls                         4
  bungeana - see PULSATILLA bungeana                                  (1)
  californica lutea - see A. drummondii 'Lutea'                       59
      "        rosea - see A. drummondii 'Rosea'                      59
  campanella - see PULSATILLA campanella                              (1)
  canadensis / P / 2' / fls white / North America                    35
  caroliniana / R / 1' / fls pink, white, violet / se United States  35
  coronaria / HH Tu / 6-12" / fls red, blue, white / Medit. region   90
     "       'DeCaen' - single flowered in wide color range           4
     "       'St. Brigid' - hort. strain, mixed colors, semi-dbl. fls 85
  crinita / P / to 18" / white fls / Siberia                         (1)
  cylindrica / P / 2' / fls greenish-white / North America           35
  decapetala - see A. caroliniana                                     9
  deltoidea / R / 6-8" / white fls, sometimes colored / w US         35
  demissa / P / 12-14" / white fls / Himalayas, w China              32
  drummondii / R / 4-12" / white fls, usually tinged / w N. America  75
       "      'Lutea' - tinged yellow                                 *
       "      'Rosea' - tinged pink                                   *
  fasciculata - see A. narcissiflora v. fasciculata                  29
  X fulgens / HH Tu / to 1' / fls scarlet / Greece                   42
     "     v. annulata - selection for larger fls                    84
     "       "       'Grandiflora' - red fls, yellowish center       56
  globosa / P / 4-20" / fls yellowish, pink, purple / nw N. America  27
  hortensis / HH Tu / 10" / fls pale purplish / c Medit. region      90
  hudsoniana - see A. multifida f. polysepala                        34
  hupehensis / P / to 3' / fls rose / c & w China                    32
     "      v. japonica - 2½', fls light purple, China               32
     "         "       'September Sprite' - see A. X hybrida 'S. S.' 44
  X hybrida 'September Sprite' - 2-3', fls rose-pink                  44
  japonica - see A. hupehensis v. japonica                           32
  X lesseri - P, 1½-2', fls rosy-purple                              42
  leveillei / P / to 2' / fls white, lilac reverse / sw China        32
  lutea - see A. palmata v. lutea                                     9
  lyallii / R / 6" / fls white or tinted blue, rose / nw N. America  75
  magellanica / R / 6-18" / creamy-yellow fls / South America        35
     "       'Major' - 10", sulphur-yellow fls                        5
     "       'Minor - see A. multifida 'Minor'                       (2)
     "       'Rosea' - see A. multifida 'Rosea'                       *
  montana - see PULSATILLA montana                                    *
     "     rubra - see PULSATILLA rubra                               90
  multifida / P / 6-18" / fls red, yellow, white / N & S America     9
     "       alba - see A. m. var. richardsiana f. leucantha         34
     "       f. polysepala - red doubled flower                      34
     "       v. richardsiana f. leucantha - 2', milky-wh. fls, nc N. Am. 34
```

(1) - YUZEPCHUK in Flora U. S. S. R. Vol. VII 1970(trans.)
(2) - BAILEY - Manual of Cultivated Plants. 1949

ANEMONE, con.
```
  narcissiflora / R / 6-16" / fls white, pink tinged / e Eu., Asia      90
      "       demissa - see A. demissa                                  32
      "       v. fasciculata - fascicled, umbellate infloresence        29
  nemorosa / R / 2-12" / fls white or flushed pink / n & c Europe       90
  obtusiloba f. patula - R, mats, fls deep blue, Himalayas              38
  occidentalis - see PULSATILLA occidentalis                           27
  palmata / Tu / to 1' / fls yellow / Portugal, Spain                  65
      "   v. alba - 6", satin white fls                                 36
      "   v. lutea - has basal lvs lobed, fls yellow                    9
  parviflora / R / 3-14" / fls white, tinged rose or blue / Arctic      63
  patens - see PULSATILLA patens                                       90
  pavonina / Tu / 6-12" / fls scarlet, pink, purple / s Europe         90
      "    'St. Bavo' - florist's strain                                4
  polyanthes / R / 6-10" / fls white / Himalayas                       32
  pratensis - see PULSATILLA pratensis                                 90
      "     nigricans - see PULSATILLA pratensis ssp. nigricans        90
  ranunculoides / R / to 1' / fls yellow / Europe                      90
  riparia / P / 2' / milk-white fls / n North America                  34
  rivularis / P / to 15" / fls white, blue reverse / India, China       42
  rupicola / R / to 1' / fls white, pink reverse / Kashmir, Sikkim      35
  sylvestris / R / 6-15" / fls white / c & e Europe                    90
      "    'Grandiflora' - fls larger than the type                    (1)
      "    f. macrantha - fls larger, free flowering                   20
  'St. Bavo' - see A. pavonina 'St. Bavo'                               4
  taurica - see PULSATILLA halleri ssp. taurica                        90
  tetrasepala / P / 3' / fls white / Himalayas                         33
  vernalis - see PULSATILLA vernalis                                    *
  virginiana / P / 2-3' / fls white / United States & Canada            35
  vitifolia / P / 2' / fls white / Himalayas, Nepal, Sikkim            (2)
```

ANEMONELLA - Ranunculaceae
```
  thalictroides / R / 6-10" / fls white to pink / ec United States      35
```

ANEMONOPSIS - Ranunculaceae
```
  macrophylla / P / 15-30" / fls pale purple / Japan                   60
```

ANETHUM - Umbelliferae
```
  graveolens / A / 8-20" / the herb Dill / India, sw Asia               91
```

ANGELICA - Umbelliferae
```
  archangelica / B / 6-8' / tiny white fls / Europe, n Asia             32
  atropurpurea / P / 4-5' / dark purple stem / e & c N. America         83
```

ANIGOZANTHUS - Haemodoraceae
```
  bicolor / Gh P / 1' / fls red, green, yellow / w Australia            16
  flavidus / Gh P / 2' / fls yellow to red / w Australia                16
  humilus / Gh P / 9" / yellow & orange fls / w Australia               16
  manglesii / Gh P / 2' / fls red & green / w Australia                 16
```

ANISTOME - Umbelliferae
```
  aromatica / HH R / to 1' / white fls / New Zealand                    78
  haastii / HH P / 1-2' / white fls / montane New Zealand                2
  imbricata / HH R / 2" / compact plant spreading by offsets / N. Z.     2
  pilifera / HH P / 1-2' / white fls / New Zealand                       2
```

(1) - BOHM - Rock Garden Flowers. 1970
(2) - KITAMURA in KIHARA - Fauna and Flora of Nepal Himalaya. 1955

ANOIGANTHUS - Amaryllidaceae
  brevifolius / HH Bb / 2-10" / bright yellow fls / South Africa   56
  luteus - see A. brevifolius   56

ANOPTERUS - Escalloniaceae
  glandulosus / HH T / 20'+ / fls white, tinged rose / Tasmania   13

ANTENNARIA - Compositae
  alborosea / R / 8-12" / fls showy, deep rose / se Yukon, e-ward   (1)
  alpina / R / 1-4" / fls white / arctic Europe & Asia   32
  aprica - see A. parvifolia   32
  asarina - strayed from ANTIRRHINUM   *
  carpatica / R / 8-20" / pappus shining white / N. Europe & Asia   63
  dioica / R / 1-4" / fls white or pinkish / arctic Europe & Asia   32
     "   'Alba' - fls white   *
     "   alborosea - see A. alborosea   (1)
     "   'Hyperborea' - trade name for pink form   51
     "   'Minima' - small form   38
     "   'Nyewoods' - fls bright rose, 3"   17
     "   'Rosea' - fls pink   38
     "   'Rosea Minima' - see 'Minima' above   38
     "   'Tomentosa' - woolly form   38
  eucosma / R / 3" / brownish fls / Newfoundland   34
  magellanica / R / 3" / fls gray & brown / South America   (2)
  microphylla / R / to 10" / fls whitish to creamy / Rocky Mts.   34
  neglecta / R / to 3" / fls whitish / ne & nc North America   82
  neodioica / R / mats / white to roseate fls / Newfoundland to Minn.   34
  oxyphylla / R / to 1' / lvs tomentose on both sides / Mont., Col.   77
  parviflora - see A. parvifolia   32
  parvifolia / R / to 6" / fls rosy / c North America   32
  rosea / R / 8-16" / fls rosy-tipped / nw North America   75
  suffrutescens / HH R / 2-6" / evergreen lvs / n Cal., s Ore.   35

ANTHEMIS - Compositae
  barrelieri - see ACHILLEA barrelieri   21
  biebersteinii / R / 6" / yellow fls; silver lvs / Asia Minor   35
        "   v. rudolphiana - more compact, longer lived   17
  compacta / R / neat / single white fls / s Alps, Pyrenees   33
  cupaniana / R / 6-10" / white fls; silvery lvs / Italy   38
  montana / R / 4-8" / white fls / Spain, Italy, Balkans   35
  nobilis / R / to 1' / white fls / w Europe   9
  rudolphiana - see A. biebersteinii v. rudolphiana   17
  sancti-johannis / P / 15" / golden daisies / Bulgaria   17
  tinctoria / P / 2½' / yellow daisies / Europe   42
      "   'E. C. Buxton' - 2-3', pale lemon fls   85
      "   'Kelway's Var.' - deep yellow fls   9

ANTHERICUM - Liliaceae
  algeriense - see A. liliago ssp. algeriense   51
  liliago / P / 18" / fls white / s Europe   42
     "   ssp. algeriense - adaptive to varied sites   55
     "   'Major' - larger in all parts   9
  liliastrum 'Major' - see PARADISEA liliastrum 'Major'   9
  ramosum / R / 12" / starlike fls, white / Europe   84

  (1) - PORSILD - Botany of se Yukon adjacent to the Canol Road. 1951
  (2) - RUFFIER-LANCHE in Bull. Am. Rock Garden Soc. 19:1

ANTHYLLIS - Leguminosae
```
  jacquinii - see A. montana v. jacquinii                                    13
  montana / Sh / 4-12" / fls rose / s & se Europe                            87
     "     'Carminea' - bright colored selection                             *
     "     v. jacquinii - with paler fls, e part of ramge                    13
     "     'Rubra' - selection for deeper colored fls                        13
  moura - see A. vulneraria ssp. maura                                       91
  vulneraria / R / to 1' / fls yellow / n Europe                            91
     "        ssp. alpestris - 1', fls pale yellow, in mts.                  91
     "        ssp. maura - 2', fls usually red, Portugal, Spain, Italy       91
     "        ssp. praepropera - 14", fls reddish, Medit. region             91
     "        ssp. pyrenaica - 10", fls pink to red                          91
```

ANTIRRHINUM - Scrophulariaceae
```
  asarina - see ASARINA procumbens                                          (1)
  grosii / HH Sh / decumbent / fls pale yellow / wc Spain                    92
  hispanicum / HH Sh / decumbent to 2' / fls white or pink / se Spain 65
  'Magic Carpet' - see A. majus 'Magic Carpet'                              85
  majus 'Magic Carpet' - HH A, 6", creeping habit, mixed col.               85
  meonanthum / HH P / to 4' / fls pale yellow / Spain, Portugal             92
  molle / HH Sh / 16" / white or pale pink fls / e & c Pyrenees             92
  sempervirens / HH Sh / 8" / fls white or cream / c Pyrenees               65
  siculum / HH P / to 2' / fls pale yellow, veined red / Sicily, Malta 92
```

APHYLLANTHES - Liliaceae
```
  monspeliensis / HH R / 4-10" / blue fls / Spain, Italy, n Africa           64
```

APLECTUM - Orchidaceae
```
  hyemale / P / to 2' / greenish or yellowish fls / n & c North Am.          34
```

APOCYNUM - Apocynaceae
```
  pumilum / P / 8-20" / fls pinkish / North America                         75
```

AQUILEGIA - Ranunculaceae
```
  akitensis - see A. flabellata v. pumila                                    60
     "     alba - see A. flabellata v. pumila 'Alba'                         *
     "     kurilensis - see A. flabellata 'Nana'                             43
     "     nana - see A. flabellata 'Nana'                                   85
  alpina / P / 6-36" / nodding fls, bright blue / Alps, n Apennines          90
     "  'Hensol Harebell' - see A. X 'Hensol Harebell'                       85
     "  'Hensol Hybrid' - see A. X 'Hensol Harebell'                         62
  atrata / P / 1½-3' / fls nodding, dark purple-violet / Alps                90
  atropurpurea - see A. viridiflora                                          85
  atroviolacea - see A. atrata                                               67
  aurea / R / 4-16" / fls suberect, yellow / Bulgaria                        90
  bertolonii / R / 4-12" / fls nodding, blue-violet / France, Italy          90
     "       'Alba' - white fls                                             *
  bicolor - see A. sibirica                                                  85
  'Biedermeier' - P, 22-25", blue fls                                       (2)
  brevistyla / P / 1-2' / blue & white fls / Rocky Mts.                      85
  buergeriana / P / 2' / fls yellow, tinged purple / Japan                   85
  caerulea / P / 1-1½' / fls blue & white / Rocky Mts.                       35
     "     'Alba' - fls white                                                9
     "     'Candidissima' - 27-34", white fls                              (2)
  canadensis / P / 1-2' / fls bright red / e & c North America               35
     "       f. flavescens - yellow-flowered form                           38
     "       'Nana' - to 1' or less                                         9
```

```
(1) - DeWOLF in Baileya  4:2
(2) - COLE in Bull. Am. Rock Garden Soc.  29:1
```

AQUILEGIA, con.
  candidissima - see A. caerulea 'Candidissima'   (1)
  chaplinii / P / to 20" / fls yellow / Texas, New Mexico   74
  chrysantha / P / 1-4' / fls yellow / New Mexico, Arizona, Mexico 85
     "   'Flavescens' - fls yellow, tinged red   9
  'Clematiflora' - spurless mutant, Scott Elliot Strain   85
  'Crimson Star' - 2', fls crimson & white   42
  dichroa / P / 8-26" / fls blue tipped white / nw Spain, Portugal 90
RW ·   discolor / R / 4-6" / fls blue & white / n Spain   90
6-79   'Dragon Fly Hybrid' - 18", long-spurred, bright colors   89
  ecalcarata - see SEMIAQUILEGIA ecalcarata   85
  'Edelweiss' - see A. vulgaris v. erecta 'Edelweiss'   (1)
  einseliana / R / 4-18" / fls nodding, blue-violet / Alps   90
  elegantula / R / 4-16" / red fls tipped yellow / Rocky Mts.   76
  flabellata / R / 6-18" / fls white, tinged violet-rose / Japan 85
     "   'Alba' - form with milky-white fls   43
     "   'Nana' - 3", sepals mid-blue, petals light yellow 43
     "   'Nana-alba' - white fls on the dwarf form   43
     "   v. pumila - 1', 1-2-flowered, alps of Japan   60
     "   "   'Alba' - white form   *
  flavescens / P / 1-2' / yellow to pinkish fls / Rocky Mts.   76
  formosa / P / 2-3' / fls red & yellow / w North America   85
     "   v. shockleyi - see A. shockleyi   *
     "   v. truncata - California form, fls smaller, spurs short 85
  fragrans / P / 1½-2' / fls white or pale purple / Himalayas   85
  glandulosa / R / 8-12" / fls bright blue / Altai Mts.   85
  'Granny's Bonnet' - common name for A. vulgaris fl.pl.   42
  'Hensol Harebell' - A. alpina X A. vulgaris, seedlings vary   85
  hirsutissima / R / 4-10" / fls pale blue to white / se France 90
  japonica - see A. flabellata v. pumila   60
  jonesii / R / 3" / fls solitary, blue / Rocky Mts.   85
  kareliniana - see A. karelinii   (2)
  karelinii / P / 8-32" / fls violet or dark red / c Asia   (2)
  kitabelii / R / to 1' / fls red-violet to blue-violet / Italy 90
  lactiflora / P / 18" / fls white or tinged blue / Altai Mts.   85
  longissima / P / 2-3' / fls pale yellow / Texas, Mexico   42
  'McKana Hybrids' - 2'+, fls various colors   (1)
  nigricans / P / 1½-3' / fls purple, large / c & se Europe   90
  olympica / P / 2' / fls claret to purple / Caucasus   85
  oxysepala / P / 2½' / fls blue / Siberia   85
     "   v. yabeana - 8-18", fls lilac-blue, Manchuria   (2)
  pubescens / R / 8-18" / fls cream to pink / s Sierra Nevadas, US 75
  pyrenaica / R / 8-16" / fls clear pale blue / Pyrenees   87
     "   discolor - see A. discolor   *
  rubicunda - variety of A. elegantula   21
  saximontana / R / 6" / fls blue & white / Rocky Mts.   35
  scopulorum / R / 6" / fls large, lavender to violet / sw N. Am. 85
     "   calcarata - see A. s. var. calcarea   43
     "   v. calcarea - petioles glandular-pubescent, Utah 43
  sibirica / R / to 1' / fls bright lilac or white / Siberia   85
  shockleyi / P / to 30" / fls red & yellow / s Calif., Nevada   74
  skinneri / HH P / 2' / fls orange & red / Mexico   85
  ullepitschii - see A. nigricans   90
  viridiflora / P / 1-1½' / fls greenish / Siberia to China   85
  vulgaris / P / 2' / fls blue, purple, white / Europe   42
     "   alba - see A. v. var. nivea   9
     "   atrata 'Major' - see A. atrata 'Major'   *
     "   'Edelweiss' - see A. v. var. erecta 'Edelweiss'   (1)
     "   v. erecta 'Edelweiss' - 19-25", fls white   (1)

(1) - COLE in Bull. Am. Rock Garden Soc. 29:1
(2) - SHISHKIN in Flora U.S.S.R. 7 1970 (trans.)

AQUILEGIA, con.
 vulgaris v. nivea - 2-3', pure white fls   9
   " 'Stellata' - spurless mutant   21
 yabeana - see A. oxysepala v. yabeana   (1)

ARABIS - Cruciferae
 albida - see A. caucasica   90
   " rosea - see A. X arendsii 'Rosabella'   95
   " variegata - see A. caucasica v. variegata   95
 allionii / P / to 18" / white fls / Europe, in mts.   90
 alpina / R / 2-16" / fls white / much of Europe, rare e   90
   " billardieri - see A. billardieri   (2)
 X arendsii 'Rosabella' - 6-8", purple-pink fls   95
 aubrietioides / R / to 6" / fls purplish-pink / Cilician Taurus   26
 bellidifolia - see A. soyeri ssp. jacquinii   90
 billardieri / R / to 1' / fls white / Asia Minor, Caucasus   (2)
 blepharophylla / R / to 1' / deep pink fls / w North America   35
   " 'Spring Charm' - selected form of above   17
 breweri / R / 2-8" / fls pink to red-purple / w United States   75
 caerulea / R / 2-6" / fls pale blue / Alps   90
 caucasica / R / 8-14" / fls white / s Europe   90
   " 'Rosabella' - see A. X arendsii 'Rosabella'   95
   " 'Snowcap' - compact plant, white fls   79
   " v. variegata - lvs variegated yellow & green   95
 corymbiflora / R, may be B / to 1' / fls white / c Europe, in mts.   90
 cypria / HH R / tufted / fls white or pale pink / Cyprus   85
 ferdinandi-coburgii / R / to 1' / fls white / Bulgaria   90
   "   'Variegata' - gray lvs with variegations   *
 hirsuta / P or A / to 2' / fls white / most of Europe   90
 jacquinii - see A. soyeri ssp. jacquinii   90
 japonica - see A. stelleri v. japonica   60
 X kellereri - R, 3", fls large, white   43
 kohleri / R / 2-16" / fls bright red to purple / sw Oregon   75
 lemmonii / R / 2-16" / fls pink or rose-purple / nw N. America   75
 lucida 'Variegata' - R, largish rosette, lvs white or yellow bordered 33
 lyallii / R / 4-12" / fls purple / nw North America   75
 lyrata / B or R / to 1' / fls white / n & c North America   83
 montana - see A. hirsuta   29
 muralis / R / to 1' / fls white, rarely pink / s & sc Europe   90
   " f. rosea - the pink form   51
 nuttallii / R / 3-4" / white fls / Montana to Washington   76
 petraea - see CARDAMINOPSIS petraea   90
 procurrens / R / to 1' / fls white / Balkan mts.   90
 pumila / R / 2-6" / fls white / Alps, Apennines   90
 purpurea / R / 3" / fls purple / Cyprian Olympus   33
 'Snowcap' - see A. caucasica 'Snowcap'   79
 soyeri / P / 6-20" / white fls / Pyrenees   90
   " ssp. jacquinii - 6-18", fls white, Alps   90
 sparsiflora / P / 10-36" / pink or purple fls / nw United States   76
 stelleri v. japonica - 8-16", fls white, Japan, Korea   60
 X sturii - R, to 6", fls large, white   6
 subpinnatifida / R / 6-16" / fls lavender or purple / Calif., Ore.   75
 X wilczekii - A. bryoides X carduchorum, tufts, fls white   20

ARALIA - Araliaceae
 elata / T / to 30' / fls small, whitish / Japan, Korea   13
 hispida / P / to 3' / the Bristly Sarsaparilla / e & ec N. America   71
 nudicaulis / P / 8-16" / black frs on leafless stem / e & c N. Am.   71

 (1) - BAILEY - Manual of Cultivated Plants. 1949
 (2) - Flora of the USSR. Vol. 8.

ARALIA, con.
  racemosa / P / 2-10' / frs purple / ne & nc North America   83
  spinosa / T / to 30' / frs red, turning black / se United States   46

ARBUTUS - Ericaceae
  unedo / HH T / 15-30' / white or pinkish fls / Medit. region   13

ARCTERICA - Ericaceae
  nana / Sh / to 4" / nodding white fls / Japan   38

ARCTOSTAPHYLOS - Ericaceae
  glandulosa 'Cushingiana Repens' - 6-8", gray lvs, white fls   (1)
  glauca / HH Sh / 6-14" / white or pinkish fls / S. California   13
  nevadensis / Sh / trailing / fls white or reddish / California   13
  patula / Sh / 3-7' / fls white or pinkish; lvs evergreen / w N. Am.   13
  tomentosa / Sh / to 5' / fls white / California, coast ranges   13
  uva-ursi / Sh / trailing / white or pink fls / n hemisphere   13

ARCTOTIS - Compositae
  stoechadifolia / A / 24-28" / fls white to violet / South Africa   32

ARENARIA - Caryophyllaceae
  arctica / R / caespitose / Fls white / arctic Asia & N. America   63
  austriaca / R / 6" / white fls / Austria   45
  balearica / R / mats / solitary white fls / Balearic Isls.   65
  capillaris / R / to 8" / fls white / Eurasia   63
        "   v. americana - of nw North America   47
  caroliniana / R / to 8" / fls in clusters, white / R. I. to Fla.   72
  cephalotes / P / 8-20" / white fls / s Ukraine, Moldavia   90
  foliosa / R / 7" / white fls / India   33
  glacialis - see A. gracilis   51
  gracilis / R / to 3" / fls white / s & w Jugoslavia   90
  grandiflora / R / to 6" / fls white / c & s Europe   90
        "   v. triflora - lvs narrowed & recurved, sandy hills, France   29
  graminifolia - see A. procera   90
  groenlandica / R / mats / white fls / Greenland & high mts. s-ward   (2)
  gypsophilioides / R / 1'+ / white fls / s & e Bulgaria, sw Asia   90
  imbricata / R / 3" / fls white / alps of the Caucasus   29
  kingii / R / to 8" / fls white / Great Basin of w United States   75
  laricifolia - see MINUARTIA laricifolia   63
  ledebouriana / R / to 10" / fls white / Turkey   26
  macrocarpa / R / mats, to 6" / solitary white fls / Alaska, Yukon   63
  montana / R / to 1' / fls white / sw Europe   90
  norvegica / R / 3" / white fls / Scandinavia, Scotland, Ireland   90
  polaris / R / to 6" / fls violet-tinged / Siberia   90
  procera / R / 8-16" / fls white / c & e Europe   90
  purpurascens / R / to 4" / fls pale-purplish, white / Pyrenees   90
  rotundifolia / R / to 8" / white fls / n Balkan Peninsula   90
  sajanensis / R / mats / white fls / circumpolar   63
  striata kitabelii - see MINUARTIA laricifolia ssp. kitabelii   90
  tetraquetra / R / cushion / fls white / s & e Spain, Pyrenees   65
  verna caespitosa - see MINUARTIA verna 'Caespitosa'   38
  verticillata - see ACANTHOPHYLLUM verticillatum   26

ARGEMONE - Papaveraceae
  alba / A / 1-3' / fls white / southern states, US & s-ward   9
  platyceras / A / 1½-4' / fls white to purple / N. & S. America   9

  (1) - BREUER in Bull. Am. Rock Garden Soc. 19:3
  (2) - Mountain Flowers of New England. Appalachiam Mt. Club. 1964

ARGYROLOBIUM - Leguminosae
  zanonii / R / 10" / yellow fls / Albania & w-ward in s Europe   91

ARISAEMA - Araceae
  atrorubens / Tu / to 2½' / fls purplish / ne & c N. America   34
  dracontium / Tu / to 1' / fls green / e North America   84
  flavum / Tu / ? / fls green to yellow / Himalayas   9
  griffithii / Tu / 2' / spathe lined violet / Himalayas, Sikkim   84
  ringens / Tu / to 10" / fls green or purple / Japan, China   60
  sikokianum / Tu / to 8" / fls dark purple / Japan   60
  tortuosum / HH Tu / 2' / green & purple spathe / w Himalayas   84
  triphyllum / Tu / 1'+ / fls green, purple or brown / e N. America   84
  wallichianum / HH Tu / ? / spathe striped purple / Himalayas   (1)

ARISARUM - Araceae
  proboscideum / Tu / 3-4" / greenish fls / Apennines   38

ARISTOLOCHIA - Aristolochiaceae
  californica / HH Cl / to 10' / fls green & purple / California   75
  chiliensis / Gh Cl / 10' / purple & green fls / West Indes   45
  durior - see A. macrophylla   13
  elegans / Gh Cl / high / purple, white & yellow fls / Brazil   41
  macrophylla / Cl / high / fls purplish / Pennsylvania to Georgia   9
  serpentaria / P / to 2' / basal fls, greenish / e United States   73

ARMERIA - Plumbaginaceae
  alliacea / P / 8-20" / fls purplish to white / w Europe   92
  allioides - see A. alliacea   92
  alpina - see A. maritima ssp. alpina   92
  arctica - see A. maritima ssp. sibirica   92
  'Beechwood' - see A. caespitosa 'Beechwood'   *
  X 'Bloodstone' - 9" hybrid, fls almost red   85
  bufleuroides - error for A. bupleuroides   *
  bupleurifolia - probable error for A. bupleuroides   *
  bupleuroides - see A. alliaceae   92
  X caesalpina - 6", fls pink   (2)
  caespitosa - see A. juniperifolia   (2)
      "   'Ardenholme' - probably best referred to A. X caesalpina   *
      "   'Alba' - probably best referred to A. X caesaplina   *
      "   'Beechwood' - probably best referred to A. X caesalpina   *
      "   'Bevan's Var.' - see A. juniperifolia 'Bevan's Var.'   *
      "   'Bloodstone' - see A. X 'Bloodstone'   *
      "   'Pearl' - probably best referred to A. X caesalpina   *
      "   'Roger Bevan' - see A. juniperifolia 'Bevans Var.'   *
      "   'Rosea' - see A. juniperifolia 'Rosea'   *
  corsica - see A. leucocephala   (2)
  girardii / R / to 6" / pink fls / sc France on dolomite   92
      "   'Alba' - white cultivar   *
  gussonei - see A. morisii   92
  juncea - see A. girardii   92
      " f. alba - see A. girardii 'Alba'   *

(1) - RAU - Illustrations of West Himalayan Flowering Plants. 1963
(2) - LAWRENCE in Am. Rock Garden Soc. Yearbook 1941

ARMERIA, con.
  juniperifolia / R / 3" / fls pale purplish or pink / c Spain   65
      "   'Alba' - probably best referred to A. X caesalpina   *
      "   'Ardenholme' - referrable to A. X caesalpina   *
      "   'Bevans Var.' - 2-4", dark rose fls   85
      "   'Bloodstone' - see A. X 'Bloodstone'   *
      "   'Pearl' - probably best referred to A. X caesalpina   *
      "   'Rosea' - probably best referred to A. X caesalpina   *
  labradorica / R / to 1' / pink to purple fls / Newfoundland   34
  leucocephala / R / 3" / fls whitish / Corsica   (1)
  maritima / R / 6" / fls in pink shades / Eu., N. Am., coastal   42
      "   f. alba - 6-9", fls white   85
      "   arctica - see A. m. ssp. sibirica   92
      "   ssp. alpina - to 10", fls deep pink, reddish or white   92
      "   ssp. halleri - to 1', fls bright pink to red, w & c Eu.   92
      "   'Laucheana' - hort. selection, bright pink fls, 6"   17
      "   ssp. purpurea - 8-14", fls purplish, Germany, Italy   92
      "   ssp. sibirica - to 8", fls pale pink, Siberia, arctic Am.   92
      "   'Splendens' - brilliant red fls   95
      "   'Vindictive' - 6", fls rosy red   85
  montana - see A. alliacea   92
  morisii / HH P / 8-16" / fls pale pink / Sardinia, Sicily   92
  'Pearl' - see A. juniperifolia 'Pearl'   *
  plantaginea bupleuroides - see A. alliacea   92
  pseudarmeria / HH Sh / 10-20" / fls usually white / Portugal   92
  pungens / HH R / to 10" / dense spiny lvs; fls pale rose / s Port.   65
  rigida - see A. alliacea   92
  setacea - see A. giraldii   (1)
      "   alba - see A. giraldii 'Alba'   *
  'Six Hills' - see A. maritima 'Laucheana'   95
  welwitschii / HH Sh / to 10" / fls pink to white / wc Portugal   92

ARNEBIA echioides - see ECHIOIDES longiflorum   (2)

ARNICA - Compositae
  alpina / R / to 1' / yellow fls / n circumpolar, South America   32
     "   sornbergeri - included in the sp.   63
  amplexicaulis / P / 1-3' / pale yellow fls / Calif., Alaska, Mont.   76
  chamissonis / P / 8-40" / fls yellow / nw North America   75
  chionopappa / R / to 1' / fls yellow / e Quebec   33
  cordifolia / P / 4-24" / fls bright yellow / Calif. to Alaska   76
  frigida / R / to 16" / yellow fls / Alaska, nw Canada, Siberia   (3)
  latifolia / P / 4-24" / fls yellow / nw North America   75
  lessingii / R / to 1' / fls pale yellow to orange / Yukon, Alaska   63
  longiflora - error for A. longifolia   *
  longifolia / P / to 2' / yellow fls / Calif., Colorado, Canada   76
  montana / R / 6" / fls deep orange / Europe in mts.   43
  unalascensis / R / 6-14" / fls yellow / Japan   60
      "   v. tschonoskyi - corollas slightly pilose   60

ARONIA - Rosaceae
  arbutifolia / Sh / 5-10' / fls white; frs red / e North America   13
      "   'Brilliantissima' - see A. f. macrocarpa   (4)
      "   f. macrocarpa - hort. form with larger frs   (4)
  melanocarpa / Sh / to 3' / fls white; frs black / e North America   69

(1) - LAWRENCE in Am. Rock Garden Soc. Yearbook. 1941
(2) - INGRAM in Baileya 6:3
(3) - WHITE - The Alaska-Yukon Wild Flowers Guide. 1974
(4) - BLACKBURN - Trees and Shrubs in Eastern North America. 1952

RW
6/79

ARRHENANTHERUM Gramineae
   elatius v. bulbosum - P Gr, 2-3', may be weedy, Europe   (1)
      "   tuberosus - see A. e. var. bulbosum   (1)

ARTEMISIA - Compositae
   absinthum / P / 3' / fls yellow; lvs silky / Europe   42
   assoana / HH R / low cushion / fls pale yellow / se & s Spain   65
   borealis / R / to 1' / silky gray lvs / circumboreal   63
   campestris ssp. maritima - HH P, 2'+, lvs fleshy, dark green, Spain 65
   douglasiana / P / tall / elliptic, unlobed lvs / Calif., Oregon   75
   eriantha / R / 6" / silvery ferny lvs / s & c Alps   33
   genipi / R / to 4" / fls yellowish / European Alps   32
   glacialis / R / 4" / yellow fls, silvery lvs / Alps   35
   lactiflora / P / 4-5' / fls creamy-white / China, India   42
   lanata / Sh / to 8" / yellow fls / c & s Europe, in mts.   20
   laxa / Sh / to 6" / fls pale yellow / s & c European mts   32
   maritima - see A. campestris ssp. maritima   65
   mutellana - see A. laxa   32
   nitida - see A. assoana   32,65
   schmidtiana 'Nana' - R, 4", bright silver lvs   17
   spicata - see A. genipi   (2)
   splendens / R / tufted / non-woolly heads / Caucasus   33
   tridentata trifida - see A. tripartita   93
   trifurcata / R / 6" / lvs densely silky / Hokkaido   60
   tripartita / Sh / to 12' / fls yellow to brown / w North America 93

ARTHROPODIUM - Liliaceae
   candidum / HH R / 10" / white starry fls / New Zealand   38
   cirrhatum / Gh / 3' / fls white / New Zealand   41
   minus / Gh / 18" / white fls / Australia   45

ARUM - Araceae
   creticum / Gh Tu / 10-15" / fls pale green & whitish / Crete   41
   dioscorides / HH Tu / to 1' / fls green mottled purple / e Medit. 84
   hygrophilum / Gh Tu / 12" / pale green & purple fls / Syria   20
   italicum / HH Tu / 18" / fls pale yellow; lvs veined white / s Eu. 84
      "   f. marmoratum - highly marbled lvs in autumn   42
      "   pictum - see A. pictum   84
   maculatum / Tu / 12" / fls green, purple spotted / England, Eu. 35
   pictum / HH Tu / 10" / fls purple, green, white / Spain, Corsica 84

ARUNCUS - Rosaceae
   dioicus / P / to 6' / showy, white fls / Eurasia, North America 91
   sylvester - see A. dioicus   91
   vulgaris - see A. dioicus   91

ASARINA - Scrophulariaceae
   procumbens / R / trailing / pale yellow fls / Pyrenees   87

ASARUM - Aristolochiaceae
   canadense / R / to 1' / fls basal, reddish purple / e North America 35
   caudatum / R / 4" / fls brownish, appendaged / w North America 35
   europeum / R / 6" / evergreen lvs; tiny purple fls / Europe   17
   hartwegii / R / 6" / fls light reddish-brown / Sierra Nevadas, US 35
   sieboldii / R / rhizomatous / large lvs; solitary fls / Honshu 60

   (1) - HITCHCOCK - Manual of the Grasses of the United States. 1935
   (2) - POLUNIN - Flowers of Europe. 1969

ASCLEPIAS - Asclepiadaceae
    curassavica / Gh P / 2' / orange-red fls / tropical America   41
    incarnata / P / 3' / rose-purple to flesh fls / e & c N. America   9
        "   v. pulchra - hirsute, fls paler, e N. Am.   9
    physocarpa / Gh Sh / 6' / whitish-cream fls / ?   89
    purpurascens / P / 1-4' / fls deep rose / e United States   72
    speciosa / P / 3' / fls large, purplish / Nebraska, w&s-ward   9
    syriaca / P / to 6' / fls pink to white / e half US & Canada   68
    tuberosa / P / 2-3' / orange fls / e & c North America   9

ASIMINA - Annonaceae
    triloba / T, in n shrubby / 10-40' / fls purplish / e & s US   13

ASPARAGUS - Liliaceae
    densiflorus 'Sprengeri' - Gh, small pinkish fls; br. red frs, Natal 41
    plumosus - see A. setaceus   41
    setaceus / Gh Cl / high / red frs / South Africa   41
    sprengeri - see A. densiflorus 'Sprengeri'   41
    verticillatus / Cl / to 15' / red-berried / Iran to Siberia   9

ASPERELLA hystrix - see HYSTRIX patula   85

ASPERULA - Rubiaceae
    cynanchica / R / 9-12" / fls light pink / Europe, Asia   35
    lilaciflora v. caespitosa - R, mats, starry pink fls, e Medit. reg. 38
    odorata / R / ground cover, 6-8" / white fls / Europe, Asia   9
    pontica / R / 2" / fls pink / ?   35

ASPHODELINE - Liliaceae
    liburnica / P / 1-2' / fls yellow / Greece, Austria, Italy   9
    lutea / P / 2-4' / fls yellow / Italy, North Africa   9

ASPHODELUS - Liliaceae
    acaulis / HH R / rosette / fls pale pink / Algeria   38
    aestivus / P / 4½' / white fls, reddish veined / Medit. reg.   65
    albus / P / 3' / white or pinkish fls / Portugal, Medit. region   65
    cerasiferus / P / 4' / white fls, pink striped / w Medit. region   (1)
    fistulosus / HH P / 8-24" / pale pinkish fls / s Europe   65
    microcarpus - see A. aestivus   65
    ramosus / P / 3' / pale brown bracts / Medit. region   65

ASPLENIUM - Polypodiaceae
    adulterinum / F / 1' / thin, light green blades / ec Europe, in mts.90
    cuneifolium / F / 8-40" / flabellate leaf-segments / s & c Europe   90
    fontanum / F / 3-4" / narrow, lanceolate fronds / c & s Europe   50
    incisum / F / to 1' / sterile fronds shorter / Far East   60
    pinnatifidum / F / 3-9" / evergreen fronds / c & s United States   34
    platyneuron / F / 6-15" / evergreen fronds / Canada to S. America   34
    ruta-muraria / F / 1-3" / on walls and basic rocks / Europe   50
    trichomanes / F / 3-5" / delicate fronds / n temperate zone   38
        "   'Cristatum' - frond crested, partly true from spores   50
        "   'Incisum' - narrow fronds, deeply cut, true-breeding   50
    viride / F / 2-6" / evergreen fronds / n Europe, n N. America   50

ASTELIA - Liliaceae
    linearis / R / acaulescent / large red fls / New Zealand   (2)
    nervosa / R / dense tuft / frs orange / New Zealand   46

    (1) - MORRIS in RHS Lily Yearbook. 1960
    (2) - ADAMS - Mountain Flowers of New Zealand. 1965

ASTER - Compositae
  alpellus 'Triumph' - R, 9", rays blue, disc orange   85
  alpigenus / R / to 16" / fls violet to lavender / Calif. to Wash.   75
  alpinus / R / 4-8" / fls mauve to rosy-purple / European Alps   42
     "   'Albus' - white form, rarely found with good fls   43
     "   'Beechwood' - lavender-blue fls; one of the best forms   42
     "   'Dolomiticus' - near purple fls   17
     "   'Goliath' - 10", violet-blue fls   17
     "   'Pirinensis' - deep rose form   21
     "   'Roseus' - rosy-pink form   *
     "   'Superbus' - large and showy form   17
     "   'Wargrave' - lilac-colored fls   10
     "   'Wolfii' - taller with blue fls, Alps   62
  amellus / P / 2-2½' / purple solitary fls / Italy   85
  asteroides / R / 2-6" / fls mauve / se Tibet, w China   85
     "   'Albus' - white-flowered   *
  azureus / P / to 3' fls deep blue or blue-violet / e North America   38
  cordifolius / P / 3-4½' / pale blue fls / c North America   79
  farreri / R / 9" / large violet-purple fls / w China, Tibet   38
     "   'Berg Garten - see A. tongolensis 'Berggarten'   85
  foliaceus / P / 1-2' / fls rose, blue, violet / n N. Am.   75
     "   v. lyallii - involucral bracts much narrower, n Idaho   47
  X frikartii - P, 2½', fls sky-blue, orange disc   32
  fruticosus / Gh Sh / 2-4' / purple fls / South Africa   (1)
  fuscescens / P / 2½' / fls pale purplish-blue / Yunnan   24
  'Golden Sunshine' - P, 4', bright golden yellow fls   (2)
  himalaicus / R / 4-12" / lilac-blue fls / Himalayas   9
  junceus - see A. junciformis   34
  junciformis / P / to 2' / fls purple, roseate, white / n N. Am.   34
  'Knapsbury' - see A. tongolensis 'Napsbury'   85
  kumleinii - see A. oblongifolius   82
  laevis / P / 2-3' / fls blue or violet / ne North America   9
  likiangensis - see A. asteroides   85
     "   albus - see A. asteroides 'Albus'   *
  linariifolius / R / 1' / fls lavender / ne North America   35
     "   f. leucactis - the white form   34
  linosyris / P / 2' / fls bright yellow / Europe   42
  meritus / R / 4" / fls purple / nw United States   75
  natalensis / R / 9" / fls clear light blue / Natal   6
  novae-angliae / P / to 6' / fls violet-purple or pink / e N. Am.   42
     "   f. roseus - roseate fls   34
  oblongifolius / P / 6-24" / fls violet-purple / c United States   82
  pappei - see FELICIA pappei   85
  paucicapitatus / P / 8-20" / fls white turning pink / Olympics, US   75
  ptarmicoides / P / to 2' / fls white / e North America   34
  pyraneus / P / to 3' / fls large, purple / ne Spain   33
  sericeus / P / 8-24" / violet-purple fls; silvery lvs / c US   82
  sibiricus / P / 1-2' / violet or lilac fls / arctic Eu., & N. Am.   9
     "   meritus - see A. meritus   75
  sikkimensis / P / 3-4' / fls purple-blue / Sikkim, Nepal   85
  soulei v. limitanus - R, 6-8", purple-violet fls / w China border   38
  spectabilis / P / 1½-2' / fls bright violet / Mass. to N. Carolina   42
  subcaeruleus - see A. tongolensis   85
  subspicatus / P / 1-3' purple fls / Aleutians to California   47
  thomsonii / P / to 3' / fls clear lilac-blue / Nepal, Kashmir   33
  tibeticus / R / 6" / fls bright blue / Himalayas   85

(1) - BAILEY - Manual of Cultivated Plants. 1949
(2) - Lamb Nursery Catalog. n.d.

ASTER, con.
  tongolensis / R / 12-16" / fls pale blue / Himalayas   85
      "   'Berggarten' - 1', fls deeper blue   89
      "   'Napbury' - 18', fls heliotrope-blue   85
  uliginosus / HH R / 2" / mauve fls / Basutoland   (1)
  'Wargrave Pink' - 5", large pink fls   3
  yunnanensis / P / to 3' / fls blue-mauve / w China, se Tibet 85
      "   'Knapsbury' - see A. tongolensis 'Napsbury' 85

ASTILBE - Saxifragaceae
  biternata / P / 3-6' / fls yellowish-white / Virginia, s-ward 9
  chinensis / P / 1½-2' / fls whitish / China 9
      "   v. davidii - 1-2', fls rose-purple, China, Korea 60
      "   v. pumila - 10", raspberry-pink fls 35
  X crispa 'Gnome' - 10", pink fls 57
  davidii - see A. chinensis v. davidii 60
    "   pumila - see A. chinensis v. pumila *
  glaberrima - see A. japonica v. terrestris 60
    "   saxatilis - see A. j. var. terrestris 'Saxatilis' 43
  japonica v. terrestris - to 20", fls white 60
    "   "   'Saxatilis' - 3", fls light purple, wh. tips 43
  simplicifolia / R / to 1' / white fls / Honshu 60
      "   'Rosea' - pink fls *
  tacquetii 'Superba' - 4', intense purple-rose fls 85

ASTRAGALUS - Leguminosae
  alopecuroides - see A. centralpinus 91
  austrinus / A or B / to 16" / fls pale purple-violet / Tex., Mex. 10
  balearicus / HH R / caespitose / fls white / Balearic Isls. 91
  caespitosus / R / small cushion / magenta-purple fls / nc N. Am.(2),21
  campestris ochroleuca - see OXYTROPIS nuriae 91
  canadensis / P / 1-4' / fls greenish cream / e & c N. America 34
  caryocarpus / P / trailing / fls pale purple-violet / w plains, US 82
  centralpinus / P / to 3'+ / yellow fls / sw Alps, Bulgaria 91
  crassicarpus - see A. caryocarpus 82
  exscapus / R / tufted / fls yellow / c Europe 91
  glycyphyllos / P / 1-3', trailing / fls cream / Europe, Siberia 32
  lusitanicus / HH P / 18" / large white fls / Portugal, sw Spain 65
  mexicanus (ex Kansas) - see A. m. var. trichocalyx 34
    "   v. trichocalyx - decumbent, fls cream, calyx white 34
  monspessulanus / R / acaulescent, fls purplish-violet / s Eu. 91
  nutzotinensis / R / 4-6" / fls large, blue & white / Alaska (3)
  onobrychis / P / 2', trailing / fls pale or dark violet / Europe 91
  poterium - see A. balearicus 91
  purpureus / R / 4-16" / purplish fls / s & w Europe 91
  purshii / R / 2" / fls cream & purple / nc North America 19
    "   v. glareosus - fls reddish-purple, Calif., Oregon 47
  schelichovii / R / 8-16" / yellowish fls / betw. Yakutsk & Okhotsk (4)
  schizopterus / R / acaulescent / purple fls / Caucasus (4)
  sinicus / B / 4-10" / reddish-purple fls / China, Japan, Taiwan 60
  sirinicus / R / caespitose / fls yellowish & violet / Balkans 91
  spatulatus - see A. caespitosus (2)
  tennesseensis / R / 20", trailing / yellowish fls / midcentral US 72

(1) - MURRAY-LYON in Bull. Am. Rock Garden Soc. 27:2
(2) - RYDBERG - Flora of the Prairies and Plains of Central N. Am. 1932
(3) - PORSILD - Botany of the se Yukon Adjacent to the Canol Road. 1951
(4) - SHISHKIN in Flora U. S. S. R. Vol. 12 1965 (trans.)

ASTRANTIA - Umbelliferae
  biebersteinii / R / to 1' / pink & white fls / Caucasus   35
  carinthiaca - see A. major ssp. carinthiaca   91
  carniolica / P / to 2' / fls whitish / se Alps   91
      "   f. rubra - 1', fls dark red   (1)
  major / P / 3'+ / fls white & purplish / s Europe   91
    " ssp. carinthiaca - with longer bracteoles, s Alps, nw Spain   91
  maxima / P / 1-2' / fls pinkish / Caucasus   42
  minor / R / to 16" / fls whitish / Pyrenees   91

ASYNEUMA canescens - see PHYTEUMA canescens   32
  "   limoniifolium - see PHYTEUMA limonifolium   *
  "   prenanthoides - see CAMPANULA prenanthoides   47

ATHAMANTA - Umbelliferae
  cretensis / P / to 2' / white fls / Spain to Jugoslavia   91
  matthioli - see A. turbith   91
  turbith / P / to 20" / white fls / nw Balkan Peninsula   91

ATHANASIA - Compositae
  parviflora / Gh P / 2½' / fls yellow / Cape of Good Hope   45

ATHYRIUM - Polypodiaceae
  filix-femina / F / 1-4' / finely-divided fronds / temperate zones   50
      "   'Fieldiae' - a cruciate form   50
      "   'Frizelliae' - 18", pinnae bead-like, Ireland   50
  goeringianum pictum - see A. iseanum 'Pictum'   60
  iseanum / F / 10" / mountain fern / Japan, Formosa   60
    "   'Pictum' - 2', gray & green fronds   60
  thelypterioides / F / 1-2½' / silvery indusia / e & c N. America   83

ATROPA - Solanaceae
  belladonna / P / 3-4' / blue-purple fls; frs poisonous / Eu., Asia   9

AUBRIETA - Cruciferae
  deltoidea / R / caespitose to trailing / fls red-purple / Greece   90
    "   'Dr. Mules' - deep violet-blue fls   38
    "   'Leichtlinii' - pink fls in abundance   9
    "   'Mrs. Lloyd Edwards' - lilac-purple fls   (2)

AUCUBA - Cornaceae
  japonica / HH Sh / 6-10' / purplish fls; scarlet frs / Japan   13

AULAX - Proteaceae
  umbellata / Gh / 2' / yellow fls / Cape of Good Hope   45

AUREOLARIA virginica - see GERARDIA virginica   34

AVENA candida - see HELICTOTRICHON sempervirens   85

AZARA - Flacourtiaceae
  gilliesii - see A. petiolaris   46
  microphylla / HH T / 15-30' / yellow fls, vanilla-scented / Chile   46
  petiolaris / HH Sh / 15' / small yellow fls / Chile   46

AZARINA procumbens - error for ASARINA procumbens   *

(1) - BLOOM - Hardy Plants of Distinction. 1965
(2) - SCHENK - The Wild Garden - A Catalog. n.d.

AZORELLA - Umbelliferae
  columnaris / HH R / close, hard, massive cushion / Peru   21

BABIANA - Iridaceae
  plicata / C / 4-12" / fls pale blue-lilac / sw Cape Province   56
  stricta / C / 6-10" / varii-colored fls / sw Cape, S. Africa   56
     "   v. rubrocyanea - fls deep purplish-blue & crimson   56
     "   v. sulphurea - fls creamy white, base stained blue   56
     "   v. villosa - deep crimson fls   84
     "   'Zwanenberg Glory' - segments alternating blue & white   36
  tubiflora / C / 1' / creamy-white scented fls / Cape Province   36
  'Zwanenberg Glory' - see B. stricta 'Z. G.'   36

BAECKEA - Myrtaceae
  camphorosmae / HH Sh / 2' / fls white or pink / w Australia   20
  virgata / Gh Sh / 3' / fls white / Australia, New Caledonia   32

BAEOMETRA - Liliaceae
  uniflora / HH Bb / 6-12" / fls red & orange-yellow / Cape of G. Hope(1)

BAERIA richardsonii - see HYMENOXIS richardsonii   *

BAILEYA - Compositae
  multiradiata / R / 8-18" / fls yellow / sw United States, n Mexico   73

BALSAMORRHIZA - Compositae
  rosea / R / to 7" / fls golden-orange / Washington   (2)
  sagittata / P / 8-32" / fls yellow / nw United States   75

BANKSIA - Proteaceae
  marginata / Gh Sh / 6' / yellow fls / New South Wales   45
  prionotes / Gh T / 15-25' / eleven inch lvs / Australia   9
  repens / Gh Sh / 1' / yellow fls / Australia   45

BAPTISIA - Leguminosae
  alba / P / 1-3' / fls white / mideast United States   9
  australis / P / 3-4' / fls blue, occasionally white / mideast US   35
  leucantha / P / to 4½' / white fls / c North America   89
  leucophaea / P / 1-2½' / fls large, cream / Michigan to Texas   9
  tinctoria / P / 2-4' / fls bright yellow / e & s United States   9

BARBAREA - Cruciferae
  vulgaris 'Variegata' - B, 18", lvs yellow-variegated / Eurasia   9

BARTSIA - Scrophulariaceae
  alpina / R / 4-8" / purple lvs & frs / mts. of north temperate zone 33

BECKMANNIA - Gramineae
  eruciformis / P Gr / ? / bulbous stem base / Europe   85
  syzigachne / A Gr / 1-3' / unusual infloresence / N Am., e Asia (3),20

BEGONIA - Begoniaceae
  evansiana / HH P / 2' / fls large, flesh-colored / Java, China   9

BELAMCANDA - Iridaceae
  chinensis / P / 2-3' / orange fls, spotted red / e Asia   9

  (1) - KIDD - Wild Flowers of the Cape Peninsula. 1950
  (2) - DAVIDSON in Bull Am. Rock Garden Soc. 31:4
  (3) - HITCHCOCK - Manual of the Grasses of the United States. 1935

BELLENDENA - Proteaceae
  montana / HH Sh / 2' / white fls; scarlet frs / Tasmania   (1)

BELLEVALIA - Liliaceae
  ciliata / Bb / to 20" / fls purplish / s Europe, e Asia   55
  dalmatica - see HYACINTHUS dalmaticus   38
  dubia / Bb / to 10" / blue to white fls / European Medit. reg.   55
    " hackelii - see B. hackelii   65
  flexuosa / Bb / to 10" / white to purple fls / Near East   86
  hackelii / Bb / 8-10" / fls bright blue / s Portugal   65
  longistyla / Bb / 12" / rusty-purple & white fls / Caucasus   54
  paradoxa / Bb / 8" / fls dark blue / Caucasus, Iran   20,85
  pycnantha / Bb / 8" / intense dark blue fls / e Turkey   56
  romana / Bb / 8-16" / fls white or bluish / Medit. region   86
  speciosa / Bb / 10-20" / yellow & brownish fls / Caucasus   54
  wilhelmsii / Bb / ? / fls brown, green banded / Caucasus   54

BELLIDASTRUM michellii - see ASTER bellidastrum   32

BELLIS - Compositae
  rotundifolia v. caerulescens - 2-3", light lavender fls, Atlas Mts. 38

BELLIUM - Compositae
  bellidioides / A / 2" / miniature white daisies / Medit. region   9
  minutum / R / 2" / fls white, deep red reverse / Levant   32

BERARDIA - Compositae
  subacaulis / R / acaulescent / woolly lvs; fls not showy / Alps   33

BERBERIS - Berberidaceae
  aggregata / Sh / 3-5' / fls pale yellow; red bloomy frs / w China   13
  aquifolium - see MAHONIA aquifolium   13
  buxifolia 'Nana' - 18", rarely flowering   13
  X 'Chenaultii' - evergreen Sh, 3'+, lvs spiny margined   46
  darwinii / HH Sh / 6-12' / evergreen lvs; orange frs / Chile   13
  dictyophylla / Sh / to 6' / pale yellow fls; red frs / w China   13
  julianae / Sh / 8-10' / evergreen lvs; blue-black frs / c China   13
  nervosa - see MAHONIA nervosa   46
  repens - see MAHONIA repens   46
  X stenophylla - HH Sh, 8-10', evergreen lvs; golden fls   13
      "   'Corallina' - fls reddish   1
      "   'Corallina Compacta' - less than 1' high   13
  thunbergii 'Atropurpurea Nana' - 2', lvs brownish red   13
      "   'Aurea' - lvs yellow   46
  valdivana / HH Sh / 10' / long purple frs / Chile   13
  verruculosa / Sh / to 6' / golden yellow fls / w China   46
  vulgaris / Sh / 8' / fls yellow; frs red / Europe, N. Africa, Asia   13
  wilsonae / Sh / 2-3' / frs soft, pinkish-red / w China   1
      "   'Globosa' - dwarf globular form   46

BERGENIA - Saxifragaceae
  beesiana - see B. purpurascens   85
  'Bullawley' - see B. purpurascens 'Bullawley'   85
  cordifolia / P / to 15" / petals rose pink / Siberia   85
  purpurascens / HH P / to 15" / petals bright pink / China, Himal.   85
      "   'Bullawley' - plant massive, deep-colored fls   85
  stracheyi / R / 1' / fls white becoming pink / Afghanistan   85
      "   alba - included in the sp.   85

  (1) - WOLFHAGEN in Bull. Am. Rock Garden Soc.   24:1

BERKHEYA - Compositae
  macrocephala / HH P / 4' / golden-yellow fls / South Africa   (1)

BESSERA - Liliaceae
  elegans / Gh Bb / 1-2' / scarlet & white fls / Mexico   41

BESSEYA - Scrophulariaceae
  bullii - see WULFENIA bullii   34
  rubra / R / rosette / hoary, red-flushed lvs / Rocky Mts.   21

BETONICA divulsa - see STACHYS officinalis   92

BETULA - Betulaceae
  albo-sinensis / T / to 35' / pink & red bark / w China   46
  humilis / Sh / 2-9' / glabrous, green lvs / Eu. & Asia, high lat.   13
  lenta / T / 70' / aromatic bark / e North America   13
  lutea / T / to 100' / trunk yellowish brown / e North America   13
  nana / Sh / 2-4' / shining dark green lvs / n Europe, N. America   13
  papyrifera / T / 65' / whitest barked of the birches / N. America   13
  pubescens v. carpatica - T, 15'+, densely branched, Icel. to Carpa.43
  pumila v. glandulifera - Sh, ½-9', lvs glandular-warty, ne N. Am.   34

BILLARDIERA - Pittosporaceae
  longiflora / Gh Cl / 6' / fls greenish-yellow / Tasmania   13
  "   'White Form' - white fruiting form, true-seeding   13

BISCUTELLA - Cruciferae
  frutescens / HH P / 20" / yellow fls; plant woolly / sw Spain   90
  laevivata / P / to 20" / yellow fls / c & s Europe   90

BLANDFORDIA - Liliaceae
  grandiflora / HH P / 2' / fls red & yellow / N. South Wales, Austr.(2)
  punicea / HH P / 1' / fls rich brown-red / Tasmania   (2)

BLECHNUM - Polypodiaceae
  discolor / HH F / 1-4' / pinnae closely-set, comblike / N. Zealand 50
  fluviatile / Gh F / 2½' / obtuse pinnae / N. Z., Australia   (3)
  lanceolatum / Gh F / to 1' / leathery texture / Austral., Polynesia 9
  penna-marina / F / 6" / dark green fronds / New Zealand   50
  spicant / F / 6-9" / evergreen fronds / Alaska to Calif., Europe 9

BLETILLA - Orchidaceae
  striata / R / 1' / fls purple / China, Japan   42
  "   'Alba' - see B. striata f. gebina   60
  "   f. gebina - the white form   60

BLOOMERIA - Liliaceae
  crocea / HH Bb / to 2' / fls orange-yellow / s coast of California 75

BLUMENBACHIA - Loasaceae
  coronata / A / 1½' / white fls; stinging hairs / South America   9
  laterita - see CAJOPHORA laterita   32

BOENNINGHAUSENIA - Rutaceae
  albiflora / P / to 3' / fls white / Asia   13

  (1) - INGWERSEN in Gardening Illustrated April 1952
  (2) - INGRAM in Baileya 13:2
  (3) - JOE in Baileya 8:3

BOLANDERA oregana - error for BOLANDRA oregana   *

BOLANDRA - Saxifragaceae
  oregana / R / 8-16" / fls purplish / Oregon & Washington   9

BOLAX - Umbelliferae
  glebaria / R / 3" / yellow fls / Falkland Islands   35

BOLTONIA - Compositae
  asteroides / P / 2-8' / fls white to violet-purple / s & e US   9
    "   v. latisquama - more showy fls, blue-violet   82
  latisquama - see B. asteroides v. latisquama   82

BONGARDIA - Berberidaceae
  chrysogonum / HH P / 12-20" / yellow fls / Iran, Iraq, Syria   26

BORAGO - Boraginaceae
  laxiflora - see B. pygmaea   92
  pygmaea / HH R / trailing / fls pale, clear azure-blue / Corsica 92

BOTRICHIUM - Ophioglossaceae
  dissectum / F / to 10" / fronds bronzing in autumn / n & c N. Am. 34

BOTTIONEA - Liliaceae
  plumosa / HH P / 3' / greenish fls / Chile   (1)

BOUTELOUA - Gramineae
  gracilis / P Gr / 8-20" / bristly, one-sided bracts / c & s US, Mex. 85
  oligiostachya - see B. gracilis   85

BOWIEA - Liliaceae
  volubilis / Gh Bb / twining climber / fls green / South Africa   9

BOYKINIA - Saxifragaceae
  aconitifolia / P / 1-3' / fls small, white / Va. to Ga., in mts. 9
  jamesii / R / 6" / fls deep pink / Colorado, in mts.   42
    "   v. heucheriformis - cherry-red fls, Medicine Wheel, Mont. (2)
  major / P / 1-3' / white fls; large lvs / Idaho, Oregon, Montana 76
  tellimoides - see PELTOBOYKINIA tellimoides   60

BRACHYCHITON - Sterculiaceae
  acerifolium / HH T / timber tree / red fls / Australia   9

BRACHYCOME - Compositae
  nivalis / R / rosette / white fls / New South Wales, Australia   (3)
  rigidula / HH R / ? / small, lavender-blue daisies / ne Victoria, Au (4)
  scapiformis / HH R / ? / lilac fls / Tasmania   21
  scapigera / R / rosette / white fls / New South Wales, Australia (3)

BRACHYGLOTTIS - Compositae
  repanda / Gh T / 6-21' / fls whitish / New Zealand   2

BRASSICA - Cruciferae
  repanda / P / to 18" / tufted plant; yellow fls / Spain, France   65

BRAVOA - Amaryllidaceae
  geminiflora / HH Tu / 18" / coral-red fls / Mexico   36

(1) - Anonymous in Quar. Bull. Alpine Garden Soc. 41:1
(2) - WOODWARD in Bull. Am. Rock Garden Soc. 29:3
(3) - VALDER in Jour. Royal Hort. Soc. Sept. 1964
(4) - SYNGE in ANDERSON - Seven Gardens. 1973

BRAYA - Cruciferae
  alpina / R / 4" / fls white / e Alps   90

BRICKELLIA - Compositae
  grandiflora / P / 1-2' / fls greenish, yellowish-white / nw US   75

BRIMEURA - Liliaceae
  amethystina / Bb / 8" / cambridge blue fls / Pyrenees   42,85
     "   'Alba' - white form of above   38,85
  fastigiata / Bb / 6" / whitish fls / Corsica, Sardinia   84

BRIZA - Gramineae
  maxima / A Gr / 1-1½' / elegant seed-heads for drying / Medit. reg. 42
  media / P Gr / to 2½' / spikelets usually purplish / Europe, Asia   85
  minor / A Gr / 9-24" / shining white, purplish spikelets / w & s Eu.85
  subaristata / HH P Gr / purplish or green spikelets / Mexico, S. Am.85

BRODIAEA - Liliaceae
  bridgesii - see TRITELEIA bridgesii   56
  californica / C / 4-12" / fls violet-blue / Sacramento Valley   85
  candida / C / 1-2' / fls white or bluish / California   9
  capitata - see DICHELOSTEMMA pulchella   56
     "   alba - see DICHELOSTEMMA pulchella 'Alba'   *
  congesta / C / to 3' / blue-violet fls / California to Washington   59
  coronaria / C / 3-9" / fls violet to lilac / B. C. to Calif.   85
     "   v. macropoda - to 8", lilac to violet fls, Calif., Ore.   59
  crocea - see TRITELEIA crocea   *
  douglasii / C / ? / pale to deep blue fls / nw N. America   47
  hendersonii / C / 4-12" fls pale yellow / sw Oregon   75
  howellii / C / 15" / fls white to blue-purple / Oregon to B. C.   75
  hyacinthina - see TRITELEIA hyacinthina   56
     "   alba - included in the sp.   *
  ida-maia - see DICHELOSTEMMA ida-maia   56
  ixioides - see TRITELEIA ixioides   56
     "   'Splendens' - see TRITELEIA i. 'Splendens'   *
  lactea - see TRITELEIA hyacinthina   56
  laxa - see TRITELEIA laxa   56
  " candida alba - see B. candida   9
  lutea - see TRITELEIA ixioides   56
     " 'Splendens' - see TRITELEIA ixioides 'Splendens'   *
  peduncularis / C / to 2' / fls white, lilac tinged / California   75
  pulchella - see DICHELOSTEMMA pulchella   56
     "   alba - see DICHELOSTEMMA pulchella 'Alba'   *
  X tubergenii - see TRITELEIA X tubergenii   56

BROMUS - Gramineae
  squarrosus / Gr, A or B / to 1½' / green or purplish fls / Medit.   85
  tectorum / A Gr / 6-24" / shining green or purplish fls / Medit.   85

BRUCKENTHALIA - Ericaceae
  spiculifolia / Sh / 9" / fls rosy / e Europe, Asia Minor   13

BUGLOSSOIDES - Boraginaceae
  purpurocaerulea / P / 2' / fls red-purple to blue / s & c Europe   92

BULBINE - Liliaceae
  bulbosa / HH R / 9" / yellow fls / Australia, Tasmania   16
  semi-barbata / HH R / 6-12" / yellow fls / Tasmania   21

BULBINELLA - Liliaceae
  floribunda / HH P / 3' / creamy-white fls / Table Mt., S. Africa   36
  hookeri / HH P / 2-3' / fls bright yellow / New Zealand   33
  robusta / HH P / ? / yellow fls / South Africa   (1)

BULBOCODIUM - Liliaceae
  vernum / Bb / 4" / reddish-violet-purple fls / mts. of Europe   84

BUPTHALMUM - Compositae
  salicifolium / P / 1½-2' / yellow fls / Austria   42
  speciosum - see TELEKIA speciosa   32

BUPLEURUM - Umbelliferae
  angulosum / P / 6-16" / petals yellow / Pyrenees   91
  falcatum / P / to 3' / petals yellow / Europe   91
  lancifolium / A / 6-30" / yellowish-green fls / s Europe   91
  longifolium / P / 1-5' / green or purplish fls / c Europe   91
  nipponicum / P / 8-16" / petals yellow / high mts. of Honshu   60
  ranunculoides / P / to 2' / yellowish fls / mts. of c & s Europe   91
       "   ssp. gramineum - with involute, linear lvs   91
  rotundifolium / A / 1½-3½' / purplish lvs; yellow-green fls / Eu.   91

BURCHARDIA - Liliaceae
  umbellata / HH P / 2' / fls white to pinkish / Australia   16,20

BURSARIA - Pittosporaceae
  spinosa / HH Sh / 8-15' / white fls / Tasmania, N.S. Wales, Austr.   9

BUTOMUS - Butomaceae
  umbellatus / P Aq / 2-4' / fls rose-pink / n Asia, Europe   42

CAILLIEA - Leguminosae
  glomerata - tropical Sh or small T, lilac-pink & white fls   (2)

CAJOPHORA - Loasaceae
  coronata - see BLUMENBACHIA coronata   9
  laterita / HH Cl / to 9' / fls orange-red / Argentina   32

CALAMAGROSTIS - Gramineae
  epigeios / P Gr / 2-6' / decorative spikelets / Eurasia   85

CALAMINTHA - Labiatae
  alpina - see ACINOS alpinua   (3)
  grandiflora / R / 4" / bright light violet fls / s Europe   9

CALANDRINIA - Portulacaceae
  caespitosa / R / 1-2" / white fls, tinged pink / Patagonia   21
  ciliata / A / low / rose-red or red-purple fls / Baja Cal. to B. C.   75
    "   v. menziesii - included in the sp.   47
  grandiflora / HH P / 1-3' / fls light purple / Chile   9
  umbellata / P gr. as A / 4-6" / fls bright crimson / Peru   42

CALCEOLARIA - Scrophulariaceae
  acutifolia / R / 4" / fls golden-yellow / Patagonia   43
  arachnoidea / Gh / 8-10" / dull reddish-purple fls / Chile   38
  biflora / R / 10-12" / yellow fls / Chile   38

  (1) - LAWRENCE - Gardens in Winter. 1961
  (2) - BIRCHER - Gardens of the Hesperides. 1960
  (3) - RUFFIER-LANCHE in Bull. Am. Rock Garden Soc. 19:1

CALCEOLARIA, con.
  brunellifolia / HH Sh / 6-12" / few large fls / Andes Mts.   21
  chelidonioides / P / 2' / golden yellow fls / Peru   32
  darwinii / R / 2-3" / orange-yellow & white fls / Patagonia   42
  dentata - see C. X fruticohybrida   9
  falklandica / R / 6" / yellow fls, purple spotted / Falkland Isls.   33
  filicaulis / Gh A / tall / yellow fls / South America   21
  fothergillii / R / 4" / pale yellow fls, red-spotted / Patagonia   38
  X fruticohybrida - Gh Sh, yellow or orange fls   9
  mexicana / A / 10" / yellow fls / Mexico, South America   32
  polyrrhiza / R / 5" / yellow fls, purple spots, Patagonia   43
  scabiosaefolia / P gr. as A / 2' / pale yellow fls / c S. America   9
  tenella / R / 4" / fls clear yellow, red spots / Chile   38
  volckmannii / R / 1' / large fls / South America, in mts.   21

CALENDULA - Compositae
  suffruticosa / A / 2' / fls bright yellow / w Medit. region   9

CALLA - Araceae
  palustris / P Aq / to 1' / white spathe / Europe, N. Am., n Asia   35

CALLIANDRA - Leguminosae
  eriophylla / HH Sh / to 4' / pink & yellow stamens / Texas, Mexico   74
  humilis / HH P / trailing / stamens bright pink / Arizona, N. Mex.   74

CALLIANTHEMUM - Ranunculaceae
  anemonoides / R / 3-10" / fls pink to white / ne Alps   90
  coriandrifolium / R / 8" / fls white / Alps, Carpathians   90
  rutifolium - either C. anemonoides or C. coriandrifolium   90
       "   anemonoides - see C. anemonoides   90

CALLICARPA - Verbenaceae
  americana / HH Sh / 3-6' / fls bluish; frs violet / se & sc US   13
  bodinieri v. giraldii - Sh, 8', lilac fls & frs, w China   13
  giraldiana - see V. bodinieri v. giraldii   13

CALLIRHOE - Malvaceae
  digitata / P / 2-4' / fls rose-red to violet / c United States   73
  involucrata / P / trailing / fls cherry-red / Minn. to Texas   35

CALLISTEMON - Myrtaceae
  citrinus / Gh Sh / 6' / crimson fls / w Australia   16
     "   'Splendens' - fls brilliant scarlet   46
  rigidus / Gh Sh / 8' / red-flowered / Australia   13
  sieberi / Gh Sh / to 15' / pale yellow fls / se Australia   13
  speciosus / Gh Sh / 8' / fls red / w Australia   16

CALLITRIS - Pinaceae
  rhomboidea / Gh T / 40' / conifer / Australia   40
  tasmanica - see C. rhomboidea   40

CALLUNA - Ericaceae
  vulgaris / Sh / 3' / purplish-pink fls / England, Scotland, e Eu.   13
     "   f. alba - the white variant   13
     "   'Crispa' - 12", white fls   (1)
     "   f. hirsuta - stems & lvs hairy, grayish   13
     "   'Mrs. H. E. Beale' - 18", silvery-pink double fls   13
     "   'Tib' - 10", lvs dark green, fls cyclamen-purple   13

  (1) - UNDERHILL - Heaths and Heathers. 1972

CALOCHORTUS - Liliaceae
  albus / C / 1-2' / fls pearly white / California   84
    " f. rosea - see C. amoenus   9
    " v. rubellus - variants with pinkish fls   56
  amabilis / C / 8-20" / bright yellow fls / n Calif., coastal   75
  amoenus / C / 8-20" / rose fls / s Half of Sierra Nevada, Calif.   75
  barbatus / Gh C / ? / fls yellow / Mexico   84
  bonplandianus / Gh C / 3' / fls yellow & purple / Mexico   9
  caeruleus / C / 3" / fls lilac & blue / Sierra Nevada, Calif.   43
  catalinae / C / 1-2' / fls white / California, coastal   9
  clavatus / C / to 3' / fls yellow / California   84
  elegans v. nanus - C, 4", cream fls, mts. of n California   9
  greenei / C / 4-12" / purplish fls / nc Calif., sw Oregon   75
  gunnisonii / C / 1-2' / light blue to white fls / Rocky Mts.   9
  howellii / C / 8-12" / yellowish-white fls / sw Oregon   75
  kennedyi / C / 4-8" / fls red, orange, yellow / Calif., Arizona   74
  luteus / C / 8-20" / fls yellow / California   84
  lyallii - see C. elegans v. nanus   9
  macrocarpus / C / 15" / purple fls, green banded / B. C. to Calif.   36
  maweanus - see C. caeruleus   43
  monophyllus / C / 3-8" / yellow fls / Sacremento Valley, Calif.   75
  neriniiflorum - error for CALOSCORDUM neriniflorum   *
  nitidus / C / 18" / fls purplish / California   36
  nudus / C / 2-4" / fls greenish-white or pale lilac / California   9
  pulchellus / C / 8-16" / canary-yellow fls / c California   9
  purpureus - see C. bonplandianus   9
  splendens / C / 1-2'/ fls pale lavender / California   84
  tolmiei / C / 4-16" / cream or white fls / Oregon, California   75
  uniflorus / C / 1-1½' / fls lilac-pink / California   42
  venustus / C / to 2' / fls variable, all blotched / n Calif.   84
    "   'El Dorado Strain' - varii-colored fls, Eldorado Co.   9
  vestae / C / to 2' / fls white to purple, blotched / n Calif.   43
  weedii / Gh C / to 18" / fls lemon-yellow, orange / s Calif.   84

CALOPOGON - Orchidaceae
  pulchellus / C / 12-18" / fls magenta-crimson / e North America   9
  tuberosus - see C. pulchellus   23

CALOSCORDUM neriniflorum - see NOTHOSCORDUM neriniflorum   (1)

CALOTHAMNUS pyroliflora - error for CLADOTHAMNUS pyroliflorus   *

CALOTROPIS - Asclepiadaceae
  procera / Gh Sh / 10' / fls white & purple / India   9

CALTHA - Ranunculaceae
  appendiculata / R / 2" / narrow-sepalled fls / Southern Andes Mts.   21
  biflora / R / 2-10" / fls white / California to Alaska   9
  howellii / R / to 1' / fls white / n Calif., s Oregon   75
  introloba / R / of alpine streams / white fls / New South Wales   (2)
  laeta / P / to 2' / varies slightly from Marsh Marigold / Europe   90
  leptosepala / R / 12" / fls white / Rocky Mts., Alaska   9
  palustris / P / 1' / fls golden yellow / Europe, N. America   42
    "   'Alba' - single white form   42
    "   v. barthei - 20", large yellow fls, Japan   60

(1) - TRAUB in Plant Life Vol.10 1954
(2) - VALDER in Jour. of the Roy. Hort. Soc. Sept. 1964

CALYCANTHUS - Calycanthaceae
  floridus / Sh / 3-6' / dark reddish-brown fls / Virginia to Fla.   9

CALYDOREA - Iridaceae
  speciosa / HH Bb / ? / violet fls / Chile   21

CALYPSO - Orchidaceae
  bulbosa / R / 6-9" / fls purple, pink, yellow / Maine to Wash., Eu. 35

CALYPTRIDIUM - Portulacaceae
  umbellatum / R / rosette / white fls / nw United States   (1)

CALYSTEGIA - Convolvulaceae
  soldanella / R / creeping / fls white to purplish / sea shores   2

CAMASSIA - Liliaceae
  angusta / Bb / 6-16" / fls lavender to pale purple / Illinois - Tex. 82
  azurea - see C. quamash v. azurea   47
  cusickii / Bb / 1½-2' / fls pale lilac-blue / w North America   42
  esculenta - see C. quamash   32
  howellii / Bb / to 2' / fls pale purple / s Oregon   9
  leichtlinii / Bb / 3' / fls cream, blue, purple / Calif. to B. C.   84
       "   'Alba' - white form   84
       "   v. angusta - see C. angusta   82
       "   'Caerulea' - selection for blue fls   *
       "   v. suksdorfii - to 4', deep violet-blue fls   59
  quamash / Bb / 2-3' / fls white to blue / w North America   42
     "   'Alba' - white fls   *
     "   v. azurea - pale bluish-violet fls, Washington   47
  scilloides / Bb / 18" / fls pale blue / ec North America   84

CAMELLIA - Theaceae
  'Donation' - see C. X williamsii 'Donation'   46
  japonica 'Alba' - HH T, 25'+, white fls   9
  X williamsii 'Donation' - Gh, orchid-pink, semi-double fls   46

CAMPANULA - Campanulaceae
  abietina / P / 2½' / fls light blue / Bulgaria, n Greece   11
  aggregata / P / 2' / blue fls / Bavaria   45
  alliarifolia / P / 16-40" / fls cream-white / Russia to Turkey   11
  allionii / R / 1-2" / fls light purple-blue / w Europe, Alps   43
     "   'Rosea' - pinker form   *
  alpina / R / 10" / fls pale to dark blue / Austria, Italy   35
     "   'Alba' - white fls   *
  americana / A / 1½-6' / fls light blue / e North America   34
     "   'Alba' - white form, botanical record not seen   *
  arvatica / R / 3" / violet to light purple fls / n Spain   35
     "   'Alba' - white stars for the blue   43
  aucheri / R / 4-5" / fls violet-purple / n Iran, Armenia   11
  barbata / P / 4-18" / fls light lilac-blue / Alps, Carpathians   35
     "   'Alba' - white fls   11
  bellidifolia / R / 6" / violet fls / c Caucasus   32
  betulaefolia / R / 6" / white fls, flushed pink / Armenia   35
  bononiensis / P / 1½-3' / fls light purplish-blue / e Eu., sw Asia   11
  'Brantwood' - see C. latifolia 'Brantwood'   85
  X burghaltii - P, 2', satiny gray-blue fls   42
  caespitosa / R / 4-8" / fls deep lilac to white / c Europe   11
  calaminthifolia - see C. orphanidea   85
  carniolica - see C. thrysoides ssp. carniolica   25

(1) - HINTON in Brittonia 27:3

CAMPANULA, con.
```
      carpatica / R / 6-12" / fls in shades of blue / e Eu., Carpathians    42
         "      'Alba' - a white form                                       11
         "      'Blue Clips' - stable 9" strain                             89
         "      'Blue Moonlight' - 6", fls light blue                       17
         "      'Chewton Joy' - 8", smoky-blue fls                          17
         "      'Nana' - dwarf form                                          *
         "      'Pallida' - see C. c. var. turbinata 'Pallida'              89
         "      'Riverslea' - large flat fls, dark blue                     33
         "      v. turbinata - flatter fls, pale blue, 4"                   17
         "          "       'Alba' - fls white                              *
         "          "       'Pallida' - fls pale blue                       89
         "          "       'Pseudoraineri' - deep violet fls, 4"           17
   cashmeriana / R / 5-6" / tubular blue fls / Afghanistan, Kashmir         38
   cenisia / R / 2-3" / fls dark to bright violet-blue / Alps               11
   cephallenica / R / trailing / blue fls / ?                               35
   cervicaria / B / 2-2½' / fls violet-blue / c & n Europe                  11
   charadze / P / 12-16" / violet fls / Caucasus                           (1)
   cochlearifolia / R / 2-4" / blue, mauve, white fls / Alps                42
         "         'Alba'-white form                                        42
   collina / R / 1' / fls deep purple / Caucasus                           35
   X 'Covadonga' - R, 6", bright blue-violet fls                            17
   crispa / B / ? / fls pale blue / Caucasus                               (1)
   X 'Chewton Joy' - see C. carpatica 'Chewton Joy'                         17
   dasyantha / P / 1½-3' / fls blue / e Siberia to Japan                    11
   elatines v. elatinoides - lvs white-tomentose, Udine, Italy              11
         "     v. fenestrellata - glabrous, glossy lvs, Adriatic reg.       11
         "     v. garganica - lvs gray-pubescent, mts. of s Italy           11
         "     v. istriaca - tomentose lvs; corolla to 3/4" long            11
   elatinoides - see C. elatines v. elatinoides                            11
   ephesia / P / 1-1½' / deep blye fls; white-tomentose lvs / w Turkey      11
   excisa / R / 4-6" / fls violet / Swiss & Austrian Alps                   11
   finitima - see C. betulaefolia                                          (2)
   formanekiana / B / 8-12" / white or light blue fls / Greece, Albania     35
   fragilis / HH R / trailing / fls deep blue / s Italy                     43
   garganica - see C. elatines v. garganica                                11
         "     hirsuta - see C. elatines v. garganica                       11
   X 'G. F. Wilson' - 4", violet-purple fls                                 17
   glomerata / P / 2' / fls violet-blue to white / Europe, Siberia          35
         "     v. acaulis - R, 3-6", fls blue-violet                        35
         "     "       'Alba' - fls white                                   17
         "     f. alba - white-flowered form of the type                    51
         "     v. dahurica - 2'+, fls variable, ne Manchuria                11
         "     f. lilacina - lilac-flowered selection                       51
         "     nana - see C. g. var. acaulis                                11
   grossekii / P / 2-2½' / fls violet / Hungary                             11
   X hallii - R, 4", white fls                                             17
   hawkinsiana / R / 4-5" / fls blue-violet / Greece, Albania               11
   hercegovina / R / 4-5" / fls blue-lilac / Jugoslavia                     11
         "       'Alba' - white flowered                                    *
         "       v. nana - compact, erect deep lilac fls, Jugoslavia        43
   incurva / P / 16-20" / fls pale violet to mauve / Greece                 11
   isophylla / Gh / 4-8" / fls deep blue-violet / peninsular Italy          11
         "     v. alba - white fls                                          11
```

9/79

(1) - SHISHKIN & BOBROV in Flora U. S. S. R. Vol. 24 1972 (trans.)

(2) - Anonymous in Quar. Bull. Alpine Garden Soc. 37:4

CAMPANULA, con.
```
  kolenatiana / P / 12-16" / fls rich violet / Caucasus                      11
  lactiflora / P / 5-6' / fls white to milky blue / Caucasus                 42
      "      'Alba' - 4', white fls                                          42
      "      'Lodden Anna' - to 4', fls flesh pink                           85
  lanata / R / trailing / fls ivory to milk-white / Bulgaria                 11
  lasiocarpa / R / 2-6" / fls blue / n Japan to Alaska                       60
      "      'Alba' - white fls                                               *
  latifolia / P / 4-5' / fls bluish-purple / Europe to Kashmir               42
      "      'Alba' - 4', white fls                                          42
      "      'Brantwood' - 4', violet-purple fls                             42
      "      'Macrantha' - bright purple large fls, taller                   44
      "      'Macrantha Alba' - white form                                   25
  latiloba - see C. persicifolia v. sessiliflora                             *
      "     alba - see C. persicifolia v. sessilifolia 'Alba'               *
  linifolia / P / 10-20" / fls lilac to rose-blue / s Europe                 11
  lingulata / B / 12-16" / fls violet in close head / Balkans                11
  longestyla / B / 1-3' / fls amethyst-violet / Caucasus                     11
  longifolia - see C. speciosa                                               11
  lourica / R / 2" / purple fls / Iran                                       33
  makaschvilii / P / 10-20" / pink fls / Caucasus                           (1)
  marchesettii / R / 12" / fls violet, trumpet-shaped / Adriatic reg.        11
  meyeriana / R / prostrate to 4" / violet fls / alps in Caucasus           (1)
  mirabilis / B / 1' / fls pale lilac / w Caucasus                           11
  moesiaca / B / 1½-2' / fls lilac-blue / Balkans                            11
  morettiana / R / 2-3' / solitary lilac fls / Italy, Tyrols                 11
  X 'Mrs. G. F. Wilson' - see C. X 'G. F. Wilson'                            *
  nitida - see C. persicifolia 'Planiflora'                                  33
  ochroleuca / P / 32" / fls ochre-yellow / Caucasus                        (1)
  orphanidea / B / trailing to 6" / fls pale to deep violet / ne Greece      11
  patula / B / 2' / large blue-violet fls / Europe                           87
  peregrina / Gh B / 2' / blue fls / Cape of Good Hope                       45
  persicifolia / P / 1-3' / blue fls / Europe incl. Britain                  42
      "      'Alba' - white form                                             11
      "      'Grandiflora' - larger fls                                      11
      "      'Planiflora' - 9", otherwise typical                           85
      "      'Planiflora Alba' - as above with white fls                     85
      "      v. sessiliflora - 2" sessile fls                                11
      "               "      'Alba' - white fls                             *
  petrophila / R / 2-5" / fls lilac, pale / e Caucasus                       11
  pilosa / R / 4"/fls lilac or blue, erect / Altai Mts., Mongolia            11
      "   dasyantha - see C. dasyantha                                       11
      "   'Superba' - 3", blue fls, Japan                                    38
  piperi / R / 3" / fls clear deep lavender / Olympics, Washington           35
      "   'Sovereigniana' - the white form                                  (2)
  planiflora - see C. persicifolia 'Planiflora'                             85
      "      'Alba' - see C. persicifolia 'Planiflora Alba'                 85
  portenschlagiana / R / 2-4" / fls light bluish-mauve / e Europe            42
      "           'Major' - a gross form?                                    33
  porscharskyana / R / trailing / pale lavender starry fls / nw Jugosl.      35
  prenanthoides / HH P / 12-32" / blue fls / California                      47
  primulifolia / P / 2-3' / fls blue-purple / c Portugal                     11
  pseudoraineri - see C. carpatica v. turbinata 'Pseudoraineri'              17
  pulla / R / 3" / fls deep rich purple / e Europe                           38
  punctata / P / 16-32" fls rose-purple / Japan                              60
      "      'Alba' - dull white fls                                         11
      "      v. microdonta - fls smaller, paler, seashores of Honshu         60
```
6/79-
kw

(1) - SHISHKIN & BOBROV - Flora U. S. S. R. Vol. 24 1972 (trans.)
(2) - ENGLISH in Bull. Am. Rock Garden Soc. 17:3

CAMPANULA, con.
  pusilla - see C. cochlearifolia   35
  X pulloides - R, 4-10", purple fls   11
     "   'Alba' - white fls   *
     "   'G. F. Wilson' - see C. 'G. F. Wilson'   *
  pyramidalis / P or B / 4' / lilac or white fls / Austria, Italy   11
  raddeana / R / 6-16" / fls deep lavender / Caucasus   35
  raineri / R / 2-4" / light blue fls / c Alps   96
  rapunculoides / P / 1-3' / deep purple-blue fls / Europe   38
     "   'Alba' - white form of above weedy sp.   11
  rapunculus / B / 2-3' / lilac fls / Europe, w Asia, N. Africa   35
  rhomboidalis / P / 6-28" / purple-blue fls / Alps, Pyrenees   96
  rigidipila / R / 6-12" / blue fls / Abyssinia   20
  rotundifolia / P / 1-2½' / fls blue-violet / n Europe, n N. Am.   35
     "   v. lancifolia - stem-lvs petioled, northern form   34
  rupestris / HH R / 4-6" / pale lilac fls / Greece   38
  sarmatica / R / 1' / soft gray-blue fls / Caucasus   35
  sarmentosa - see C. rigidipila   85
  sartorii / R / 6-9" / glistening white fls / Andros Is., Greece   35
  saxatilis / R / 3-4" / lilac fls / Crete   11
  saxifraga / R / 5-6" / fls purplish-blue / Caucasus, Asia Minor   38
  scabrella / R / 2-5" / fls bright blue-lilac / California to Wash.   11
  scheuchzeri / R / 1' / dark blue-violet fls / Europe, in mts.   11
     "   'Covadonga' - see C. X 'Covadonga'   17
  scouleri / P / 12-20" / blue to violet fls / Pyrenees   87
  spicata / B / 6-30" / blue-violet fls / Switzerland, Italy   11
  X stansfieldii - R, 4-6", fls violet-purple   11
  thrysoides / R / 6-12" / yellow fls / European Alps   38
     "   ssp. carniolica - P, 2', yellow fls, Alps   25
  thomasiana - probable error for C. tommasiniana   *
  tommasiniana / R / 5-14" / fls pale lilac / Jugoslavia   35
  trachelium / P / 2-3' / fls lilac to white / Europe, Asia   11
     "   'Alba' - the white variant   11
  trautvetteri / R / to 1' / fls lilac / Caucasus in alpine meadows   (1)
  tridentata / R / 5-6" / purplish-blue fls / Caucasus   38
  tubulosa / B / 8-15" / lavender-blue fls / Crete   11
  X van houttei - P, 18", fls indigo-blue or violet   11
  versicolor / P 2' / fls light violet / Greece, c Italy   11
  vidallii / HH P / 1-2' / fls white or cream / Azores   11
  waldsteiniana / R / 4-10" / lavender fls / Jugoslavia   11
  X wockii - R, 2-5", lavender fls   11
  zoysii / R / 3-4" / fls pale lilac, tubular / e Alps   11

CAMPSIS - Bignoniaceae
  radicans / Cl / 30' / fls orange to scarlet / Pa., Fls., Texas   69

CAMPTOSORUS - Polypodiaceae
  rhizophyllus / F / 6" / Walking Fern / nc North America   83

CARAGANA - Leguminosae
  aurantiaca / Sh / 4' / fls orange-yellow / c Asia   13
  pygmaea / Sh / 3-4' / fls yellow / Caucasus, Siberia   13
  tragacanthoides / Sh / 1-1½' / fls yellow / Tibet, n China   13

(1) - SHISHKIN & BOBROV - Flora of the USSR. Vol. 24 1972(trans.)

CARDAMINE - Cruciferae
```
 asarifolia / P / 8-16" / white fls / Pyrenees, Alps            90
 bulbifera / P / 1-2' / fls pale purple / Europe               90
 enneaphyllos / R / to 1' / pendant fls, pale yellow, white / c Eu.  90
 heptaphylla / P / 1-2' / white, pink, purple fls / w & c Europe  90
 pentaphyllos / P / 1-2' / fls white or pale purple / w & c Eu. mts.  90
```

CARDAMINOPSIS - Cruciferae
```
 neglecta / R / 2-8" / purple fls / Carpathians                90
 petraea / R / 4-12" / fls white or purplish / n & c Europe    90
```

CARDIOCRINUM - Liliaceae
```
 cordatum / Bb / to 6' / creamy-white fls / Japan              60
     "   v. glehnii - Bb, 3'+, greenish-white fls, Japan       52
 giganteum / Bb / to 10' / white lilies / Himalayas to Tibet   84
```

CARDUNCELLUS - Compositae
```
 mitissimus / R / sessile / mauve fls / c Spain               (1)
 pinnatus / R / sessile / purplish fls / n Africa              38
     "    f. acaulis - R, sessile, silvery lvs, Atlas Mts.    (2)
 rhapontocoides / R / sessile / fls light violet / n Africa    85
```

CARDUUS - Compositae
```
 kerneri / P / 3' / fls rosy-purple / Bulgaria                 80
 nutans / to 3' / Musk-thistle, showy / Europe, adventive in e N. Am. 34
```

CAREX - Cyperaceae
```
 atrata / P / 6-20" / Black Sedge / ne Europe, nw Asia, Greenland  63
 baldensis / R / tufted, to 8" / Mt. Baldo Sedge / c Europe    85
 buchananii / P / ? / reddish foliage / New Zealand            85
 comans / P / 1½' / grass-like edging plant / New Zealand      85
 grayii / P / to 3' / inflated gray-green lvs / e & c N. America  34
 mertensii / P / to 3' / dense, caespitose / Calif. to Yukon, Montana 59
 morrowii 'Variegata' - HH P, 8-16", white-striped lvs, Japan  60
 pendula / R / 2-6", tufted / spiked pendulous / s Eu., England  85
```

CARLINA - Compositae
```
 acaulis / R / 2" / fls in heads; silky, shiny white / Alps    38
     "   f. caulescens - with longer flower stems              17
 vulgaris / B / 6-15" / purple fls / Europe                   (3)
```

CARMICHAELIA - Leguminosae
```
 australis / HH Sh / 3-12' / fls pale purple / New Zealand     13
 compacta / HH Sh / 3' / purple & white fls / New Zealand      2
 ensyii / Sh / 6-12" / fls bright violet / South Island, New Zealand 13
     "   compacta - see C. ensyii v. nana                      *
     "   v. nana - to 1'+ in height                            43
 monroi / Sh / 6" / white fls, purple veined / New Zealand     2
 odorata / HH Sh / 10' / fragrant fls, lilac-rose / New Zealand 13
```

CARPENTERIA - Saxifragaceae
```
 californica / HH Sh / 6-15' / fls white / California          13
```

CARPINUS - Betulaceae
```
 betulus / T / 35'+ / gray, fluted trunk / Europe, Asia Minor  46
 caroliniana / T / to 40' / American Hornbeam / e North America 13
```

```
 (1) - GORER in Gardeners Chronicle  May 3, 1967
 (2) - Anonymous in Quar. Bull. Alpine Garden Soc.  35:4
 (3) - WEBB - An Irish Flora.  1963
```

CARUM - Umbelliferae
  carvi / B / to 5' / Caraway Seed / Europe, adventive in e US.   34,91

CARYOPTERIS - Verbenaceae
  X clandonensis - Sh, 2', fls bright blue   13

CASSIA - Leguminosae
  artemisioides / HH Sh / 4' / fls yellow / temperate Australia   16
  corymbosa / HH Sh / 5-6' / rich yellow fls / Argentina   13
  covesii / HH Sh / 2' / yellow fls / New Mexico, s & Baja Calif.   74
  didymobotrya - see CHAMAESENNA didymobotrya   (1)
  fasciculata / P / 3' / yellow fls / Mass., Minn., Fla., N. Mex.   73
  marilandica / P / 4' / fls rich yellow / e & c United States   95
  mexicana / HH Sh / 6-10' / petioles and branches velvety / Mexico   29
  nicticans / P / 2' / yellow fls / Mass., Kan., Fla., Texas   71
  stipulacea / HH Sh / 3' / yellow fls / Chile   45

CASSINIA - Compositae
  fulvida / HH Sh / 4' / white fls; yellowish lvs / New Zealand   13
  vauvilliersii / HH Sh / 2-6' / fls white / New Zealand   13

CASSIOPE - Ericaceae
  hypnoides / Sh / 2" / bright pink fls / circumpolar   63
  lycipodioides / Sh / 1-3" / fls white / Japan, Alaska   13
  tetragona / Sh / to 10" / fls white, tinged red / circumpolar   63

CASTILLEJA - Scrophulariaceae
  applegatei / P / 8-20" / fls bright red / California, Oregon   75
  coccinea / A or B / 1-2' / bright scarlet fls / e & c North America   9
  indivisa / A / 8-16" / red fls / Texas, Oklahoma   73
  lindheimeri / R / 1' / fls rose to brick-red / Texas, Colorado   10
  miniata / P / 26-32" / red & green fls / nw United States   75

CATANANCHE - Compositae
  coerulea / P / 2-3' / fls deep mauve / s Europe   42
     "   'Alba' - white fls   9

CATHCARTIA - Papaveraceae
  villosa / R / 8-12" / yellow fls / Nepal, Sikkim, Bhutan   32

CAULOPHYLLUM - Berberidaceae
  thalictroides / P / 2' / blue frs / e North America   35

CAUTLEYA - Zingiberaceae
  lutea / HH P / 18" / fls yellow / Himalayas   32

CEANOTHUS - Rhamnaceae
  americanus / Sh / 3' / fls dull white / e & c United States   13
  integerrimus / HH Sh / 10' / fls white or pale blue / California   13
  prostratus / HH Sh / few inches / fls blue / Calif. to Wash.   13
  pumilus / Sh / small-leaved extreme of C. prostratus, Siskiyous   13
  repens - see C. thyrsiflorus v. repens   (2)
  sanguineus / HH Sh / 10' / white fls; red branches / Ore., Wash.   (3)
  thyrsiflorus prostratus - see C. t. var. repens   13
       "   v. repens - Sh, prostrate, fls pale blue, California   13
  velutinus / HH Sh / 8-10' / fls dull white / California   13

  (1) - SMALL - Manual of the Southeastern Flora. 1933
  (2) - MATHIAS & McCLINTOCK - Checklist of Woody Orn. Pl. of Calif. 1963
  (3) - HAYES & GARRISON - Key to Imp. Woody Plants of e Ore. & Wash.1960

CEDRELA - Meliaceae
  sinensis / T / to 50' / white fls; woody frs / China   69

CEDRONELLA - Labiatae
  mexicana / HH P / 1-3' / bright pink fls / Mexico in mts., Ariz.   9

CELASTRUS - Celastraceae
  scandens / Cl / high / orange frs / e United States   13

CELMISIA - Compositae
  allanii / R / small / gray lvs / New Zealand   21
  alpina / R / 4" / gray-green to white-tomentose lvs / S. Isl., N. Z.   2
  angustifolia / R / low, spreading / gray-green lvs / New Zealand   (1)
  argentea / R / to 8" / close cushions; grayish-white lvs / N. Z.   2
      "   spectabilis - see C. spectabilis   2
  armstrongii / P / 6-24" / fls white daisies / New Zealand   21
  asteliaefolia - see C. gracilenta   2
  bellidifolia - probable error for C. bellidioides   *
  bellidioides / R / 1" / mat of shining green lvs / New Zealand   38
  brevifolia / R / cushion / near woody branches / New Zealand   21
  compacta / Sh / prostrate / buff tomentose lvs / New Zealand   2
  coriacea / P / 10-18" / white fls / South Island, New Zealand   42
      "   v. stricta - narrower silvery lvs; more rigid plant   2
  densiflora / P 1-2' / white fls / South Island, New Zealand   21
  discolor / Sh / prostrate / white satiny leaf-reverse / New Zealand   2
  du reitzii / Sh / 8" / diverse leaf-forms, often wh.-tomentose / N. Z.   2
  glandulosa / R / 6" / glandular bright green lvs / New Zealand   2
  gracilenta / R / low tufted / silvery lvs; fl stems to 16" / N. Z.   2
  haastii / R / compact / slender-stemmed daisies / New Zealand   21
  hectori / R / prostrate / silvery lvs / South Island, New Zealand   33
  hieracifolia / R / 8" / reverse of lvs buff-woolly / New Zealand   43
  hookeri / HH P / 2' / 4-5" daisies / low altitudes in New Zealand   58
  incana / R / small / gray lvs / New Zealand   21
  insignis / R / 12" / narrow-leaved / New Zealand   21
  lanceolata / P / 2' / large lvs / New Zealand   21
  lindsayi / HH R / 8" / crowded, leathery lvs / New Zealand   33
  longifolia / HH R / 9" / white fls / Tasmania, w Australia   16
  lyallii / R / 6-12" / stiff lvs / New Zealand in mts.   33
  mackaui / P / 1-2' / green-leaved / New Zealand   33
  major v. brevis - dwarfed form, silvery-white lvs, New Zealand   2
  monroi / R / to 15" / near to C. coriacea / New Zealand   33
  petiolata / R / 1' / dark green rosettes / S. alps of New Zealand   42
  petriei / P / 2' / fierce foliage / New Zealand   21
  pro-repens / R / low / sticky lvs, 3" long / New Zealand   21
  X pseudolyallii - less rigid lvs, more woolly   2
  ramulosa / R / 1' / semi-shrubby / New Zealand   85
  rigida / R / 1' / tawny-woolly lvs; good fls / New Zealand   21
  saxifraga / HH R / low / pointed silvery lvs / Tasmania   21
  sessiliflora / R / 4" / densely tufted / New Zealand   85
  spectabilis / R / 10" / green lvs, felted beneath / New Zealand   2
  stricta - see C. coriacea v. stricta   2
  traversii / P / 18" / leaf reverse fawn-velvet / S. Is., N. Zealand   33
  verbascifolia / P / 12-16" / tomentose plant / New Zealand   2
  viscosa / R / 6" / stumpy-rayed fls / New Zealand   21
  walkeri / R / creeping / large fls / New Zealand   21
  webbii / Sh / 4-8" / felted gray-green lvs / New Zealand   38

(1) - WARREN in The World of Plants. Rock Garden Conf. Report. 1971

CELSIA - Scrophulariaceae
```
  acaulis - see VERBASCUM acaule                                          92
    "   'Alba' - see VERBASCUM acaule 'Alba'                              *
  arcturus - see VERBASCUM arcturus                                       92
  bugulifolia - see VERBASCUM bugulifolium                                92
  cretica - see VERBASCUM creticum                                        92
  roripifolia - see VERBASCUM roripifolium                                92
  suwarowiana / R / ? / yellow fls / Iran                                (1)
```

CENTAUREA - Compositae
```
  atropurpurea / P / 2-3' / fls black-purple / Hungary                    9
  bella / R / 8-12" / rosy fls / Caucasus                                 32
  cretica / R / nearly stemless / oval lvs, white-hoary / Crete           26
  cyanus / A / 1-2' / varii-colored fls / se Europe                       9
  kerneriana / R / 10" / fls reddish / Bulgaria                           21
  macrocephala / P / 3-4' / yellow fls / Armenia                          9
  montana / P / 1½' / fls purple / Europe                                 42
  nervosa / P / 2-2½' / fls deep purple / c Europe                        9
  pulchra / P / 1-2' / fls deep pink / Kashmir                           (2)
  rhenana - see C. stoebe ssp. rhenana                                   (3)
  rupestris / P / 2½' / fls yellow or orange / se Europe                  10
  scabiosa / P / ? / purplish fls / Europe                                34
  spinosa / HH P / 2' / purple fls / Crete                                45
  simplicicaulis / R / to 12" / fls lilac-pink / Armenia                  6
  stoebe ssp. rhenana / ? / ? / ? / Bulgaria                             (3)
  stricta / R / 12" / blue fls / Hungary                                  45
  uniflora / R / 1' / fls purplish / c Europe                             21
```

CENTAURIUM - Gentianaceae
```
  caespitosum - see C. chloodes                                         29,92
  chloodes / A / 2' / fls rose-red / France                               32
  diffusum - see C. scilloides                                            92
  erythraea / B / to 20" / fls pink to pinkish-purple / Europe            92
     "     ssp. tauricum - scabrid-margined, narrower lvs                 92
  floribundum / A / 4-20" / pink fls / California                         75
  littorale / B / to 10" / pink fls / seasides, n Europe                  92
     "     ssp. uliginosum - B, 16", pinkish fls, ec & c Europe           92
  massonii - see C.scilloides                                             21
  minus - see C. erythraea                                                92
  pulchellum / A / to 8" / rosy-purple fls / Europe                       92
  scilloides / A / tufted / deep rose-pink fls / Eu., including Brit.     38
  umbellatum - see C. erythraea                                           85
  vulgare - see C. erythraea ssp. tauricum                                92
  uliginosum - see C. littorale ssp. uliginosum                          92
```

CEPHALANTHERA - Orchidaceae
```
  damasonianum / P / to 2' / white or cream fls / Eu., Asia Minor         30
```

CEPHALANTHUS - Rubiaceae
```
  occidentalis / Sh / 3-6' / creamy-white fls / e North America          13
```

CEPHALARIA - Dipsaceae
```
  alpina / P / 5-6' / sulphur-yellow fls / European Alps                  9
  leucantha / P / 16-32" / creamy-white fls / s Europe                   9,32
```

```
  (1) - PARSA - Flore de l'Iran. Vol. 4 1952
  (2) - BLOOM - Hardy Plants of Distinction. 1965
  (3) - STOYANOFF & STEFANOFF - Flora of Bulgaria (Bulgarian text) 1943
```

CERASTIUM - Cruciferae
  alpinum / R / 2-8" / fls white / n Europe, s in mts.   90
    "   ssp. lanatum - plant grayish to whitish-lanate   90
  arvense ssp. lerchenfeldianum - R, to 1', Carpathians   90
    "   ssp. thomasii - R, caespitose, lvs sessile, c Italy   90
  beeringianum / R / low tufts / few-flowered / As. & Canadian arctic   63
  bialnickii - see C. beeringianum   63
  biebersteinii / R / t0 1' / white-lanate lvs, invasive / Crimea   90
  candidissimum / R / to 1' / white to yellowish-lanate / Greece   90
  carinthiacum / R / 8" / white fls; shining lvs / Alps, Carpathians   90
  latifolium / R / to 4" / white fls / Alps, Apennines   90
  lerchenfeldianum - see C. arvense ssp. lerchenfeldianum   90
  maximum / P / 8-16" / white fls / N. Asia, N. North America   90
  purpurascens / R / 4" / fls white / Asia Minor   9
  pyrenaicum / R /.to 4" / fls white / e Pyrenees   90
  thomasii - see C. arvense ssp. thomasii   90
  tomentosum / R / vigorous creeper / lvs Grayish-woolly / Europe   9
  uniflorum / R / 4" / lvs soft bright green / Alps, Carpathians   90

CERATOSTIGMA - Plumbaginaceae
  plumbaginoides / R / to 1' / fls deep blue / China   9
  willmottianum / HH Sh / 2-4' / bright blue fls / w Szechuan   13

CERCIS - Leguminosae
  canadensis / T / to 40' / fls pale rose / e & c United States   13
  chinensis / Sh / 18' / pink fls / China   13
  occidentalis / HH Sh / 15' / fls reddish-purple / California   46
  siliquastrum / HH T / 40' / fls purplish-rose / Europe   13

CERCOCARPUS - Rosaceae
  ledifolius / HH T / 40' / evergreen lvs / Oregon to New Mexico   13
  montanus / HH Sh / to 10' / frs long-tailed / Oregon, California   13

CERINTHE - Boraginaceae
  major / A / 6-15" / fls yellow & purple / Medit. region   9
  minor / A or B / 6-24" / fls yellow / c & e Europe   92

CETERACH - Polypodiaceae
  officinarum / F / to 10" / dry rock fern / Europe   90

CHAENOMELES - Rosaceae
  japonica / Sh / to 3' / fls orange to blood-red / Japan   13
  lagenaria - see C. speciosa   13
  maulei - see C. japonica   13
  speciosa / Sh / to 10' / fls scarlet to blood-red / China   13

CHAENORHINUM - Scrophulariaceae
  glareosum / R / 6" / fls mauve-tipped / Spain   17
  origanifolium / R / 6" / fls rose-purple / Pyrenees   33
  villosum / R / to 1' / lilac & yellow fls / s Spain, sw France   92

CHAMAECYPARIS - Pinaceae
  lawsoniana / HH T / 200' / bark reddish-brown / Oregon, California   13
    "   'Columnaris' - to 20', narrowly conical   28
  nootkatensis 'Lutea' - to 100', young shoots yellow   13
    "   'Pendula' - erect trunk, branches hang vertically   13
  obtusa / T / 100' / soft feathery foliage / Japan   13
  thyoides / T / 50' / columnar, branches fan-shaped / e N. America   13
    "   'Andeleyensis' - 18', narrowly columnar, part juvenile lvs   46

CHAMAECYTISUS - Leguminosae
  albus / Sh / 12-32" / white fls / c & se Europe   91
  austriacus / Sh / 6-28" / deep yellow fls / ec & se Europe   91
  banaticus / Sh / 12-32" / pale yellow fls / ec Europe, ne Balkans   91
  hirsutus / Sh / 3' / fls yellow or pinkish-yellow / c & e Europe   91
  purpureus / Sh / to 1' / fls lilac-pink to purplish / s & se Alps   91
      "   'Roseus' - selection for pink fls   *
  pygmaeus / Sh / to 6" / yellow fls / e Balkans   91
  ratisbonensis / Sh / 1-1½' / fls yellow, orange spots / c Europe   91
  supinus / Sh / to 2' / yellow fls / c & s Europe   91

CHAMAEDAPHNE - Ericaceae
  calyculata / Sh / 2-3' / white fls / e N. America, Europe, Asia   13

CHAMAENERION latifolium - see EPILOBIUM latifolium   91

CHAMAESENNA - Leguminosae
  didymobotrya / HH Sh / ? / large yellow fls / Africa   (1)

CHARIEIS - Compositae
  heterophylla / A / 6-12" / blue fls / w Cape of Good Hope   9

CHASMANTHE - Iridaceae
  aethiopica / Gh C / 3' / scarlet fls / Ethiopia   36
  floribunda / Gh C / 2' / orange fls / Cape Province   36

CHEILANTHES - Polypodiaceae
  argentea / F / 4" / white farina, reddish rachis / Siberia   50
  gracillima / F / 4" / minute bead-like pinnae / Idaho, California   9
  marantae / F / 6-10" / evergreen, rusty red scales / s Europe   50
  siliquosa / F / to 1' / continuous revolute indusium / n N. Am.   34

CHEIRANTHUS - Cruciferae
  allionii - see ERYSIMUM perofskianum   42
  linifolius - see ERYSIMUM linifolium   90
  semperflorens / Gh Sh / 9-24" / pale lilac & white fls / Morocco   85

CHELIDONIUM - Papaveraceae
  majus 'Flore Plena' - P, 2', double yellow fls   (2)
      " v. laciniatum (Bowles Var.) - single fls; cut lvs   90

CHELONE - Scrophulariaceae
  glabra / P / 2-3' / white fls / e & c North America   35
  lyoni / P / 3-4' / fls clear pink / s United States   44
  obliqua / P / 2' / fls deep rose / sc United States   9

CHERLERA sedoides - see MINUARTIA sedoides   90

CHIASTOPHYLLUM - Crassulaceae
  oppositifolium / R / 10" / small golden-yellow fls / Caucasus   6

CHILIOTRICHUM - Compositae
  amelloides diffusum - see C. diffusum   46
  diffusum / HH Sh / 3-5' / evergreen lvs; white daisies / s S. Am.   46

  (1) - SMALL - Manual of the Southeastern Flora. 1933
  (2) - HADFIELD in Gardeners Chronicle April 2, 1960

CHIMAPHILA - Ericaceae
S'82 - maculata / R / 6" / waxy white fls / e North America   35
   menziesii / R / 2-6" / white fls / nw North America   75
F79 umbellata / R / 5" / fls white or roseate / Asia, Europe   60
     "   v. occidentalis - coarser plant to 1' in N. Am.   34

CHIMONANTHUS - Calycanthaceae
   fragrans - see C. praecox   13
   praecox / Sh / 8' / early yellow-green fls / China   13
     "   'Grandiflorus' - has showier yellow fls   13

CHIOGENES gaultheria hispidula - see GAULTHERIA hispidula   *

CHIONODOXA - Liliaceae
   gigantea / Bb / 10" / fls pale purple-blue / Turkey   84
     "   'Alba' - good white form   84
   luciliae / Bb / 6" / blue & white fls / Turkey   42
     "   'Alba' - white form   84
     "   'Gigantea' - see C. gigantea   *
     "   'Pink Giant' - 6", tall pink form   84
     "   'Rosea' - 5", fls lilac-pink, white eye   4
   sardensis / Bb / to 8" / fls porcelain-blue / Turkey   42
   tmoli / Bb / 4" / fls violet-blue, white eye / Boz Dagh, Turkey   4

CHIONOGRAPHIS - Liliaceae
   japonica v. hisauchiana - R, white fls, Honshu   60

CHLORAEA - Orchidaceae
   magellanica / HH P / 18" / white fls, black veins & lip / Magellan St37

CHLORANTHUS - Chloranthaceae
   serratus / P / 12-20" / small white fls / Japan, China   60

CHLOROGALUM - Liliaceae
   pomeridianum / HH P / 2-9' / fls white / California, Oregon   9

CHORIZEMA - Leguminosae
   cordatum / Gh Sh / 2-4' / orange or red fls / Australia   41

CHRYSANTHEMUM - Compositae
   alpinum / R / 6" / glistening white daisies / Alps of Europe   35
     "   v. tomentosum - ash gray down, Corsica   33
   anserinifolium / P / 2' / cut lvs; good daisies / Orient   81
   arcticum / R / 3-15" / large white fls / arctic Eurasia   9
   aricerinifolium / R / 6" / green lvs; single fls / ?   81
   atratum / R / to 1' / white daisies / European Alps   32
   catananche / HH R / 4" / crimson backed white daisies / Morocco   43
   coccineum / P / 1-2' / varii-colored fls / Caucasus, Iran   9
   coronarium / A / 3-4' / light yellow to white fls / Medit. region   9
   frutescens / Gh / 3' / white or lemon yellow fls / Canary Isls.   9
   haradjani - see TANACETUM haradjani   85
   hispanicum / R / 2-10" / white, yellow, purple fls / alps of Spain   33
   hosmariense / HH R / 6" / white fls / Morocco   85
   leucanthemum / P / 1-2' / the common & weedy Field Daisy / Eurasia   9
   nipponicum / P / 2' / fls bright white / Japan   9
   pallasianum japonicum - see C. rupestre   60

CHRYSANTHEMUM, con.
  parthenium / P / 1-3' / small white fls / Europe to Caucasus   9
     "   'Aureum' - golden lvs   (1)
     "   'Golden Feverfew' - see C. p. 'Aureum'   *
     "   'Lemon Ball' - 12-18", light yellow fls   (1)
  roseum - see C. coccineum   9
  rupestre / R / to 7" / silvery lvs; rayless fls / Honshu, in mts.   60
  tomentosum - see C. alpinum v. tomentosum   *
  vulgare / P / 2'+ / fls yellow / Far East   60
  weyrichii / R / 4-6" / pink ray florets / Kamchatka   85

CHRYSOBRACTRON hookeri - see BULBINELLA hookeri   33

CHRYSOGONUM - Compositae
  virginianum / R / 6-9" / fls yellowish gold / e N. Am.   42

CHRYSOPSIS - Compositae
  falcata / R / 1' / golden daisies / Massachusetts to New Jersey   35
  mariana / P / 1-2' / golden-yellow fls / New York to Florida   35
  pinifolia / HH P / 8-16" / yellow fls / Taylor County, Georgia   (2)
  villosa / P / 8-40" / golden-yellow fls / c North America   35
    "   v. rutteri - in the tallest range, later fls   9

CHUSQUEA - Gramineae
  cummingii / Gh Sh / 6-10' / Bamboo / Andes Mts, Chile   13

CICHORIUM - Compositae
  intybus / P / 1-8' / sky-blue fls / Medit. region; weedy in US   68

CIMICIFUGA - Ranunculaceae
  acerina / P / 20-48" / fls white / Japan   60
  americana / P / 5' / white fls / New York & southwards   35
  dahurica / P / 6' / fls white / c Asia   32
  elata / P / 3-7' / white or pinkish fls / w Washington, nw Oregon   75
  japonica v. acerina - see C. acerina   60
  racemosa / P / 5-7' / fls creamy-white / North America   42

CIRCAEA - Onagraceae
  lutetiana / P / 1-3' / small white fls / e N. Am., in wet woods   9

CIRSIUM - Compositae
  acaule / R / large rosette / fls purplish, rarely flesh / Europe   32
  casabonae / P / 3' / fls pale purple / s Europe   32
  diacanthum / P / 3' / purple fls / e Asia, Syria   32
  eriophorum / P / to 4½' / blue-violet fls / c Europe, Russia   32
  japonicum / P / to 3' / fls purplish to rose / Japan   60
  spinosissimum / P / 16-20" / yellowish-white fls / Alps   32
  virginianum / B / to 3'+ / fls purplish / New Jersey to Florida   34

CISSUS - Vitaceae
  striata / Gh Cl / low / fls yellowish / Chile, s Brazil   9

CISTUS - Cistaceae
  albidus / HH Sh / 5' / fls pale rosy-lilac / sw Europe, n Africa   13
  crispus / HH Sh / 2' / fls purplish red / sw Europe, n Africa   13
  X cyprius - HH Sh, 6-8', fls white, red-blotched   13
    " v. albiflorus - petals without blotch   13

(1) - BOOTH - An Encyclopedia of Annual and Biennial Plants. 1957
(2) - SMALL - Manual of the Southeastern Flora. 1933

CISTUS, con.
  incanus / HH Sh / 3' / fls purplish pink / s Europe   91
  ladanifer / HH Sh / 3-5' / fls white, red blotched / s Eu., n Afr.   13
      "   v. albiflorus - pure white fls   13
  laurifolius / HH Sh / 6-8' / white fls / sw Europe   13
  monspeliensis / HH Sh / white fls / s Europe, n Africa   13
  palhinhae / HH Sh / to 2' / satin white fls / Algarve, Portugal   13
  palinhaii - error for C. palhinhae   *
  psilosepalus / HH Sh / 3'+ / fls white / Portugal, w Spain   91
  salvifolius / HH Sh / 2' / fls white, yellow at base / Medit. reg.   13
  'Silver Pink' - 2', fls clear pink   6
  symphytifolius / HH Sh / 2-6' / fls purplish-pink / Canary Isls.   13
  villosus - see C. incanus   91

CITRULLUS - Cucurbitacaea
  colocynthis / HH Cl / high / pale yellow fls / India   85

CLADOTHAMNUS - Ericaceae
  pyroliflorus / Sh / 3-6' / fls rosy / Alaska, British Columbia   13

CLADRASTIS - Leguminosae
  lutea / T / 50' / fls white / se United States   13

CLARKIA - Onagraceae
  purpurea ssp. quadrivulnaria - A, to 20", lavender-purple or red fls 59
  quadrivulnaria - see C. p. ssp quadrivulnaria   (Wash., Calif.)   59
  rubicunda v. blasdalei - A, 1-3', rose-pink to lavenderfls, Calif.   59

CLAYTONIA - Portulacaceae
  megarhiza v. nivalis - R, 2", deep rose fls, Wenatchee Mts., Wash.   (1)
  nivalis - see C. megarhiza v. nivalis   (1)
  sibirica / R / 6-18" / fls white to rose / Alaska to Montana   (1)
  umbellata / R / 5" / fls rose or white / c & n Sierra Nevada, US   75
  virginica / R / 4-8" / fls white, pink-striped / e & c US   35

CLEMATIS - Ranunculaceae
  addisonii / P / to 3' / fls reddish to purplish / West Virginia   34
  afoliata / HH Cl / 3'+ / fls greenish-white / New Zealand   13
  albicoma / P / 2' / fls purplish / Virginia, West Virginia   34
      "   v. coactilis - with felty lvs   34
  alpina / Cl / 8' / blue fls / n Eu., n Asia - s-wards in mts.   13
      "   'Alba' - see C. alpina v. sibirica   9
      "   'Pamela Jackson' - rich, deep azure fls   (2)
      "   v. sibirica - the white form   9
  aristata / HH Cl / high / fls white; evergreen lvs / Australia   9
  australis / HH Cl / high / fls white or pale yellow / New Zealand   10
  baldwinii / HH P / 1-2' / fls blue or lavender / Florida   72
  campaniflora / Cl / to 20' / fls white, tinged violet / Portugal   13
  campanifolia - error for C. campaniflora   *
  chrysocoma / HH Sh / 6-8' / white fls, tinged pink / Yunnan   13
  cirrhosa / HH Cl / 10' / fls whitish / s Europe, Asia Minor   9
      "   v. balearica - less hardy, dark green lvs, finely cut   13
  columbiana / Cl / 5' / fls violet-blue or white / Texas to Montana   (3)
      "   v. dissecta - P, 18"+, fls reddish-violet, Wash. in mts.   (3)
      "   v. tenuiloba - P, 3', fls violet-blue, Mont.-S. Dakota   (3)

(1) - DAVIS in Brittonia 18:4
(2) - PRINGLE in Baileya 19:2
(3) - PRINGLE in Brittonia 23:4

CLEMATIS, con.
'Crimson King' - Cl, large wine-red fls 32
crispa / Cl / to 8' / fls bluish-purple / se United States 13
douglasii / P / 2' / fls pale purple, deeper within / Mont., N. Mex. . 9
    "   v. scottii - 2', fls purple, Montana to New Mexico 9
    "   "   'Rosea' - lighter colored form .... *
'Ernest Markham' - see C. viticella 'E. M' .... *
fargesii / Cl / 18' / white fls / w China 46
flammula / Cl / 10' / fragrant white fls / s Europe 13
gentianoides / HH P / 1' / single fl to a stem / Australia 32
glaucophylla / Cl / low / fls reddish-purple / sc United States 34
'Hagley' - Cl, to 6', large shell-pink fls 85
'Henryi' - see C. lawsoniana 'Henryi' .... *
heracleaefolia / P / 4' / fls light blue / China 9
    "   v. davidiana - fls brighter blue 9
hirsutissima / P / 8-28" / fls purplish-brown / Mont., Wash., Ore. . 74
integrifolia / P / 3' / fls violet or blue / Europe, Asia 13
lanuginosa v. candida - Cl, 5', white fls 9
lasiantha / Cl / high / fls white / California 9
X lawsoniana 'Henryi' - HH Cl, large white fls .... (1)
ligusticifolia / Cl / 20' / fls white / w North America 13
macropetala / Cl / 6' / fls violet-blue / China, Siberia 13
    "   f. alba - white fls .... (2)
    "   markhamii - see C. m. 'Markhams Pink' 85
    "   'Markhams Pink' - fls rose-colored 85
    "   f. rosea - purplish-pink fls .... (2)
marata / HH Cl / small / greenish-yellow fls / New Zealand 2
microphylla / Gh Cl / ? / white fls / Australia 29
'Mme. Edouard Andre' - Cl, velvety-red fls, large 32
'Mrs. Cholmondeley' - Cl, large pale blue fls 85
montana / Cl / 20' / large white fls / Himalayas 13
    "   'Rosea' - pinkish fls .... *
    "   'Rubens' - Chinese variety with rosy-red fls 13
'Nellie Moser' - Cl, large pale mauve-pink fls with carmine bar . 85
occidentalis / Cl / to 10' / fls pinkish-violet / Va. to Ontario . (3)
ochroleuca / P / 1-2' / yellow fls / New York to Georgia 9
orientalis / Cl / to 20' / fls yellow / Caucasus, Iran, Manchuria . 13
    "   'Sherriffs Var.' - nodding yellow bells 85
paniculata / HH Cl / high / white fls / New Zealand 13
petriei / HH Cl / high / greenish-yellow fls / New Zealand 2
pitcheri / Cl / 12' / fls purplish-blue / c United States 13
quadribracteolata / HH R / trailing / fls dull light purple / N. Z. . 2
'Ramona' - Cl, large lavender-blue fls .... (4)
recta / R / 1' / fls white / s & e Europe 42
   "   v. mandshurica - taller and slenderer 9
   "   f. purpurea - purple lvs early in the season 42
rehderiana / HH Cl / 25' / primrose-yellow fls / w China 13
scottii - see C. douglasii v. scottii 13
    "   rosea - see C. douglasii v. scottii 'Rosea' 9
stans / P / to 3'+ / fls pale purple-blue / Honshu 60
tangutica / Cl / to 15' / fls rich yellow / c Asia 13
    "   v. obtusiuscula - free flowering and strong growing . 46
tenuiloba - see C. columbiana v. tenuiloba .... (3)
texensis / Cl / high / fls in shades of red / Texas 13
    "   'Gravetye Beauty' - cherry-red fls 85

(1) - MATHIAS - Color for the Landscape. 1973
(2) - PRINGLE in Baileya 19:2
(3) - PRINGLE in Brittonia 23:4
(4) - SPINGARN in National Horticultural Mag. 14:1

CLEMATIS, con.
  'The President' - Cl, large purple-blue fls   85
  verticillaris - see C. occidentalis   (1)
      "   v. columbiana - see C. columbiana   (1)
  'Ville de Lyon' - Cl, carmine-red fls   85
  viorna / Cl / to 10' / fls dull reddish-purple / e United States   13
  virginiana / Cl / 20' / fls dull white / e North America   13
  viticaulis / P / 2' / purplish fls / Bath Co., Virginia   34
  viticella / Cl / 12' / fls blue, purple, rosy-purple / s Europe   13
    "   'Ernest Markham' - dark petunia-red fls   32

CLEOME - Capparidaceae
  spinosa 'Helen Campbell' - A, 3', white fls   89

CLETHRA ⚬ Clethraceae
  barbinervis / Sh / to 10' / fls white / Japan   13

CLIANTHUS - Leguminosae
  puniceus / HH Cl / 8' / crimson fls / New Zealand   (2)
    "   'Albus' - white form   46

CLIFTONIA - Cyrillaceae
  monophylla / HH T / 30'+ / fls white or pinkish / Ga., Fla., La.   69

CLINTONIA - Liliaceae
  andrewsiana / R / to 1½' / fls pink, nodding / s Oregon, Calif.   35
  borealis / R / 1-2' / greenish fls; blue frs / ne North America   35
  nivalis - error for CLAYTONIA nivalis   *
  umbellata / R / 15" / white fls; black frs / ne North America   35
  umbellulata / R / 1' / white fls / Allegheny Mts. & s-wards   9
  uniflora / R / 6" / white fls / California to Alaska   35

CLITORIA - Leguminosae
  ternatea / Gh A Cl / 15' / bright blue fls / India   41

CNEORUM - Cneoraceae
  tricoccon / HH Sh / 3' / yellow fls; red frs / coastal Spain   65

CNICUS - Compositae
  acaulis - see CIRSIUM acaule   *
  benedictus / P / 2' / fls yellow / Medit. region, Caucasus   9
  casabonae - see CIRSIUM casabonae   32
  diacantha - see CIRSIUM diacantha   32
  spinosissimum - see CIRSIUM spinosissimum   32

COCCULUS - Menispermaceae
  carolinus / HH Cl / 12' / red frs / Virginia to Texas   9

COCHLEARIA - Cruciferae
  alpina / B / to 20" / fls white or mauve / Britain   90

CODONOPSIS - Campanulaceae
  clematidea / P / 1'+ / fls pale blue / mts. of Asia   35
  convolvulacea / P / 2-3' / blue fls / Himalayas, w China   38
  dicentrifolia / P / 2' / violet-blue fls / Nepal   85
  handeliana / P / twining to 3' / yellow fls / w China   11
  lanceolata / P / twining to 3' / purple fls / e Asia   (3)
  meleagris / P / 2' / yellowish fls / sw China   35

(1) - PRINGLE in Brittonia 23:4
(2) - MATHIAS - Color for the Landscape. 1973
(3) - STEWARD - Vascular Plants of the Lower Yangtze. 1958

CODONOPSIS, con.
  mollis / P / ? / fls bluish purple / Tibet   (1)
  ovata / R / 6-12" / fls china-blue / Himalayas   42
  rotundifolia / P / 3' / fls gray-blue to purple / Kashmir   11
     "   v. angustifolia - fls dull green, se Tibet   (1)
  tangshen / P / 3'+ / greenish fls / w China   32
  tubulosa / P / 15', twining / yellowish-green fls / ?   25
  ussuriensis / P / twiner / purplish fls / Manchuria   11
  vinciflora / P / twining / lilac fls / w China   9
  viridiflora / P/ twining to 4' / fls yellowish-green / w China   11

COELOGLOSSUM - Orchidaceae
  viride / Tu / 4-14" / fls greenish-yellow / n hemisphere   30

COLCHICUM - Liliaceae
  alpinum / Tu / 1" / rosy lilac fls / European Alps   36
  arenarium / Tu/2" / fls reddish-lilac / Balkans   32
  atropurpureum / Tu / ? / deep reddish-purple fls / ?   56
  autumnale / Tu / 4-8" / fls soft rosy-lilac / Europe   42
     "   f. album - white fls on 4" stems   4
     "   alpinum - see C. alpinum   56
     "   f. minor - small form, rosy-mauve fls   43
  boissieri / Tu / ? / deeply colored fls / Greece   21
  bornmulleri - see C. speciosum v. bornmulleri   84
  corsicum / Tu / ? / lilac-rose fls / Corsica   43
  giganteum / Tu / 1' / pale pink fls / Turkey   (2)
  hydrophilum / Tu / ? / pink fls / Taurus Mts., Asia Minor   18
  illyricum - confused name in Colchicum   18
  kesselringii / Tu / 6" / white fls, striped / s Russia, Afghanistan   (2)
  sibthorpii / Tu / 6" / lilac fls / Greece   36
  speciosum / Tu / 10" / variable purple shades / Asia Minor   42
     "   f. album - 6", large white fls   4
     "   'Atrorubens' - rich purplish-crimson fls   84
     "   v. bornmulleri - 6", lilac fls, Turkey   4
     "   giganteum - see C. giganteum   56
     "   illyricum - see C. giganteum   (3)
     "   'Violet Queen' - deep purplish-violet   84
  stevenii / HH Tu / 3" / rosy mauve fls / Palestine   36

COLLINSIA - Scrophulariaceae
  bicolor - see C. heterophylla   34
  heterophylla / A / 8-20" / white & violet fls / California   75
  verna / A / 6" / blue & white fls / e & c United States   71

COLLOMIA - Polemoniaceae
  grandiflora / A / 4-40" / fls salmon to light yellow / w N. America   75

COLURIA - Rosaceae
  geoides / R / to 10" / bright yellow fls / Siberia   (4)
  laxmannii - see C. geoides   (4)

COLUTEA - Leguminosae
  arborescens / Sh / to 12' / yellow fls / se Europe   13
  X intermedia - see C. X media   *
  X media - to 10', fls brownish-red or coppery   13
  orientalis / Sh / to 6' / fls reddish brown / Caucasus to Turkestan   69

  (1) - FINLAY in Jour. Royal Hort. Society. Feb. 1972
  (2) - FURSE in RHS Lily Yearbook 1968
  (3) - BURTT in RHS Lily Yearbook 1962
  (4) - KOMAROV - Flora U. S. S. R. Vol. 10

COLUTEOCARPUS - Crucuferae
  reticulatus - see C. vescicaria   26
  vescicaria / R / to 7" / white fls / Transcaucasia   26

COMARUM palustre - see POTENTILLA palustris   63

COMBERA - Solanaceae
  paradoxa / R / rosette / white & bluish fls / Argentina, sub-alpine 21

COMMELINA - Commelinaceae
  benghalensis / A / creeping / small pale blue fls / tropical Asia   60
  coelestis / HH Tu / to 8" / fls blue / Mexico, in mts.   32
  dianthifolia / HH Tu / 4-6" / clear blue fls / Mexico, Texas   56
  sikkimensis / HH R / prostrate / sky-blue fls / Sikkim, Khasia Hills 37

CONANDRON - Gesneriaceae
  ramondioides / R / to 1' / fls purple / Japan   60

CONANTHERA - Tecophilaeaceae
  bifolia / HH C / 3½-12" / fls purple / Chile   56
  campanulata / HH C / to 1' / fls variable, white to purple / Chile 56
  simsii - see C. campanulata   9

CONVALLARIA - Liliaceae
  majalis / R / 6-8" / fls white / Europe, Asia   38
    "   'Flore Plena' - doubled fls   57
    "   'Fortins Var.' - fls ten days later than the type (1)
    "   'Rosea' - a pink form   38

CONVOLVULUS - Convolvulaceae
  althaeoides / R / trailing / fls pale red or lilac / Medit. region 85
  calvertii / R / to 1' / fls white to pink / sw Asia, Crimea   92
  cantabrica / P / 5-16" / fls pink / s & sc Europe   92
  cneorum / HH Sh / 2-3' / fls white tinged pink / s Europe   13
  demissus / R / dwarf / purple-pink fls / Andes Mts., Chile   21
  mauritanicus - see C. sabatius   92
  sabatius / HH P / 5-20" / fls pink to blue / nw Italy   92
  soldanella - see CALYSTEGIA soldanella   92
  tauricus - see C. calvertii   92

COOPERIA pedunculata - see ZEPHRANTHES drummondii   (2)

COPROSMA - Rubiaceae
  brunnea / HH Sh / sprawling / fls small; translucent blue frs / N.Z. 78
  cheesemannii / HH Sh / prostrate / orange globose frs / N. Zealand 78
  nitida / HH Sh / 3' / fls white; orange frs / alpine Tasmania, Vict. 16
  petriei / HH Sh / 2-3" / blue frs; dioecious / New Zealand   13
    "   v. atropurpurea - with port-wine frs   13
  pseudocuneata / HH Sh / to 9' / scarlet frs / New Zealand   2
  pumila / HH Sh / prostrate / orange frs / New S. Wales, Australia (3)

COPTIS - Ranunculaceae
  groenlandica / R / to 5" / fls white / e North America   34
  trifolia / R / to 4" / fls white / Europe, Asia   60
    "   groenlandica - see C. groenlandica   34

  (1) - THOMAS in Jour. Royal Hort. Soc. May 1967
  (2) - GOULD - Texas Plants: A Checklist & Ecological Summary. 1962
  (3) - VALDER in Jour. Royal Hort. Soc. Sept. 1964

CORALLORHIZA - Orchidaceae
maculata / P / 1½-2' / usually crimson-purple fls / United States   23
mertensiana / P / 8-15" / greenish or purplish fls nw N. America   9
trifida / R / 1' / yellowish-white to purple fls / n temperate zone   23

CORALLOSPARTIUM - Leguminosae
crassicaule / HH Sh / to 6' / leafless, green stems / New Zealand   78

CORDYLINE - Liliaceae
australis / Gh T / 25' / used as juvenile seedlings / New Zealand   9
banksii / Gh Sh / narrow lvs to 5' long / New Zealand   32
indivisa - mostly referrable to C. australis   9

COREOPSIS - Compositae
angustifolia / P / 1-3' / fls yellow / s United States   9
auriculata / P / 6-24" / fls yellow / Virginia to Kentucky & s-ward   72
    " 'Nana' - 4-6", orange-yellow fls   44
X 'Baby Sun' - 20", bright yellow fls, uniform from seed   44
grandiflora saxicola - see C. saxicola   *
lanceolata / P / 1-2' / yellow fls / e United States   9
maritima / P gr. as A / 1-3' / yellow & gold fls / s California   74
palmata / P / 2-3' / yellow fls / Canada to Oklahoma   76
pubescens / P / 1½-3' / yellow fls / se United States   83
saxicola / HH P / to 3' / yellow fls / Georgia, Alabama   72
verticillata / P / 1½-2' / small yellow fls / e United States   42

CORETHROGNE - Compositae
californica / HH Sh / prostrate / flesh-pink daisies / Calif.   43

CORIARIA - Coriariaceae
terminalis v. xanthocarpa - Sh, 2-4', yellow frs, Sikkim   13

CORNUS - Cornaceae
alternifolia / Sh / to 20' / black frs, bloomy / e North America   13
amomum / Sh / to 10' / frs pale blue / e North America   13
canadensis / R / 6" / creamy-white bracted fl head / North America   42
candidissimum - see C. racemosa   13
florida / T / 10-20' / showy white bracts / e United States   13
    " f. rubra - bracts in some shade of pink   13
kousa / T / to 20' / creamy-white bracts / Japan, China   13
    " v. chinensis - 30', showier bracts, Hupeh   13
mas / Sh / to 25' / early yellow fls / Europe   13
nuttallii / HH T / to 50' / white-bracted / w North America   13
occidentalis / Sh / 6-18' / yellowish fls; white frs / B. C. to Cal.   13
racemosa / Sh / 8-10' / white frs on red stalks / e & c U. S.   13
stolonifera / Sh / to 8' / red-barked; white frs / North America   13
    " occidentalis - see C. occidentalis   93
suecica / R / to 10" / whitish bracts / n Europe   91

COROKIA - Cornaceae
cotoneaster / HH Sh / to 8' / fls bright yellow / New Zealand   13

CORONILLA - Leguminosae
coronata / P / 12-28" / yellow fls / c Europe   91
emerus / Sh / 6' / bright yellow fls / c & s Europe   46
glauca / HH Sh / to 10' / rich yellow fls / s Europe   13
minima / Sh / 1' / fls yellow / c Europe   91
montana - see C. coronata   91
vaginalis / Sh / to 32" / fls yellow / Europe, in mts.   91

CORTADERIA - Gramineae
argentea pumila - see C. selloana 'Pumila'   85
richardii / HH Gr / 4-10' / panicles silvery-white / New Zealand   85
selloana 'Pumila' - 6', silvery-white panicles   85
toe-toe - common name for C. richardii   85

CORTUSA - Primulaceae
matthioli / R / 6" / clean rosy purple fls / Swiss Alps   35
    "   'Alba' - a white form   38
    "   v. pekinensis - the north-Asian variety   32
pekinensis - see C. matthioli v. pekinensis   32
turkestanica / P / to 2' / violet fls / c Asia   (1)

CORYDALIS - Papaveraceae
angustifolia / R / 4-8" / pale yellow or white fls / Iran   90
aurea / A / 6" / fls golden yellow / North America   9
bulbosa / R / to 14" / fls purplish / Europe   90
cashmeriana / R / 6" / clear blue fls / Kashmir   38
cava - see C. bulbosa   90
chaerophylla / P / to 30" / bright yellow fls / c Himalayas   (2)
cheilanthifolia / R / 8" / fls yellow / China   38
glauca - see C. sempervirens   85
lutea / P / to 28" / fls golden yellow / c & e Alps   90
  " 'Alba' - cream-white fls, true from seed   33
micrantha / P / 8-20" / pale yellow fls / c United States   34
nobilis / P / 1-1½' / fls pale yellow / Siberia   85
ochroleuca / R / 1' / fls yellowish white / Italy, Jugoslavia   32
ophiocarpa / P / to 32" / fls greenish-yellow / w Asia   60
rupestris / R / compact / high alpine, thick tap-root / Iran   (2)
scouleri / P / 2-4' / fls pink or white / Oregon to British Columbia   75
sempervirens / A or B / to 3' / fls light pale purple & yel. / N. Am   (2)
solida / Tu / 4" / purple fls / Europe   42
wilsonii / HH R / 7" / fls bright yellow / China   35

CORYLOPSIS - Hamamelidaceae
spicata / Sh / 6'+ / bright yellow fls / Japan   46

CORYLUS - Corylaceae
colurna / T / 60' / catkins early (Feb.) / se Europe, w Asia   46

CORYPHANTHA - Cactaceae
vivipara / R / 4" / showy pink fls / New Mexico, Arizona   74

COTINUS - Anacardaceae
coggyria f. purpureus - Sh, 10', purplish-gray lvs   46

COTONEASTER - Rosaceae
adpressus / Sh / to 1½' / frs bright red / China   46
bullatus / Sh / 10-12' / brilliant red frs / w China, Tibet   13
congestus / Sh / to 2½' / frs bright red / Himalayas   13
conspicuus / Sh / low / white fls; purple-red frs / se Tibet   13
dammeri / Sh / creeping / frs coral-red / c China   13
  " v. radicans - with smaller lvs, w China   69
divaricatus / Sh / to 6' / egg-shaped red frs / w China   13
foveolatus / Sh / 7' / fls pink; frs black / China   46
franchetii / Sh / to 10' / frs orange-scarlet / w China   13
horizontalis / Sh / 2-3' / frs scarlet-red / China   13

(1) - FEDEROV - Flora U. S. S. R. Vol. 18 1967 (trans.)
(2) - RYBERG - A Taxomical Survey of the Genus Corydalis. 1955

COTONEASTER, con.
  'Hybridus Pendulus' - evergreen, red frs, prostrate branches   46
  microphyllus / Sh / 2-3' / frs scarlet-red / sw China   13
      "   v. cochleatus - slow-growing prostrate form   46
      "   v. thymifolius - nearly prostrate, lvs narrow   13
  multiflorus / Sh / 10-12' / fls white; red frs / Asia   13
  nanshan - see C. adpressa   69
  radicans - see C. dammeri v. radicans   69
  wardii / HH Sh / ? / leaf reverse white-tomentose / se Tibet   69

COTULA - Compositae
  atrata / R / 6" / fl-heads blackish / South Island, New Zealand   85
    "   v. dendyi - flower-heads yellow   2
    "   luteola - see C. atrata v. dendyi   2
  coronopifolia / HH R / creeping / yellow button heads / N. Zealand   78
  pyrethrifolia / R / 5" / yellow daisies / New Zealand   21

COTYLEDON simplicifolia - see CHIASTOPHYLLUM oppositifolium   42

COWANIA - Rosaceae
  mexicana - see C. stansburiana   69
  stansburiana / Sh / to 6' / fragrant white fls; aromatic lvs / w N Am 69

CRASPEDIA - Compositae
  glauca / HH P / 18" / yellow fls / n Australia   45
  incana / R / to 1' / yellow fls, snow-white lvs / high mts., N. Z.   2
  lanata / R / to 1' / yellow or white fls; greyish lvs / N. Zealand   2
  robusta / HH P / 2' / yellow fls / New Zealand   2
  uniflora / A or P / 4-12" / yellow spheres / Tasmania, Australia   58
    "   robusta - see C. robusta   2

CRASSULA - Crassulaceae
  sarcocaulis / Gh / semi-dwarf / tiny red fls / S. Africa   (1)

CRATAEGUS - Rosaceae
  mollis / T / 30' / showy red frs / e North America   46
  phaenopyrum / T / 30' / scarlet, persistent frs / se United States   13
  punctata / T / 30'+ / white fls; frs dull crimson / e N. America   46

CRAWFURDIA - Gentianaceae
  speciosa / HH P / twining / pale blue fls / Nepal   29

CREMANTHODIUM - Compositae
  arnicoides / P / strong-growing / yellow fls / ?   21
  delavayi / P / ? / golden-yellow fls / G. Forrest coll.   21
  nanum / R / 6" / orange-yellow fls / Himalayas   (2)
  reniforme / P / 18" / yellow fls / n India   38

CREPIS - Compositae
  aurea / R / 2" / coppery-orange fls / European Alps   38
  blattarioides / P / 20-28" / golden-yellow fls / Europe, in mts.   32
  incana - see C. rosea   38
    " rosea - see C. rosea   38
  jacquinii / R / to 1' / bright golden fls / e Alps, Carpathians   67
  nana / R / dwarf / crowded heads of yellow fls / n N. America   63
  rosea / R / 8" / gray lvs; pale pink dandelions / Greece   38
  rubra / A / 6-18" / fls red / Italy, Greece   9
  sibirica / P / 4'+ / bright golden fls / w Siberia   32

(1) - ROSS in New York Times 8/4/74
(2) - KITAMURA in KIHARA - Fauna and Flora of Nepal Himalaya. 1964

CRINODENDRON - Elaeocarpaceae
  decipiens - see C. patagua   13
  hookeranum / Gh T / 10-30' / rich crimson fls / Chile   13
  patagua / Gh T / 30' / fls white, bell-shaped / Chile   13

CRINUM - Amaryllidaceae
  macowanii / Gh Bb / 2' / lilac-pink fls / Natal   36

CRISTARIA - Malvaceae
  glaucophylla / HH R / prostrate / flesh-colored fls / Chile   21

CRITHMUM - Umbelliferae
  maritimum / P / 1' / the edible samphire / coastal Europe   9

CROCANTHEMUM canadense - see HELIANTHEMUM canadense   34

CROCOSMIA - Iridaceae
  masonorum / HH Bb / 3' / bright orange-red fls / South Africa   85

CROCUS - Iridaceae
  aerius / C / 4" / fls usually pale lilac-blue / Turkey, Iran   56
  alatavicus / C / 4-12" / whitish & purplish fls / c Asia   54
  albiflorus / C / 4" / white fls varying to purple / European Alps   56
  ancyrensis / C / 3" / brilliant orange fls / Asia Minor, Turkey   84
  angustifolius / C / 4-12" / orange fls / sw Russia, Crimea   (1)
  asturicus / C / 5" / fall-fl., purple f;s / Spain   84
      "   v. atropurpureus - fls very dark   56
  aureus - see C. flavus   (1)
  balansae / C / 4" / orange fls / w Asia Minor   84
  banaticus - see C. heuffelianus   32
  biflorus / C / 4" / purple stripes on white fls / Italy, Asia Minor 84
      "   'Albus' - white fls   *
      "   v. argenteus - with darker stripes, Italy   9
  boryi / Gh C / 3" / fls cream / Greece, Crete   56
  cambessedesii / C / 3" / fls pale lilac-purple / Balearic Isls.   84
  cancellatus / C / 3" / fall-fl., fls white, lilac, mauve / Greece   84
      "   v. cilicicus - pale lilac-mauve fls, Asia Minor   84
      "   v. mazzianicus - included in the sp.   56
  candidus / C / 4" / creamy yellow fls / Levant   36
      "   'Subflavus' - pale yellow fls, Asia Minor   84
  carpetanus / C / 3" / fls pale violet / c & n Portugal, c Spain   65
  cartwrightianus albus - see C. hadriaticus v. chrysobelonicus   56
  caspius v. lilacinus - C, 4-12", fall-fl., fls rosy-lilac tinted   18
  chrysanthus / C / 4" / many cvs; wild plants yellow-flowered/ Greece 42
  clusii / C / 3" / fall-fl., mauve to purple fls / w Spain, Portugal 84
  corsicus / C / 6" / lilac & purple fls / Corsica   42
  danfordiae / C / 2" / small varii-colored fls / Turkey   84
  etruscus / C / 4" / fls lilac with yellow throat / w Italy   56
  flavus / C / 6-12" / yellow fls / Balkans   18
      " aureus - a synonym not a variety   *
  fleischeri / C / 3" / fls white striped purple / Asia Minor   84
  gargaricus / C / 2" / fls orange-yellow / w Turkey   56
  goulimyi / C / 4-5½" / blue-mauve fls / Greece   85
  hadriaticus / C / 4" / white fls, veined purple / Greece   84
      "   v. chrysobelonicus - red-purple veins, w Greece   18
  heuffelianus / C / 10-14" / fls white to violet / c Europe   32
      "   'Albus' - the white form   *
      "   scepusianus - see C. scepusianus   56
  imperati / C / 4" / bright mauve & buff-yellow fls / s Italy   42
      " f. albus - white form found in wild   36
  (1) - LAWRENCE in Baileya 2:4

CROCUS, con.
  karduchorum - see C. kotschyanus v. leucopharynx   4
  korolkowii / C / 4-8" / fls deep yellow / Afghanistan, Turkestan   84
  kotschyanus / C / 4" / fall-fl., pale lilac fls / A. Minor, Lebanon   42
      "   v. leucopharynx - lavender fls with white throat   4
  laevigatus / C / 3" / fls white to lilac / Greece   56
  longiflorus / C / 5" / purplish-lilac fls / s Italy, Sicily   84
      "   v. melitensis - prominently feathered fls, Malta   84
  minimus / C / 2" / purple shades / Corsica, Sardinia   42
   napolitanus / C / 4" / large purple fls / s Alps   56
  nevadensis / C / ? / fls pinkish-white / s Spain   65
  niveus / C / 5" / fall-fl., fls white or pale lilac / Greece   56
  nudiflorus / C / 4" / fall-fl., fls pale to deep purple / Pyrenees   56
  ochroleucus / C / 4" / fls white or pale cream / Lebanon, n Palestine   84
  pestalozzae / C / ? / blue or white fls / Turkey   18
  pulchellus / C / 3" / fall-fl., pale lavender fls / Asia Minor, Turk.   42
      "   'Zephyr' - white fls shaded gray   4
  purpureus - see C. napolitanus   56
  salzmannii / C / 3" / fall-fl., large lilac fls / s Spain, n Africa   84
  sativus / C / 4" / large deep purple fls / cult. clone for saffron   56
      "   v. cartwrightianus - smaller than the cult. clone, Greece   56
      "   "   f. albus - white fls, scarlet stigma   36
      "   cartwrightii - see C. s. var. cartwrightianus   56
      "   v. elwesii - lilac-pink fls, Turkey & Iran   56
  scepusiensis / C / ? / white to deep purple fls, hairy throat / Poland   56
  scharojanii / C / 4-10" / fls bright yellow / Caucasus   54
  siculus - similar to C. albiflorus from Sicily   56
  sieberi / C / 5" / lavender-purple shades / Greece   56
      "   f. atticus - deep mauve fls; Atticus, Mt. Parnassus   84
      "   'Violet Queen' - smaller fl, deeper color   4
  speciosus / C / 5" / fall-fl., pale blue-mauve fls / e Eu., Iran   42
      "   'Aitchesonii' - largest form, fls pale lavender-mauve   9
      "   'Albus' - the white form   9
      "   'Globosus' - globe-shaped fls   (1)
  stellaris / C / ? / yellow fls / not known in the wild   56
  susianus - see C. angustifolius   (2)
  suterianus / C / 3" / butter to deep golden-yellow fls / A. Minor   84
  tomasinianus / C / 4" / mauvish-blue & br. lilac-mauve fls / s Italy   42
      "   'Barrs Purple' - soft lilac-mauve fls   36
  tournefortii / C / 4" / fall-fl., bright lilac-blue fls / Greek Isls.   84
  veluchensis / C / 4" / lilac-purple fls / mts. of n Greece   84
  vernus - see C. albiflorus   56
      "   albiflorus - see C. albiflorus   56
      "   caeruleus - see C. napolitanus   56
      "   siculus - see C. siculus   56
  versicolor / C / 4" / fls pale or dark purple / s France   9
      "   v. picturatus - purple markings on white fls   84
  zonatus - see C. kotschyanus   (3)

CROSSOSOMA - Crossosomataceae
  bigelowii / HH Sh / 3'+ / fls white or purplish / Ariz. to se Calif.   (4)

CRUCIANELLA stylosa - see PHUOPSIS stylosa   38

    (1) - LAWRENCE in Baileya 2:3
    (2) - LAWRENCE in Baileya 2:4
    (3) - LAWRENCE in Baileya 2:2
    (4) - LAWRENCE - Taxonomy of Vascular Plants. 1951

CRYPTOGRAMMA - Polypodiaceae
  acrosticoides - see C. crispa v. acrostichoides   34
  crispa / F / 3-6" / the parsley fern / England, Scotland   50
  "   v. acrostichoides - 8", the North American variant   34

CRYPTOSTEGIA - Asclepiadaceae
  madagascariensis / Gh Cl / ? / fls white or pinkish / Madagascar   9

CRUCKSHANKIA - Rubiaceae
  glacialis / R / rosette / bright lemon-yellow fls / alpine Chile   21
  pumila / A / 3-6" / yellow bracted fls / Chile   (1)

CUNILA - Labiatae
  mariana - see C. origanoides   34
  origanoides / R / 1' / fls purple-pink / e United States   71

CUPRESSUS - Pinaceae
  arizonica / HH T / 75' / evergreen with small needles / sw US 13
  bakeri / T / 35-50' / conspicuous resin glands / n California 40
  macnabiana bakeri - see C. bakeri   (2)
  macrocarpa / HH T / to 70' / large-coned / s California   46

CURTONUS - Iridaceae
  paniculata / HH Bb / to 4' / orange-red fls / Transvaal, Natal   84

CYANANTHUS - Campanulaceae
  integer - see C. microphyllus   17
  lobatus / R / 4" / deep violet-blue fls / Himalayas   42
  "   'Albus' - a white color form   38
  "   v. insignis - with larger fls   35
  "   'Sherriff's Form' - see C. sherriffii   38
  microphyllus / R / mat / fls deep violet / Himalayas   42
  sherriffii / R / procumbent / periwinkle-blue fls / s Tibet   38

CYANOGLOSSUM magellensis - error for CYNOGLOSSUM magellense   *

CYATHEA - Cyathaceae
  smithii / F / to 24' / lowland tree-fern / New Zealand   2

CYATHODES - Epacridaceae
  colensoi / HH Sh / 6-12" / white fls; rose-red frs / New Zealand   38
  fraseri / Sh / to 6" / small fls; frs orange to yellow / N. Zealand 2
  juniperina / HH Sh / to 15' / minute fls; frs white to purple / N. Z. 78
  parviflora / HH Sh / to 6' / variable colored frs / New Zealand   2

CYCLAMEN - Primulaceae
  africanum - HH Tu, like C. hederifolium except faintly fragrant   85
  X atkinsii - Tu, perhaps only a good form of C. coum   85
  "   'Album' - white fls   84
  "   'Roseum' - fls deep pink   84
  "   'Rubrum' - darker fls   *
  balearicum / HH Tu / small white fls, scented / Balearic Isls.   65
  cilicium / HH Tu / 3-5" / pale pink fls / s Turkey   42
  "   'Album' - white fls   *
  "   alpinum - see C. c. 'E. K. Balls'   (3)
  "   'E. K. Balls' - 2", fls white or pale pink, Asia Minor   (3)

(1) - MORRISON in GOODSPEED - Plant Hunters in the Andes. 1961
(2) - WOLF & WAGENER - The New World Cypresses. 1948
(3) - SAUNDERS - Cyclamen. 1973

CYCLAMEN, con.
  coum / Tu / 2-5" / white or pink fls / n Turkey, Asia Minor   (1)
    " 'Album' - white fls   84
    " 'Atkinsii' - here treated as C. X atkinsii   85
    "   "   Album' - see C. X atkinsii 'Album'   *
    "   "   Roseum' - see C. X atkinsii 'Roseum'   *
    " ssp. caucasicum - differs in pink or pale purple eye, Caucasus   (1)
    " 'Hiemale' - early-flowering, strong magenta-carmine fls, Turkey 84
    " 'Roseum' - pink fls with spot   4
    " vernum - obsolete synonym of the sp.   (1)
  creticum / HH Tu / 4" / fls mostly white / Crete   85
  cyprium / HH Tu / 4" / white or pinkish fls, fragrant / Cyprus   84
  europeum - see C. purpurascens   (1)
  graecum / Tu / 6" / like C. hederifolium; velvety lvs / Greece   84
  hederifolium / Tu / 6" / rose-pink fls / Mediterranean Basin   (1)
    "   'Album' - beautiful albino form   (1)
  hiemale - see C. coum 'Hiemale'   42
  ibericum - see C. coum   42
    " 'Tubergens Var.' - see C. pseudibericum 'T. V.'   (1)
  libanoticum / HH Tu / large salmon-pink fls / Lebanon   42
  neapolitanum - see C. hederifolium   (1)
    "   'Album' - see C. hederifolium 'Album'   (1)
  orbiculatum - see C. coum   42
    "   coum album - see C. coum 'Album'   *
  persicum / HH Tu / 6"+ / fls white, pink shades / Cyprus, Greek Is. 84
    "   'Album' - pure white fls   (1)
  pseudibericum / HH Tu / 4-6" / near purplish fls / s Turkey   85
    "   'Tubergens Var.'-deeper in color   (1)
  pseudograecum - Cretan form referred to C. graecum   (1)
  'Puck' - Gh Tu, hybrid of C. purpurascens & persicum   61
  purpurascens / Tu / 6" / rose-pink or carmine fls / Italy, Bulgaria (1)
  repandum / Tu / fls white, pink, crimson / c & s Italy   42
    "   'Album' - pure white form found in Corsica   (1)
  vernum - see C. coum   85
    "   album - see C. coum 'Album'   84

CYDONIA japonica - see CHAENOMELES japonica   13

CYMBALARIA - Scrophulariaceae
  muralis / P / 2', trailing / fls lilac to violet / s Europe   92
    " f. alba - from the rarely white wild strain   92
    " 'Alba-Compacta' - dwarfed form   (2)
    " 'Globosa' - neat little hummocks   17
    " 'Globosa Alba' - selected for white fls   *
    " 'Globosa' - light pink fls   17
    " 'Rosea' - light pink fls   17
  pallida / R / 8" / fls pale lilac-blue / c Italy, in mts.   92

CYMOPTERUS - Umbelliferae
  multinervatus / R / 3" / fls purple / w Texas to s California   73

CYNANCHUM - Asclepiadaceae
  vincetoxicum / P / 1-2' / fls greenish-white / Eu., escaped in N.Y. 34

CYNARA - Compositae
  scolymus / HH P / 3-5' / the Garden Artichoke / cult. plant   9

  (1) - SAUNDERS - Cyclamen. 1973
  (2) - PARKER in Quar. Bull. Alpine Garden Soc. 37:3

CYNOGLOSSUM - Boraginaceae
  amabile / P / 2' / bright blue fls / w China   32
     "   'Firmament' - A, 18", sky-blue fls   61
     "   f. roseum - pink fls   32
  columnae / A / 10-18" / fls deep blue / c & e Medit. region   92
  'Firmament' - see C. amabile 'Firmament'   61
  grande / P / 2' / violet or blue fls / California   9
  magellense / R / 8-12" / fls reddish / c & s Apennines   92
  nervosum / P / 1½-2' / intense blue fls / Himalayas   42

CYPELLA - Iridaceae
  herbertii / HH Bb / 12-20" / mustard-yellow & purple fls / S. Am.   56
  peruvana / HH Bb / 8-16" / apricot-yellow fls, shaded purple / Peru   56
  plumbea v. platensis - HH Bb, to 30", sky-blue fls , Brazil, Uruguay   56

CYPRIPEDIUM - Orchidaceae
  acaule / R / to 12" / fls rose-pink, pouched / ne & nc N. Am.   35
     "   f. albiflorum - lip white, sepals & petals oale   34
  calceolus / P / 15" / yellow & brown fls / Europe   42
     "   v. parviflorum - see C. c. var. pubescens   23
     "   v. planipetalum - petals flat or merely undulate, e Canada   34
     "   v. pubescens - North American form   35
  californicum / P / 10-18" / dull yellow fls / Oregon, California   23
  montanum / P / 10-40" / white lipped fls / nw North America   23
  pubescens - see C. calceolus v. pubescens   35
  reginae / P / to 1½' / white & pink fls / n United States   42

CYRILLA - Cyrillaceae
  racemiflora / HH Sh / 4'+ / fls white / S. Am., N Am. to Virginia   13

CYRTOMIUM - Polypodiaceae
  fortunei / F / to 2' / papery pinnae / Japan, s Korea, China   60

CYSTOPTERIS - Polypodiaceae
  bulbifera / F / 8-24" / bearing bulb-like bodies / e N. America   9
  dickiana / F / 2-3" / tight mass, deciduous / e Scotland   50
  fragilis / F / 4-8" / gray-green fronds / n & s hemisphere   60

CYTISUS - Leguminosae
  albus - see CHAMAECYTISUS albus
  albus pallidus - see CHAMAECYTISUS banaticus   91
  ardoinii / Sh / 4-5" / fls golden-yellow / Maritime Alps, Europe   91
  austriacus - see CHAMAECYTISUS austriacus   13
  battandieri / HH Sh / to 15' / fls golden-yellow / Morocco   91
  X beanii - Sh, 6-18", deep golden-yellow fls   13
  biflorus - see CHAMAECYTISUS ratisbonensis   13
  'Cornish Cream' - see C. scoparius 'Cornish Cream'   91
  decumbens / Sh / 4-6" / fls bright yellow / s Europe   13
  demissus / Sh / 3-4" / yellow fls / Greece   13
  diffusus / Sh / 3-10" / bright yellow fls / se Europe   13
  hirsutus - see CHAMAECYTISUS hirsutus   13
  leucanthus - see CHAMAECYTISUS albus   91
  monspessulanus - see TELINE monspessulana   91
  multiflorus / HH Sh / to 10' / fls white / Spain, Portugal   91
     "   albus - is an old synonym   13
  nigricans - see LEMBOTROPIS nigricans   91
  X 'Porlock' - Gh Sh, fls butter-yellow, large semi-evergreen   91
  X praecox - Sh, to 10', sulphur-yellow fls   46
                                                                        ·13

CYTISUS, con.
 purpureus - see CHAMAECYTISUS purpureus   91
 scoparius / Sh / 6' / golden-yellow fls / w, s & c Europe   91
   " 'Andreanus' - Sh, 5-6', brownish-crimson fls   13
   " 'Cornish Cream' - cream & yellow fls, bushy open habit 13
 supinus - see CHAMAECYTISUS supinus   91
   " capitatus - synonymous with sp.   9

DABOECIA - Ericaceae
 azorica / HH Sh / 6-10" / rosy-crimson fls / Azores   38
 'Bearsden' - seedling from D. azorica   (1)
 cantabrica / Sh / to 2' / white to purple fls / w Europe   35
   "   'Alba' - glistening white fls, Ireland   43
   "   'Atropurpurea' - rich wine-colored fls   43
 polifolia - see D. cantabrica   43
   "   'Atropurpurea - see D. cantabrica 'Atropurpurea'   9
 X 'William Buchanan' - fls garnet-red, D. azorica X cantabrica 13

DACRYDIUM - Podocarpaceae
 laxifolium / HH Sh / 2-3' / smallest of conifers / New Zealand 40

DACTYLIS - Gramineae
 glomerata 'Variegata' - Orchard Grass, lvs striped green & white 85

DACTYLORHIZA ericetorum - see ORCHIS ericetorum   30
   "   pratermissa - see ORCHIS praetermissa   30

DALIBARDA - Rosaceae
 repens / R / creeping / white fls / ne North America   9

DANAE - Liliaceae
 racemosa / HH Sh / 4' / small whitish fls; red frs / Greece to Iran 9

DAPHNE - Thymelaeceae
 alpina / Sh / decumbent / fragrant white fls / s & c Eu., in mts. 91
 arbuscula / Sh / low / lilac-pink fragrant fls / Hungary   43
 cneorum / Sh / trailing / fragrant pink fls / c Europe, in mts.   9
 giraldii / Sh / 2' / golden yellow fls / China   38
 jasminea / HH Sh / to 1' / purple & whitish fls / se Greece   91
 kamtschatica / Sh / ? / yellow fls / Korea, Russian Far East   13
 laureola / Sh / 2-4' / fls yellowish green / s & w Europe   13
 mezereum / Sh / to 5' / deep rosy-purple fls / Europe, Asia Monor 42
   " v. alba - white fls; yellow frs   91
 oleoides / HH Sh / 3' / white fls; orange-red frs / Medit. region 43
   " jasminea - see D. jasminea   13
 pontica / Sh / to 3' / pale yellow fls / Bulgaria, Turkey   91
 retusa / Sh / to 3' / dark buds; blush-pink fls / w China   42
 tangutica / Sh / to 3' / rosy-purple fls / nw China   69

DARLINGTONIA - Sarraceniaceae
 californica / Gh / 10-30" / green & yellow & brown fls / Calif.   9

DATURA - Solanaceae
 metel / A / 3'+ / fls variable in color / India   (2)
 meteloides - see D. wrightii   73
 suaveolens / HH Sh / 10-15' / white trumpet fls / Mexico   9
 wrightii / P gr. as A / 4' / white fls / Texas & w-ward to Calif. 73

 (1) - UNDERHILL - Heaths and Heathers. 1972
 (2) - DeWOLF in Baileya 4:1

DAUCUS - Umbelliferae
  carota ssp. maximus - Mediterranean wild form of the carrot   91
  maximus - see D. carota ssp. maximus   91

DAVALLIA - Davalliaceae
  mariesii / F / to 8" / epiphytic fern / Far East   60

DEINANTHE - Hydrangeaceae
  bifida / P / to 2' / white fls, green bracted / Japan   60

DELOSPERMA - Mesembryanthemaceae
  cooperi / HH Sh / prostrate / purple fls / Orange Free State   (1)

DELPHINIUM - Ranunculaceae
  'Azure Fairy' - see D. grandiflorum 'Azure Fairy'   85
  bicolor / R / 6-12" / blue & white fls / nw North America   9
  brunonianum / R / 10-15" / fls violet shaded purple / Tibet   42
  cardinale / HH P / 2-3½' / red fls / California   9
  carolinianum / P / 1-2' / blue fls / Georgia to Texas & Arkansas   7
  cashmerianum / R / 10-18" / black & green fls / Himalayas   9
  X coeruleum - P, 2', blue fls, 1847 hybrid   45
  'Connecticut Yankee' - P, 2½', varii-colored fls   61
  consolida / A / 5-20" / variously colored fls / Europe, Asia Minor   7
  elatum / P / 16-80" / blue to violet fls / c Europe, n & c Russia   90
  flexuosum / P / 2-3' / dark blue fls / Caucasus   26
  glaucum - see D. scopulorum v. glaucum   7
  grandiflorum / P / 2-3' / large blue fls / Siberia   9
         "   'Azure Fairy' - 18", Cambridge blue   85
         "   'Blue Butterfly' - 18", rich deeo blue fls, brown spot   85
         "   'Blue Mirror' - gentian-blue fls   44
         "   chinense - included in the sp.   9
  hesperium / P / 3' / fls blue to white / California   7
  likiangense / R / 4-8" / fls rich blue to lilac / Yunnan   7
  menziesii / R / 6-18" / blue fls / California to Alaska   38
  muscosum / R / 4-6" / large, deep blue-violet fls / Bhutan   85
  nudicaule / HH R / 1' / fls red & yellow / n California   38
       "   v. luteum - pale yellow fls, coast of c California   7
  nuttallianum / P / 4-32" / fls bright blue to purplish / Ore., Wash.   75
  oreganum / P / 3' / narrowly segmented lvs / Oregon   21
  oxysepalum / R / 4-20" / fls blue to blue-violet / Carpathians   90
  parryi v. blockmannae - 1', dark blue fls, s California   (2)
  przewalskii / R / 6-10" / brownish & white fls / w Mongolia   7
  pylzowii / R / 6-10" / dark violet fls / w China   7
  scopulorum v. glaucum - 3'+, fls blue to purplish, s Calif. Alaska   7
  tatsienense / R / 12" / prussian blue fls / s China   6
  tricorne / P / 2' / purplish or deep blue fls / ec United States   72
  trollifolium / P / 6' / fls deep blue / Oregon, California   7
  vestitum / P / tall / blue fls / Himalayas   7
  virescens / P / 1-3' / yellowish fls / c North America   7
  xantholeucum / P / 12-32" / fls pale yellow / Wenatchee Mts., Wash.   76
  zalil / P / 2' / primrose-yellow fls / Iran   7

ARGS S'81 (margin note)

DENTARIA bulbifera   see CARDAMINE bulbifera   90
       "   digitata - see CARDAMINE pentaphyllos   90
       "   pinnata - see CARDAMINE heptaphylla   90

(1) - JACOBSEN - A Handbook of Succulent Plants. 1960, trans.
(2) - WILDE - Studies of the Genus Delphinium. 1931

DEUCHESNIA indigo - error for DUCHESNIA indigo   *

DEUTZIA - Philadelphaceae
  X rosea - Sh, compact, pink fls   46

DIANELLA - Liliaceae
  caerulea / Gh P / 1'+ / blue fls; blue frs / e Australia   9
  intermedia / Gh P / 10-18" / white fls; purple-blue frs / N. Zealand 41
  laevis / Gh P / to 3' / fls blue / e temperate Australia   16
  tasmanica / Gh P / 2-4' / fls pale blue / Tasmania, Australia   9

DIANTHUS - Caryophyllaceae
  X allwoodii - P, 9-16", fragrant fls, variable in color   8
    "   'Alpinus' - 6" strain of above   89
  alpestris - see D. furcatus   90
  alpinus / R / 4" / pink or deep rose fls / European Alps   42
    "   'Albus' - non-fragrant white fls   38
  amurensis / R / 8" / mauve fls / Manchuria   (1)
  anatolicus / P / to 14" / white fls / Turkey   26
  arboreus / HH Sh / 3-5' / rose fls, fragrant / Isles in Medit. Sea   90
  arenarius / P / to 1½' / white fls / e Europe   90
  armeria / A / 1-2' / fls lilac-purple / Europe, w Asia   8
  X arvernensis - R, to 14", purplish fls, c France   8
  barbatus / B / to 2' / varii-colored fls / s & e Europe   42
    "   'Messenger' - an early-flowering strain, mixed-col. fls   85
    "   'Newport Pink' - 18", salmon-pink fls   61
  bicolor - see D. marschallii   90
  'Blue Hills' - R, 3", tufted plant, magenta-purple fls   17
  brachyanthus - see D. subacaulis ssp. brachyanthus   90
  'Bravo' - see D. chinensis 'Bravo'   85
  brevicaulis / R / cushion / purplish fls / Turkey   26
  'Brilliancy' - R, 1', vivid carmine fls   (2)
  broteri - see D. malacitinus   90
  caesius - see D. gratianopolitanus   8
  callizonus / R / to 8" / carmine fls / Carpathians   90
  calocephalus - see D. cruentus   90
  campestris / P / 14" / pink or purplish fls / e & s Russia   90
  capitatus / P / 12-16" / purplish fls / se Europe to Siberia   8
  carmelitarum / P / to 16" / carmine red fls / Turkey   26
  carthusianorum / P / 2' / pink to purple fls / s, w & c Europe   90
    "   v. atrorubens - tall with dark red fls   8
    "   v. nanus - 3-4", fls purple   8
  caryophyllus / HH P / to 32" / fls variable in color / Medit. reg.   90
    "   v. corsicus - possibly a wild form   33
  chinensis / B / 6-30" / varii-colored fls / China   8
    "   'Bravo' - A, 6", bright scarlet fls   85
    "   v. laciniatus - fringed petals   95
    "   v. macrosepalus - P, to 1', fls bright red   9
  corsicus - see D. caryophyllus v. corsicus   33
  crinitus / P / 7-25" / white to pale pink fls / Armenia   34
  croaticus - see D. giganteus ssp. croaticus   90
  'Crossways' - R, 6", intense crimson-carmine fls   17
  cruentus / P / to 40" / fls reddish-purple / Balkans   90
  deltoides / R / 6-9" / white, pink or crimson fls / n Europe   42
    "   'Albus' - white fls   9
    "   'Brilliant' - bright deep rose fls   17
    "   'Erectus' - deep rose fls, upright 6-8"   17

(1) - HECKER in Quar. Bull. Alpine Garden Soc. 41:1
(2) - LLOYD in Jour. Royal Hort. Soc. June 1975

DIANTHUS, con.

7/79

DIANTHUS, con.
'Pikes Pink' - habit a close rug, fls soft rose-purple   (1)
'Pink' - see D. latifolius 'Pink'   8
pindicola - see D. haematocalyx ssp. pindicola   90
plumarius / P / to 16" / fls white or bright pink / ec Europe   90
   "   'Highland Queen' - see D. 'Highland Queen   49
   "   lumnitzeri - see D. lumnitzeri   90
pontederae / P / 6-18" / red-purple fls, rose below / ec Europe   90
praecox - of uncertain designation   8
preobraszhenskii / R / to 1' / fls pink, yellow below / Caucasus   (2)
X pulcherrimus - a Sweet William of short statue   49
pungens / R / to 8" / pink fls / e Pyrenees   90
X 'Rainbow Loveliness' - 1', superbus type, varii-colored fls   (3)
repens / R / 2-10" / fls pink or purplish / arctic Russia   90
'Roysii' - 4-6", cultivar with deep rose fls, large   8
scardicus / R / 4" / pink fls / s Jugoslavia in mt. pastures   90
'Scaynes Hill' - mounded plant, 4-6" stems, fls carmine-purple   17
seguieri / P / to 20" / pink fls, yellowish below , c Europe   26
serotinus / P / to 16" / cream-colored fls / n Balkans   90
shinanensis / P / 8-16" / rose-purple fls / Honshu   60
spiculifolius / R / 5-7" / rose, pink, white fls / e Carpathians   90
X 'Spencer Bickham' - 4", deep rose-pink fls   49
squarrosus / R / to 1' / white or pink fringed fls / c Russia   35
sternbergii - see D. monspessulanus ssp. sternbergii   90
strictus / P / 24-32" / white fls / sw Asia   90
subacaulis / R / 1-8" / pale pink fls / mts. of sw Europe   90
   "   ssp. brachyanthus - densely caespitose, Pyrenees   90
suendermannii - see D. petraeus   90
superbus / P / to 3' / pink or purplish fls / Europe   90
   "   'Albus' - white fls   *
   "   alpinus - material grown referrable to D. s. ssp. speciosus   *
   "   v. amoenus - dwarfed in statue   49
   "   v. longicalycinus - widespread in the Far East   60
   "   'Rainbow Loveliness' - see D. X 'Rainbow Loveliness'   49
   "   ssp. speciosus - glaucous purplish calyx   90
sylvestris / R / 4" / pink fls / European Alps   90
tatrae - see D. hungaricus   8
'Tiny Rubies' - 2", masses of pink fls   81
tristis / P / 16" / pink fls / Balkans   90
velebiticus - included in D. carthusianorum   90
viscidus / R / 1' / fls purple, spotted / Greece   90
'White Hills' - 4", small pink fls, crimson zone   (4)
'Windward Rose' - 6", deep rose-pink fls; ash-gray lvs   49
X winteri - compact hardy border pink strain   8
'Zing' - see D. deltoides 'Zing'   61
zonatus / R / to 1' / deep pink fls, yellow below / Turkey   26

DIAPENSIA - Diapensiaceae
lapponica / R / 2" / glistening white fls / New England, on mt. tops 35

DIASCIA - Scrophulariaceae
cordata / HH R / 8" / fls rose-purple / Natal   6

(1) - JACKMAN in Jour. Royal Hort. Soc. October 1968
(2) - SHISHKIN in Flora U.S.S.R. Vol. 6 1970 (trans.)
(3) - LLOYD in Jour. Royal Hort. Soc. June 1975
(4) - HECKER in Quar. Bull. Alpine Garden Soc. 41:1

DICENTRA - Papaveraceae
  chrysantha / P / 2-3' / fls gold en yellow / California   9
  cucullaria / R / to 10" / fls white, tipped gold / e & c North Am.   35
      "   'Ozark Form' - with pinkish fls   82
  eximia / P / 1½' / rosy-purple fls / e United States   42
    "   'Alba' - a good white form   42
    "   'Bountiful' - 1', rosy-red fls   85
  formosa / P / 2' / rose to white fls / nw North America   85
    "   'Alba' - 12", with all white fls   5
  ochroleuca / HH P / 5' / fls cream tipped purple / s California   74
  oregana / R / 4" / fls cream tipped rose / nw United States   43
    "   'Rosea' - a rosy-hued form   81
  peregrina v. pusilla - 3", fls deep pink & white, Japan   42
  spectabilis / P / 2' / rosy-pink & white fls / Siberia, Japan   42
    "   v. alba - weaker growth, white fls   9
  uniflora / R / 3" / white or pink fls / nw United States   35

DICHELOSTEMMA - Liliaceae
  pulchella / Bb / 1-2' / lilac-blue fls / California, Oregon   56
    "   'Alba' - white fls   *
  ida-maia / Bb / 10" / bright crimson fls, green tipped / Calif.   56

DICOPOGON - Liliaceae
  strictus / Gh / small / mauve fls / temperate Australia   16

DICRANOSTIGMA - Papaveraceae
  franchetianum / A or B / 3' / yellow fls / China   (1)
  lactucoides / P / 1-2' / clear yellow fls / Tibet   (1)

DICTAMNUS - Rutaceae
  albus / P / 2-3' / fls white / e Europe, Asia   42
    " albiflorus - superfluous   *
    " 'Purpureus' - a purplish-pink form   42
    " 'Roseus' - see D. albus 'Purpureus'   *
    " 'Rubra' - rosy-purple fls, veined   9
  fraxinella - see D. albus   9
  rubra - see D. albus 'Rubra'   9

DIERAMA - Iridaceae
  pendulum / HH C / to 3' / white, pink or purple fls / S. Africa   62
  pulcherrimum / HH C / 2-6' / blood-red to purple bells / S. Africa   42

DIETES - Iridaceae
  grandiflora - see MORAEA iridioides   41
  vegeta / HH C / 1-2' / white fls, brown flecked / South Africa   32

DIGITALIS - Scrophulariaceae
  alba - see D. purpurea 'Alba'   *
  ambigua - see D. grandiflora   85
    "   grandiflora - also see D. grandiflora   *
  davisiana / P / 20" / fls pale yellow, dark inner net / Anatolia   85
  dubia / HH R / 6-9" / soft purplish-pink fls / Spain   38
  'Excelsior' - see D. purpurea 'Excelsior'   61
  ferruginea / B or P / 4-6' / fls rusty red / s Europe to Iran   9
  'Foxy' - see D. purpurea 'Foxy'   61
  gloxinaeflora - see D. purpurea v. gloxinaeflora   9
  grandiflora / B or P / 2-3' / yellow fls / e & c Europe   92
  kishinskyii / P / 2' / brown fls, dense spike / Russia   *

(1) - CULLEN in Baileya 15:3

DIGITALIS, con.
  laevigata / P / 2-3' / fls yellow, purple marked / w & c Balkans   9
  lanata / B or P / 2-3' / fls whitish, brown veins / Balkans   9
  lutea / P / to 28" / pale cream fls / w & nc Europe   32
  mertensiana - error for D. X mertonensis   *
  X mertonensis - B, 3', strawberry-red fls   20
  obscura / HH Sh / 1-3' / fls orange-yellow to brown / e,s&c Spain   92
  orientalis / P / 2' / fls nearly white / Asia Minor   21
  parviflora / P / 1-2' / fls reddish-brown & white / n Spain   92
  purpurea / B / 2-4' / purple spotted fls / w, sw & wc Europe   9
      "   'Alba' - fls white   9
      "   'Excelsior' - B, 5', large-flowered   89
      "   'Foxy' - B, 3', varii-colored fls   61
      "   'Gloxinaeflora' - robust, fls more flaring   9
      "   ssp. mariana - white-tomentose lvs; purple fls, Spain, Port.   92
  sibirica - habit of D. grandiflora; fls of D. lanata, Siberia   9
  thapsi / P / 2½-3' / cream fls suffused pink / Spain, Portugal   44
  viridiflora / P / 20-32" / dull greenish-yellow fls / Balkans   92

DIMORPHOTHECA - Compositae
  barberiae / P gr. as A / 1' / purplish-pink fls / South Africa   42
      "   v. compacta - 9", hardier   42

DIONAEA - Droseraceae
  muscipula / HH R / 6" / white fls; insectiverous lvs / N. & S. Car.   9

DIONYSIA - Primulaceae
  aretioides / R / loose cushion / white lvs; yellow fls / Iran   21

DIOTIS candidissima - see OTANTHUS maritima   64

DIPCADI - Liliaceae
  serotinum / HH Bb / 4-12" / fls greenish-brown / s Europe, N. Africa   9

DIPHYLLEIA - Berberidaceae
  biphylla - not a recognized specific name   *
  cymosa / P / to 3' / white fls; blue frs / streamsides, Va. to Ga.   34
      " grayii - see D. grayii   60
  grayii / P / 1-2' / white fls; blue frs / high mts., Japan   60

DIPIDAX - Liliaceae
  triquetra / Gh P / 12-18" / whitish fls, brown veins / South Africa   9

DIPLARRHENIA - Iridaceae
  moraea / HH P / to 2' / fls whitish / Australia, Tasmania   9

DIPSACUS - Dipsacaceae
  fullonum / B / 6' / strong hooked floral scales / Europe, A. Minor   9
  sylvestris / B / 6' / lilac or white fls / Europe   68

DIPTERONIA - Aceraceae
  sinensis / HH T / 30' / pinnate lvs; orbicular samaras / c China   9

DISCARIA - Rhamnaceae
  serratifolia / HH Sh / 10'+ / fragrant fls / Chile, Patagonia   46

DISPHYMA - Aizoaceae
  australe / Gh / prostrate / fleshy lvs; pink to white fls / N. Z.   2

DISPORUM - Liliaceae
  hookeri / P / 1-3' / cream or greenish fls / nw United States 75
    "   oreganum - see D. smithii .... (1)
  maculatum / P / 2' / yellow fls, spotted purple / ec US 35
  oreganum - see D. smithii .... (1)
  smithii / P / 1-3' / white fls / nw North America 75

DODECATHEON - Primulaceae
  alpinum / R / 8-10" / fls bright purplish-crimson / Nevada, Calif. 42
  amethystinum / R / to 1' / fls deep red-purple / w Va. to Minn. 34
  clevelandii / R / 8-16" / fls magenta to white / s California 75
    "   'Alba' - the white form .... (2)
    "   ssp. insulare - yellow pollen-sacs, coastal .... (2)
    "   ssp. patulum - dark pollen-sacs, in mts. .... (2)
  conjugans / R / 3-10" / white to magenta fls / ne California 75
  cusickii - like pulchellum except glandular pubesence, nw US .... (2)
  dentatum / R / 8-10" / fls white, purple at base / nw US 35
    "   ssp. ellisiae - with yellow filaments, se Ariz., N. Mexico .... (2)
  ellisiae - see D. dentatum ssp. ellisiae .... (2)
  glastifolium / R / 8" / lilac-purple fls / California 21
  hendersonii / R / 5-18" / light orchid to darker fls / nw N. Am. 75
  integrifolium / R / 10" / fls lilac-purple to pink / Br. Columbia 43
  jeffreyi / R / 6-24" / fls purple to white / nw North America 35
  latifolium - see D. hendersonii .... (2)
  X lemoineii - R, 1', pale rose fls .... (3)
  macrocarpum - believed to be D. pulchellum .... *
  meadia / P / 1-1½' / fls rosy / c & sc United States 42
    "   'Album' - graceful white form 42
    "   'Rubrum' - deep colored selection .... *
  patulum - see D. clevelandii ssp. patulum .... (2)
  pauciflorum - see D. pulchellum .... (2)
    "   'Red Wings' - see D. pulchellum 'Red Wings' .... (2)
  poeticum / R / ? / very dark filament tube / n Oregon, s Wash. .... (2)
    "   'Red Wings' - see D. pulchellum 'Red Wings' .... (2)
  pulchellum / R / 2-20" / magenta or lavender fls / c US to Mexico 74
    "   'Red Wings' - brilliant rosy fls .... (2)
    "   ssp. watsonii - 2½', Vancouver Is. to Montana .... (2)
  radicatum - see D. pulchellum .... (2)
    "   watsonii - see D. pulchellum ssp. watsonii .... (2)
  redolens / P / 10-24" / lavender to magenta fls / s Calif. to Utah 75
  salinum - alkaline soil segregate of D. pulchellum, Idaho 21
  tetandrum - see D. pulchellum .... (2)

DODONAEA - Sapindaceae
  viscosa / HH Sh / 15' / greenish fls / pan-tropical 9

DOLIA - Nolanaceae
  tomentosa / HH R / creeping / white fls; gray-green lvs / Chile .... (4)

DORONICUM - Compositae
  austriacum / P / to 2' / yellow fls / Austria, in mts. 95
  carpaticum / R / 6" / yellow fls / ? 21
  caucasicum / P / 1-1½' / fls deep yellow / Europe, Asia 42
    "   'Spring Beauty' - double fls 42

(1) - ELLIOTT in Jour. Royal Hort. Soc. February 1973
(2) - INGRAM in Baileya 11:3
(3) - Floraire - Plantes Alpines et Vivaces. n.d.
(4) - MYHR in Bull. Am. Rock Garden Soc. 30:3

DORONICUM, con.
  clusii / R / 4-16" / fls yellow / c & e Alps   96
  columnae / P / 1-2' / golden yellow fls / se Europe, Asia   32
  cordatum - see D. columnae   32
  glaciale / R / 2-10" / yellow daisies / Swiss Alps   67
  hirsutum - may be error for DORYNCIUM hirsutum   *
  pardalianches / P / 20-32" / yellow fls / e & n Europe   32
  plantagineum / P / 3-5' / yellow daisies / w Europe   44
  'Spring Beauty' - see D. caucasicum 'Spring Beauty'   42

DORYNCIUM - Leguminosae
  germanicum - see D. pentaphyllum ssp. germanicum   91
  hirsutum / P / 8-32" / fls white or pink / Medit. region   91
  pentaphyllum ssp. germanicum - 8-32", white fls, c Eu. & Balkans   91
  rectum / HH P or Sh / 1-5' / white or pink fls / Medit. region   91

DOUGLASIA - Primulaceae
  dentata / R / loose rosettes / violet-pink fls / Rocky Mts.   35
  laevigata / R / compact / carmine to rose-pink fls / Cascade Mts.   35
  montana / R / tight tuffet / varying pink fls / Cascade Mts.   35
  nivalis / R / loose tufts / pale pink fls / British Columbia   38
  vitaliana / R / prostrate mat / clear yellow fls / Europe   38
      "   f. praetutiana - grayish lvs; citron-yellow fls, s Alps   33

DOWNINGIA - Campanulaceae
  elegans / A / 4-20" / blue or violet & white fls / Calif. to Oregon   75

DRABA - Cruciferae
  acaulis / R / cushion / golden-yellow fls / Cicilian Taurus Mts.   43
  aizoides / R / 2-4" / fls yellow / c & s Europe, in mts.   90
      "   ssp. bertolonii - 2" segregate   33
      "   'Grandiflora' - larger-sized flower   *
  aizoon - see D. lasiocarpa   90
  alpina / R / to 8" / bright yellow fls / arctic & subarctic Eu.   90
    " ssp. demissorum - 4", lanceolate-leaved   (1)
    " glacialis - see D. glacialis   90
  altaica - see D. subcapitata   63
  andina / R / 2" / pale yellow fls / Andes Mts., South America   43
  arabisans / R / large mound / white fls / North America   (2)
      "   v. canadensis - lower, pods narrower   34
  arbuscula / T / half-shrubby tuft / yellow fls / alpine Venezuela   21
  aspera / R / 2-4" / yellow fls / Europe, in mts.   90
    "   v. eriocarpa - hairy frs   90
    "   v. erioscapa - hispid scape   90
  athoa / R / to 5" / large yellow fls / Greece, w Balkans   90
    " f. laicaita - smaller, tighter tuffet   33
    " f. leiocarpa - smooth-fruited   *
  aurea / B / 1'+ / deep yellow fls / e arctic Canada, Greenland   63
  austriaca - see D. stellata   90
  barbata - see D. alpina   63
  belli / R / 4" / fls dull yellow / Spitzbergen   90
  bertolonii - see D. aizoides ssp. bertolonii   33
  borealis / R / to 8" / fls white / Hokkaido, Kuriles   60
  bruniifolia / R / 3" / bright yellow fls / Caucasia, n Iran   26
      "   v. diversifolia - included in the sp.   26
      "   ssp. olympica - with villous scape, Turkey   26
  bryoides / R / 1"+ / fls golden yellow / Caucasus   43
      "   v. imbricata - 1-2", bright yellow fls, Caucasus   42

(1) - PETERSON in Bull Am. Rock Garden Soc. 25:2
(2) - BABB in Bull. Am. Rock Garden Soc. 13:4

DRABA, con.
```
  cappadocica / R / rounded tufts / yellow fls / Turkey, Kurdistan      26
  carinthiaca / R / to 6" / white fls / c & s Europe, in mts.           90
  chamaejasme - no bot. recognition; some seed produces D. aizoides      *
  cinerea / R / 1'+ / fls white / fully circumpolar                     63
  compacta / R / very dwarf / deep yellow fls / n Balkans               90
  crassifolia / R / 2"+ / fls pale yellow / N. America, arc. Scandinav. 90
  cretica / R / dwarf /        yellow fls / Crete, in mts.              90
  cuspidata / R / dwarf / large yellow fls / Crimea                     90
  daurica / R / to 10" / cream fls / arctic Europe, Scandinavia mts.    90
  dedeana / R / 3" / fls white / n & e Spain, in mts.                   90
     "    'Mawii' - fewer blossoms, green sepals                        33
     "    v. zapateri - 1½", bright white fls, purple calyx             33
  demissorum - see D. alpina ssp. demissorum                           (1)
  dubia / R / to 8" / white or cream fls / c & s Europe, in mts.        90
  fladnizensis / R / 3" / fls white / arctic Europe, Scandinavia        90
  frigida - see D. fladnizensis                                         33
  glacialis / R / to 8" / bright yellow fls / arctic Norway, Russia     90
  globosa v. sphaerica - 1", yellow fls, pilose plant, Oregon           10
  haynaldii / R / very dwarf / yellow fls / Carpathians                 90
  heterocoma / R / to 4" / fls yellow / Asia Minor                      90
  hirta - see D. daurica                                                90
  hispanica / R / dwarf / yellow fls / e & s Spain                      90
  hoppeana / R / very dwarf / yellow fls / European Alps                90
  incana / B / 1'+ / fls white / n Europe                               90
  incerta / R / 4" / large clear yellow fls / Wash., Mont., & n-ward    35
  kitadakensis - similar to D. borealis, 3", Japan                      52
     "       koizumii - G. Koidzumi author of the sp.                   52
  kotschyii / R / 8" / white or creamy fls / s Carpathians              90
  lacaithae - see D. athoa f. lacaita                                   33
  lasiocarpa / R / to 8" / deep yellow fls / Balkans, Austria           90
  lemmonii / R / 1-5" / yellow fls / s Sierra Nevada, US                75
  linearis - see ERIOPHILA verna ssp. praecox                          26
  loiseleurii - Corsican form of D. hispanica                          90
  longipes / R / 2-9" / white fls / Alaska & nw Canada                  63
  longirostra - see D. aspera                                           90
     "        erioscapa - see D. aspera v. erioscapa                    90
  lutescens / A / 5½" / small pale yellow fls / s Spain, s France       90
  macrocarpa - see D. oblongata                                        63
  mollissima / R / 1½" / fls yellow / Caucasus                          85
  muralis / A / to 1' / white fls / Europe                              90
  nemorosa / A / 1' / pale yellow fls / across N. Am. & Europe          34
  nivalis / R / 2" / white fls / arctic Europe & mts. of Norway         90
  norica / R / to 9" / fls cream / Austria                              90
  norvegica / R / to 8" / white fls / subarctic Europe, Scotland        90
  oblongata / R / to 4" / densely tufted / probably circumpolar         63
  oligosperma / R / ½-4" / whitish fls / mts. of w North America        75
  olympica - see D. bruniifolia ssp. olympica                          26
  oreadum / HH R / ? / white fls / Morocco                              21
  oxycarpa / HH R / dense / yellow fls / Lebanon                        33
  paysonii / R / ½-2½" / whitish fls / Calif. to B. C. e to Rockies     75
     "     v. treleasii - yellow fls                                   (2)
  polytricha / R / 1½" / fls bright yellow / Transcaucasia              26
  repens - see D. sibirica                                              34
  rigida / R / 2-4" / yellow fls / Armenia                              26
  rupestris - see D. norvegica                                          90
```

(1) - PETERSON in Bull. Am. Rock Garden Soc. 25:2
(2) - ZWINGER & WILLARD - Land Above the Trees. 1972

DRABA, con.
```
  X salamonii - R, 2", white fls                                    5
  sauteri / R / 1½" / yellow fls / Alps                            90
  scardica / R / dwarf / small yellow fls / Balkan Peninsula, in mts.  90
  sibirica / R / creeping / yellow fls / e Russia, Asia, Greenland  90
  stellata / R / to 4" / fls white or cream / e Alps on limestone  90
  stylaris - perennial, otherwise close to D. incana               90
  subalpina / R / ? / large white fls / c Utah                    (1)
  subcapitata / R / 1½" / fls yellow / probably fully circumpolar  63
  X thomasii - see D. stylaris                                     90
  tomentosa / R / to 8" / white fls / Pyrenees, Alps, on limestone  96
  ussuriensis / R / caespitose / white fls / Far East             (2)
  vestita - see D. globosa v. sphaerula                           10
```
(handwritten in left margin: 979)

DRACOCEPHALUM - Labiatae
```
  argunense / R / 6-14" / blue-purple fls / Far East              60
     "    'Rubrum' - fls reddish                                    *
  austriacum / R / 6-12" / fls deep violet / Alps, Pyrenees       96
  botryoides / R / 6" / blue purple fls / Caucasus                10
  forrestii / P / 12-18" / deep purplish-blue fls / Yunnan        24
  grandiflorum / R / 6-9" / violet-blue fls / Siberia             38
  hemsleyanum / P / to 20" / fls purplish-blue / Tibet            10
  isabellae / P / 12-20" / dark lilac-blue fls / c China          32
  mairei - see D. renatii                                         (3)
  moldavica / A / to 2' / fls violet or white / Siberia & c Asia  92
  nutans v. alpinum - R, 12", bright blue fls, c Asia             10
  purdomii / R / 8" / purple fls / c Asia                         38
  renatii / R / 6" / creamy-white fls / Morocco                  (3)
  rupestre / R / 1' / dark bluish-violet fls / China             (3)
  ruyschiana / R / to 1' / blue-violet fls / Pyrenees, Alps       96
  setigerum / R / 6" / whitish fls / Armenia                      21
  tanguticum / R / 8-12" / vivid blue fls / China                 38
  wendelboii / R / ? / cobalt blue fls / Afghanistan             (4)
```

DRACOPHYLLUM - Epacridaceae
```
  pronum / R / hard wiry mats / waxy white fls / South Island, N. Z.  (5)
```

DRACUNCULUS - Araceae
```
  vulgaris / Tu / to 2' / Large reddish-maroon fls / s Europe     42
```

DRIMYS - Magnoliaceae
```
  winteri / HH T / to 25' / ivory-white fls / South America       46
```

DROSERA - Droseraceae
```
  anglica / R / to 8" / fls white or pinkish / N. Am., Eurasia    34
  arcturi / Gh P / 6" / white fls / New Zealand, Tasmania          2
  capensis / Gh / 6" / purple fls / South Africa                  41
  intermedia / R / to 10" / white fls / ne North America          34
  rotundifolia / R / to 12" / white fls, rarely pink / N. Am., Eurasia  34
```

DRYANDRA - Proteaceae
```
  formosa / HH Sh / 10' / orange-yellow fls / w Australia          16
```

```
  (1) - RIPLEY in Quar. Bull. Alpine Garden Soc. 40:3
  (2) - BUSH in Flora of the USSR. Vol. 8 1970(trans.)
  (3) - FURSE in Quar. Bull Alpine Garden Soc. 37: 3
  (4) - DRAKE in The Scottish Rock Garden Club Jour. 15:3
```

DRYAS - Rosaceae
  drummondii / R / 4" / creamy-yellow fls / n North America   35
  integrifolia / R / dense mats / creamy-white fls / arctic regions   63
  octopetala / R / mat / fls white & egg-yellow / Alps, Scotland   42
       "   integrifolia - see D. integrifolia   63
       "   lanata - see D. o. var. vestita   32
       "   v. minor - smaller and more compact   38
       "   v. tenella - with gray-woolly small lvs   35
       "   v. vestita - white-hairy lvs, compact growth   32
  X suendermannii - yellow buds opening to white fls   35
  tenella - see D. o. var. tenella   35

DRYMIS winteri - correctly DRIMYS winteri   *

DRYOPTERIS - Polypodiaceae
  arguta / F / 14" / evergreen fronds / w North America   81
  atrata / F / 8-18" / evergreen fronds / Far East   60
  borreri 'Cristata' - 2-3', crested form true from spores, England   50
  carthusiana / F / to 2' / deciduous fronds / England   50
  cristata / F / to 20" / Crested Wood-fern / n & c North America   34
  erythrosora / F / ? / young fronds coppery pink / Far East   50
  goldiana / F / to 4' / large deciduous fronds / ne & c N. America   50
  marginalis / F / 2' / evergreen fronds / North America   (1)
  phegopteris - see THELYPTERIS phegopteris   (1)
  spinulosa / F / to 20" / Woods or Florist Fern / North America   (2)
  thelypteris / F / to 2' / fronds herbaceous / northern hemisphere   34

DUDLEYA - Crassulaceae
  cymosa / Gh / 8" / yellow or red fls / s California   74
  farinosa / Gh / 1' / lemon-yellow fls / sea cliffs, Calif. to Ore.   74

DYSSODIA - Compositae
  tenuiloba / P gr. as A / 4-8" / yellow daisies / Rio Grande region   73

EBENUS - Leguminosae
  cretica / HH Sh / to 20" / fls bright pink / Crete   91

ECCREMOCARPUS - Bignoniaceae
  scaber / Gh A Cl / 10-15' / vivid orange fls / Chile   41
    " 'Aureus' - bright golden-yellow fls   9
    " f. lutea - see E. s. 'Aureus'   *
    " 'Ruber' - reddish fls   32

ECHIUM - Boraginaceae
  rubrum - see E. russicum   92
  russicum / B / to 20" / fls dark red / ec & se Europe   92

ECHINACEA - Compositae
  angustifolia / P / 18" / fls purplish to white / s North America   9
  X 'Bright Star' - 2½-3', bright rose-red fls   44
  purpurea / P / 3-5' / purplish fls / e & c United States   44
  tennesseensis / R / to 1' / purplish fls / Arkansas, Tennessee   (3)
  'White Lustre' - P, 3½', large white fls, deep orange center   85

ECHINOCACTUS - Cactaceae
  texensis / R / 6" / fls blended scarlet & white / N. Mexico, Texas   (4)

(1) - MOHLENBROCK - The Illustrated Flora of Illinois - Ferns. 1967
(2) - Appalachian Mt. Club - Mountain Flowers of New England. 1964
(3) - SMALL - Manual of the Southeastern Flora. 1933.
(4) - GOULD - Texas Plants: A Checklist & Biological Summary. 1962

ECHINOCEREUS - Cactaceae
  viridiflorus / R / 1-8" / brownish to yellowish-green fls / c US   (1)

ECHINOPS - Compositae
  banaticus / P / ? / blue fls / Hungary   9
  exaltatus / B / tall / fls blue / Russia   9
  ritro / P / 3'+ / steely-blue fls / e Europe   42
  sphaerocephalus / P / 5-7' / fls white or bluish / s Europe   9

ECHIOIDES - Boraginaceae
  longiflorum / R / 1' / yellow fls / Armenia, Caucasus   (2)

ECHIUM - Boraginaceae
  vulgare / P / 1-3' / brilliant blue fls / adventive weed in US, Eu. 34

EDRAIANTHUS - Campanulaceae
  bosniacus - intermediate between E. graminifolius & tenuifolius   21
  caudatus - see E. dalmaticus   11
      "   albus - see E. dalmaticus 'Albus'   *
  croaticus / R / 4" / fls violet-½ Croatia, Dalmatia   32
  dalmaticus / R / 4-6" / fls violet-blue / w Jugoslavia   11
      "   'Albus' - white fls   *
  dinaricus / R / low / fls violet-blue / Dinarian Alps   11
  graminifolius / R / 3" / narrow purple bells / Dalmatia   38
      "   'Albus' - white fls   *
  intermedius - coarser leaved and less silvery than E. pumilio   21
  kitabelii / R / 2-3" / fls blue-violet / Balkans   32
  parnassi / R / 12" / small purple bells / Balkans   33
  pumilio / R / cushion / strong violet-blue fls / Balkans   42
  serbicus / R / tufted / blue-violet fls / Bulgaria, Jugoslavia   11
  serpyllifolius / R / 4" / intense violet-blue fls / Dalmatia   42
      "   dinaricus - see E. dinaricus   11
  tasmanicus - see WAHLENBERGIA tasmanica   10
  tenuifolius / R / 4-6" / fls violet-blue / Jugoslavia   11
      "   'Albus' - white fls   *

EHRETIA - Ehretiaceae
  tinifolia / Gh T / 18-40' / white or cream fls, fragrant / Cuba   (3)

ELAEAGNUS - Elaeagnaceae
  umbellata / Sh / 12-18' / silvery-white fls; reddish frs / Far East 13

ELMERA - Saxifragaceae
  racemosa / R / 6" / fls white / Olympic & Cascade Mts., w US   75

ELEORCHIS - Orchidaceae
  japonica / R / to 12" / rose-purple fls / Hokkaido, Honshu, Kuriles 60

ELSHOLTZIA - Labiatae
  stauntonii / Sh / 5' / fls lilac-purple / n China   9

ELYMUS - Gramineae
  dahuricus / P Gr / erect / foliage basal, good ground cover / Siberia (4)
  interruptus / P Gr / 28-52" / of open rich soil / Wyo. to Mexico   (5)
  sibiricus / P Gr / 1-3' / attractive spikes for drying / Eurasia   85

  (1) - STEVENS - Kansas Wild Flowers. 1948
  (2) - INGRAM in Baileya. 6:3
  (3) - ADAMS - Flowering Plants of Jamaica. 1972
  (4) - WEINTRAUB - Grasses Introduced into the United States. 1953
  (5) - HITCHCOCK - Manual of the Grasses of the United States. 1935

EMBOTHYRIUM - Proteaceae
coccineum / HH T / to 20' / bright crimson-scarlet fls / Chile 13
    "   v. lanceolatum 'Norquinco' - hardier form, Argentine mts. 13

EMILIA - Compositae
flammea - see E. sagittata 32
sagittata / A / 1-2' / scarlet fls / India, China 32

EMPETRUM - Empetraceae
hermaphroditum - see E. nigrum ssp. hermaphroditum 63
nigrum / Sh / dwarf / purplish fls; black frs / n hemisphere 35
    "   ssp. hermaphroditum - tetraploid form, hermaphrodite fls 63

ENDYMION - Liliaceae
hispanicus / Bb / 9" / varii-colored fls / Spain, Portugal 84
    "   'Albus' - white fls .... *
    "   'Excelsior' - deep blue fls 42
    "   'Rose Queen' - pink selection .... *
    "   'Roseus' - pinkish fls .... *
nonscriptus / Bb / to 18" / fls in several colors / w Europe 42

ENKIANTHUS - Ericaceae
campanulatus / Sh / to 8' / white or pink fls / Japan 42
perulatus / Sh / 3-6' / white fls / Japan 13

EPACRIS - Epacridaceae
impressa / HH Sh / 3' / fls red or white / Australia 9

EPIDENDRUM - Orchidaceae
schomburgkii / Gh / 2-3' / fls vermilion / Guiana, Brazil 9

EPIGAEA - Ericaceae
asiatica / Sh / prostrate / fls white to rose / Japan 60
gaultherioides / Sh / semi-prostrate / pink fls / Asia Minor .... (1)
repens / Sh / trailing / pink & white fls / e & c North America 35

EPILOBIUM - Onagraceae
alpinum / R / 2-12" / pink or lilac fls / w North America 75
angustifolium / P / 3-5' / fls violet or purplish / world-wide 91
    "   'Album' - compacter, pure white fls .... *
crassum / R / trailing / pink or white fls / New Zealand 33
dodonaei / P / 8-42" / violet or purplish fls / c & s Europe 91
fleischeri / R / decumbent / purple to violet fls / Alps 91
glabellum / R / 9" / creamy-white fls / New Zealand 17,33
    "   'Album' - whiter selection .... *
kai-koense / R / 4" / rosy-pink fls / Japan 38
latifolium / R / decumbent / violet or purplish fls / n hemisphere 91
luteum / P / 1-2' / fls bright yellow / Oregon to Alaska 9
niveum / R / 4-8" / red-violet fls / California in Coast Ranges 75
nummularifolium / R / ground-hugging / bronze-green lvs / N. Zealand 17
obcordatum / R / 4" / deep rose-pink fls / Nevada, California 38
rigidum / R / close mounds / bright pink fls / Siskiyou Mts. 35

EPIPACTIS - Orchidaceae
gigantea / P / to 5' / pink, red, purple fls / w & wc N. America 75
helleborine / P / to 4' / fls of many colors / Europe, Asia 38
latifolia - see E. helleborine 30

(1) - FINLAY in Jour. Royal Hort. Soc. May 1972

EPIPACTIS, con.
```
  palustris / R / 10-12" / varii-colored fls / Europe, Siberia         38
  thunbergii / P / 1-2' / greenish to purplish fls / Japan, Korea      60
```

ERANTHIS - Ranunculaceae
```
  cilicica / Tu / 3" / finely divided flower bracts / Cilicica         42
  hyemalis / Tu / 8" / fls bright golden yellow / Europe               42
     "    v. cilicica - see E. cilicica                                32
  X tubergenii - Tu, 2", fls shining golden yellow, sterile?           36
```

EREMURUS - Liliaceae
```
  aitchisonii / P / 5'+ / pink fls / Afghanistan                       85
  altaicus / P / to 4' / yellow fls / w Siberia, c Asia                54
     "    v. fuscus - fls partly brown                                 54
  bungei - see E. stenophyllus                                         85
  elwesii - referred to E. aitchisonii                                 85
  fuscus - see E. altaicus v. fuscus                                   54
  himalaicus / P / to 5' / white fls / Himalayas                       85
  olgae / P / 28-40" / fls pink or white / Iran to Tadjikstan          85
  regelii / P / to 9' / rose fls / ?                                   54
  robustus / P / to 10' / pink fls / Tien-Shan, Pamir-Altai            85
  stenophyllus / P / to 4' / clear yellow fls / Iran                   85
```

ERICA - Ericaceae
```
  arborea / HH Sh / to 20' / fls almost white / Eurasia, Asia Minor    13
  baccans / Gh Sh / sturdy / rose-pink fls / Cape of Good Hope in mts. 70
  carnea 'King George' - see E. herbacea 'King George'                 13
     "    'Praecox Rubra' - see E. herbacea 'Praecox Rubra'            13
  cerinthoides / Gh Sh / to 6' / scarlet fls / Africa                  70
  cinerea 'Coccinea' - 4", dark scarlet fls                            46
     "    'Mrs Dill' - compact shrub with pink fls                     (1)
     "    'Velvet Knight' - blackish-purple fls                        46
     "    'Victoria' - 6", large fls of rich purple                    (2)
  elegans / Gh Sh / 6" / green fls / Cape of Good Hope                 45
  formosa / Gh Sh / 1-2' / white fls / South Africa                    9
  glauca v. elegans - Gh Sh, pinkish fls, South Africa                 70
  glomiflora / Gh Sh / 1' / white fls / Cape of Good Hope              45
  herbacea 'King George' - 6-10", rosy-crimson fls; dark green lvs     13
     "      'Praecox Rubra' - 10", early deep red fls                  13
  holosericea / Gh Sh / ? / pink & red fls / Cape of Good Hope         70
  inflata / Gh Sh / 18" / white & red fls / Cape of Good Hope          45
  mammosa 'Coccinea' - robust greenhouse shrub, Cape of Good Hope      70
  tetralix / Sh / 18" / rose fls / n & w Europe                        42
     "    f. alba - fls white                                          13
     "    'Mollis' - light gray lvs; white fls                        42
     "    'Rubra' - 6", very compact, fine red fls                     (2)
  vagans / Sh / 2' / fls rosy-pink or white / w Europe & Medit. reg.   42
     "    'Mrs. D. F. Maxwell' - 15", dark pink fls                    95
     "    'St. Keverne' - 15", salmon-pink fls                         95
```

ERIGERON - Compositae
```
  alpinus / R / 6-8" / mauve fls / alpine & arctic regions of Europe   38
  atticus / P / to 2' / intense purple fls / Alps, Carpathians         67
  aurantiacus / R / 1' / orange fls / Turkestan                        38
  aureus / R / 3" / fls bright golden yellow / w North America         42
  borealis / R / to 10" / white to pink-purple fls / n hemisphere      63
  caespitosus / R / to 8" / fls white or blue / n & wc North America   22
```

```
  (1) - HEATH - Shrubs for the Rock Garden and Alpine House.  1954
  (2) - UNDERHILL - Heaths and Heathers.  1972
```

ERIGERON, con.
  compositus / R / 3-4" / white or pale mauve fls / w N. America   38
        "   v. discoideus - rayless heads   20
  'Darkest of All' - 2½', deep blue fls   85
  eatonii / R / 2-12" / fls white, rarely blue, pink / Wyo. & w-ward   76
  flagellaris / R / carpeting / fls rose or white / w North America   32
  flettii / R / 2-6" / white fls / Olympic Mts., Washington   75
  glabellus / P / 12-16" / violet, purple, white fls / Wisc. to Utah   32
  glaucus / HH R / 6-10" / purple daisies / Pacific Coast of N. Am.   38
        "   'Albus' - white fls   *
        "   'Roseus' - rosy daisies, seaside California   79
  grandiflorus / R / to 6" / pale lavender fls / alp. & arc. nw N. Am.(1)
  howellii / P / 8-20" / white fls / Columbia River Gorge   75
  humilis / R / 6" / white to purplish fls / Alaska   63
  karwinskianus / HH R / 8" / white & purple fls / Mexico   32
  lanatus / R / 2" / fls white, blue, pink / nw Montana, Colorado   76
  leiomerus / R / close mat / violet fls / Utah, Wyoming   33,35
  linearis / R / 2-12" / yellow fls / Yosemite Park, n & e-wards   75
  mucronatus - see E. karwinskianus   32
  multiradiatus / P / 6-24" / fls purplish / Himalayas   9
  oreganus / R / 2-6" / blue, pink, white fls / Columbia River Gorge   75
  philadelphicus / P / 1-3' / fls pinkish to roseate / e N. America   34
  'Pink Jewel' - 18-24", lavender-pink fls   44
  pinnatisectus / R / 4-6" / mauve daisies / Rocky Mts.   38
  poliospermus / R / to 6" / fls pink or violet / Wash., w Oregon   76
  polymorphous / R / to 1' / reddish-lilac fls / Alps, Balkans   67
  pulchellus / P / ½-2'+ / fls blue-purple to white / e & c N. America   34
  radicatus / R / 2" / mauve fls / Central Rockies   33,38
  scribneri / R / 3" / white daisies / Great Plains of the US   (2)
  simplex / R / 4-6" / deep mauve daisies / nw North America   38
  speciosus / P / 12-16" / dark violet to lavender-blue fls / w Ore.   32
  thunbergii / R / 4-15" / fls blue-purple / Honshu   60
        "   v. angustifolius - 2', blue-purple fls, Japan   60
  trifidus / R / 1'+ / pale lavender fls / Rocky Mts.   43
  unalaschensis - see E. humilis   63
  uniflorus / R / 4" / white or mauve-pink fls / Pyrenees, Alps   96

ERINACEA - Leguminosae
  anthyllis / HH Sh / spiny hummock / blue-violet fls / s & e Spain   65
  pungens - see E. anthyllis   46

ERINUS - Scrophulariaceae
  alpinus / R / 3-4" / rosy fls / w & c Europe, in mts.   35
        "   'Abbotswood Pink' - pink selection   89
        "   'Albus' - the white form comes true from seed   35
        "   'Dr. Hanele' - deep crimson fls   38
        "   'Mrs. Charles Boyle' - clear pink form   38

ERIOCEPHALUS - Compositae
  africanus / Gh Sh / 5' / white-rayed fls, purple center / S. Africa 70

ERIOGONUM - Polygonaceae
  allenii / P / 1-1½' / yellow fls / Virginia & West Virginia   83
  campanulatum / R / to 1' / yellow fls / Nebraska, Colorado, Utah   (3)
  compositum / P / to 16" / cream or yellow fls / n coast of Calif.   75
  crocatum / R / to 1' / white-woolly plant; yellow fls / s Calif.   74

(1) - PORSILD - Illustrated Flora of the Canadian Archipelago. 1957
(2) - TOTTEN in Bull. Am. Rock Garden Soc. 15:3
(3) - RYDBERG - Flora of the Prairies & Plains of Central N. Am. 1932

ERIOGONUM, con.
  diuglasii / R / 8" / yellow fls / c Washington, ne California   76
  flavum / R / 4-10" / fls bright yellow / wc North America   27
  grande pubescens - error for E. grande f. rubescens?   *
       "   f. rubescens - 12", fls rose-red. Santa Cruz Island, Calif. (1)
  jamesii / R / 4-12" / fls whitish to cream / wc United States   27
  latifolium / P / 2' / fls white, rose, yellow / s Calif. & n-ward   74
  nudum / P / to 3' / fls white or tinged rose, yellow / Wash., Nev.   27
  ovalifolium / R / 3-8" / fls white or yellow / w North America   38
       "   v. nivale - the white form   (2)
  proliferum / R / 6-12" / fls white turning purplish / e Wash., Idaho 27
  saxatile / HH P / 3-24" / fls white to pale yellow / s Calif.   20
  strictum / P / 18" / fls cream, yellow, white / Wash. to Montana   76
  subalpinum / R / 4-12" / fls light yellow / B. C. to Nevada   27
  umbellatum / R / variable hts. / fls yellow / nw North America   27
       "   subalpinum - see E. subalpinum   27

ERIOPHYLLUM - Compositae
  lanatum / R / 6-8" / golden-yellow daisies / w North America   38

ERITRICHIUM - Boraginaceae
  caucasicum - from subalpine belt, n slope, Great Caucasus   (3)
  howardii / R / tufts and mats / bluest of all blue fls / Col., Mont,(4)
  nanum / R / dense cushion / soft blue fls / Alps   38
     " ssp. jankae - lvs more densely white-villous, e Alps   92
  rupestre / R / 4-8" / fls sky-blue / Kashmir   32
     "   v. pectinatum - 6", blue fls, Himalayas   43
  strictum - see E. rupestre v. pectinatum   43

ERODIUM - Geraniaceae
  acaule / R / 6" / lilac fls / Portugal, Medit. region   91
  atlanticum / R / to 1' / violet-pink fls / Atlas Mts.   33
  carvifolium / R / 6" / purple fls, black at base / nc & wc Spain   91
  cazorianum / R / 7" / pale lilac to purplish fls / se Spain   91
  chamaedryoides - see E. reichardii   91
       "   'Roseum' - see E. reichardii 'Roseum'   *
  chrysanthum / R / 6" / bright yellow fls / c & s Greece, in mts.   91
  corsicum / HH R / 3" / pale magenta-pink fls / Corsica   42
     "   'Rubrum' - fls deeper pink   42
  daucoides / R / 5" / fls pale pink or purplish / Spain, in mts.   65
     "   cazoriense - see E. cazorianum   91
  gruinum / A or B / to 20" / violet fls / Sicily, Aegean region   91
  hymenodes / R / 1' / lilac-white & crimson fls / nw Africa   17,26
  macradenum - see E. petraeum ssp. glandulosum   91
       "   'Roseum' - see E. petraeum ssp. glandulosum 'Roseum'   *
  manescavi / R / to 1' / purple fls / w & c Pyrenees   91
  pelargonifolium / R / 6-12" / white fls, violet veins / Turkey   26
  petraeum / R / stemless / finely cut lvs / Spain, sw France   65
     "   ssp. crispum - white-woolly lvs, pale pink or lilac fls   65
     "   ssp. glandulosum - aculescent, violet-purple fls, Pyrenees 65
     "   "   'Roseum' - pink selection   *
  reichardii / HH R / acaulescent / white fls / Balearic Isles   91
       "   'Roseum' - 2", deep pink fls, Majorca   43

  (1) - LENZ - Native Plants for California Gardens. 1956
  (2) - ZWINGER & WILLARD - Land Above the Trees. 1972
  (3) - SUKACHEV - Studies on the Flora & Vegetation of High Mt. Areas
                                      1960 (trans. 1965)
  (4) - BARR in Bull. American Rock Garden Soc. 26:2

ERIOPHILA - Cruciferae
　verna / A / to 8" / white or reddish fls / Europe   90
　　" ssp. praecox - Mediterranean region form   90

ERYNGIUM - Umbelliferae
　agavifolium / Gh P / to 6' / sword-like lvs to 5' / Argentina   9
　alpinum / P / 1½-2' / fls metallic blue / Europe   42
　amethystinum / P / 8-20" / fls bluish / Balkans, Italy   91
　aquaticum / P / t6 4' / whitish fls / New Jersey to Florida   71
　bourgatii / P / 18" / blue fls / Pyrenees, Spain   65
　bromeliaefolium / HH P / 9-10' / greenish fls / Mexico   9
　caeruleum / P / 3' / blue fls / Caucasus   9
　campestre / P / to 28" / fls pale greenish / Europe, s England   91
　delaroux / HH P / 30" / gunmetal-blue fls / Mexico   91
　giganteum / B / 3-4' / silvery-blue fls / Caucasus   42
　　" 'Miss Willmott's Ghost' - B, 3', gray-blue fls   (1)
　maritimum / P / 6-24" / bluish fls / seacoasts of Europe   91
　X oliverianum - P, 3', blue fls   9
　pandanifolium / Gh P / to 8' / dark purple fls / s Brazil, Argentina   9
　planum / P / 1-3' / bluish fls / c & se Europe   91
　protaeflorum / HH P / 3'+ / white fls / Mexico   9
　tricuspidatum variifolium - see E. variifolium   *
　tripartitum / P / 2' / blue-gray fls / ?   42
　　" variifolium - see E. variifolium   85
　variifolium / HH P / 2' / silver-blue fls / Atlas Mts., Morocco   85
　X 'Violetta' - 2-2½', large violet-blue fls   44
　yuccifolium / P / to 6' / greenish fls / e United States   73

ERYSIMUM - Cruciferae
　X allionii - P, 1½', orange fls   32
·　alpinum / R / 6" / sulphur-yellow fls / Scandinavia   38
　　" 'Moonlight' - luminous primrose-yellow fls   38
　asperum / B / 6-10" / coppery-yellow fls / California to Texas   38
　arkansanum - see E. capitatum   82
　　" 'Golden Gem' - see E. capitatum 'G. G.'   82
　capitatum / B / 8-10" / pale yellow fls / c & w United States   82
　　" 'Golden Gem' - fls deeper color   20
　concinnum / HH R / 2-6" / yellow fls / coast of Calif. & Oregon   75
　cuspidatum / A Or B / 3'+ / yellow fls / se Europe   90
　decumbens / P / to 16" / yellow fls / Pyrenees, sw Alps   90
　dubium - see E. decumbens   90
　helveticum / P / 2' / fls yellow / Balkans, Alps, Pyrenees   90
　linifolium / R / 12" / fls soft purple / Spain, Portugal   6
　ochroleucum - see E. decumbens   90
　pachycarpum / P / to 2' / fls orange-yellow / Tibet, Sikkim   90
　perofskianum / A / 1-2' / fls bright orange / Caucasus, Afghanistan   33
　pumilum 'Golden Gem' - see E. capitatum 'G. G.'   *
　rupestre / R / tufted / yellow fls / Mt. Olympus, Bithynia   29
　torulosum / A / 8" / fls yellow / Turkey   26

ERYTHRINA - Leguminosae
　crista-galli / HH Sh / 6' / crimson-scarlet fls / Brazil   42
　herbacea / HH P / 4'+ / fls deep scarlet / Florida, Texas, N. Car.   71

ERYTHRONIUM - Liliaceae
　albidum / Tu / 4-8" / fls white / e North America   71
　　" v. mesochorum - shades of blue-lavender fls, c US   82
　californicum / Tu / to 1' / fls creamy-white / California   84
　　" v. helenae - see E. helenae   (2)

　(1) - FOX - Variations on a Garden. 1974
　(2) - WATSON & WOODWARD in Quar. Bull. Alpine Garden Soc. 42:1

ERYTHRONIUM, con.

citrinum / Tu / 6" / fls creamy-white / Oregon, California	84
dens-canis / Tu / 6" / white or pink fls / Europe	42
" v. sibiricum - large fls with yellow base	9
giganteum - either E. grandiflorus or E. oreganum	56
grandiflorum / Tu / 1-2' / golden yellow fls / Calif., Wash.	84
" v. pallidum - white or cream anthers	84
helenae / Tu / to 1' / white fls / Mt. St. Helena, California	74
hendersonii / Tu / 1' / pale lilac fls / Oregon	84
japonicum / Tu / to 1' / fls rose-purple / Japan, Korea	60
klamathense / Tu / 6" / white fls / nw Calif., sw Oregon	75
mesochorum - see E. albidum v. mesochorum	82
obtusatum / Tu / 1' / fls white or cream / Wyoming to Montana	10
X 'Pagoda' - deep canary-yellow fls	4
revolutum / Tu / 5'+ / rose-pink fls / coastal, Calif. to B. C.	75
" v. johnsonii - fls dark rose; mottled lvs	9
" 'Rose Beauty' - deep rose selection	81
" 'White Beauty' - see E. X 'White Beauty'	4
sibiricum - see E. dens-canis v. sibiricum	9
tuolumnense / Tu / 1' / golden yellow fls / s California, Nevada	75
" 'Pagoda' - see E. X 'Pagoda'	56
X 'White Beauty' - 2', large fls, good grower	4

ESCALLONIA - Escalloniaceae

illinita / HH Sh / to 10' / fls white; evergreen lvs / Chile	13
pulverulenta / Gh Sh / to 12' / white fls, lvs evergreen / Chile	13

ESCHSCHOLTZIA - Papaveraceae

caespitosa / R / 1' / fls bright yellow / c California & s-ward	74
californica / A / 9-19" / orange, yellow, cream fls / California	42
lobbii / A / 4-12" / yellow fls / Sierra Nevada, Calif.	75
stauntonii - error for ELSHOLTZIA stauntonii	*

EUCALYPTUS - Myrtaceae

citriodora / Gh / juvenile / lemon-scented lvs / Australia	9
cloeziana / HH T / 30-45' / dark brown bark / Queensland, Australia	(1)
coccifera / HH T / large / pruinose shoots / Tasmania	85
gunnii / HH T / to 100' / flaking bark / Tasmania	13
macrocarpa / Gh Sh / to 13' / red fls; lvs mealy / Australia	58
niphophylla / HH T / 20' / good foliage & bark / Victoria, Australia	85
parvifolia / HH T / to 30' / small green lvs / Australia	85
saligna / HH T / tall / lanceolate lvs / Australia	(1)

EUCOMIS - Liliaceae

autumnalis / Bb / 1' / green to whitish fls / South Africa	84
bicolor / Bb / 1-1½' / greenish-yellow fls / South Africa	42
comosa - see E. punctata	32
pole-evansii / Gh Bb / 5-6' / greenish-yellow fls / Transvaal	36
punctata / Bb / 2' / yellowish-green fls / South Africa	32
zambesiaca / Bb / 2' / fls green, unspotted / Africa	20

EUCRYPHIA - Eucryphiaceae

cordifolia / HH T / to 100' / large white fls / Chile	(2)

EUGENIA - Myrtaceae

uniflora / HH Sh / to 7½' / white fls; edible red frs / Brazil	(3)

(1) - BIRCHER - Gardens of the Hesperides. 1960
(2) - MENNINGER - Flowering Trees of the World. 1962
(3) - ADAMS - Flowering Plants of Jamaica. 1972

EUONYMUS - Celastraceae
    alatus / Sh / 8' / corky branches, fine fall color / Far East   42
        "   'Compactus' - subglobose habit   69
    americanus / Sh / 8' / pink frs / New York to Texas   9
    atropurpureus / Sh / 6-12' / purplish fls; crimson frs / e & c US   13
    bungeanus / T / to 30' / yellowish fls; orange & pink frs / n China   13
    europaeus / Sh / to 18' / scarlet capsules / Europe   46
        "   'Red Cascade' - 15', brilliant scarlet frs   85
    fortunei 'Vegetus' - Sh, 6'+, freely fruiting,evergreen lvs   69
    hamiltonianus v. maackii - 12', pink frs, ne Asia   85
    latifolius / Sh / 20' / frs bright red / sc & se Europe   91
    maackii - see E. hamiltonianus v. maackii   85
    nanus / Sh / 1-3' / brown-purple fls; pink & orange frs / Caucasus   13
    planipes / Sh / to 12' / frs bright red & orange / Far East   13
    radicans 'Vegetus' - see E. fortunei 'Vegetus'   46
    'Red Cascade' - see E. europaeus 'Red Cascade'   85
    sachalinensis - in cultivation is E. planipes   13

EUPATORIUM - Compositae
    coelestinum / P / to 3' / fls bluish-violet / e & c United States   34
    glechonophyllum / Gh Sh / low / white fls / Chile   9
    ligustrinum / Gh Sh / to 9' / creamy-white fls / e Mexico   13
    maculatum / P / to 5' / purple fls / North America   34
    micranthum - see E. ligustrinum   32
    purpureum / P / 3-6' / fls purplish-pink / North America   42
    rugosum / P / to 4' / fls bright white / North America   34

EUPHORBIA - Euphorbiaceae
    biglandulosa - see E. rigida   85
    characias / HH P / to 32" / pale green & purple fls / Medit. region   64
        "   ssp. wulfenii - 4'+, yellow fls, e Medit. region   91
    coralloides / HH P / to 2' / purplish fls / c & s Italy, Sicily   85
    epithymoides / P / 8-16" / yellow or purple tinged fls / c & se Eu.   91
    hyberna / P / 1-2' / warty seed capsules / w Europe, Ireland   85
    lathyris / A / 2-3' / yellow-green fls / Europe   85
    marginata / A / 3'+ / green & white fls / North America   85
    mellifera / HH Sh / 6'+ / yellow flower heads / Madeira   85
    myrsinites / P / 1', trailing / yellow fls / s Europe, Asia Minor   9
    nicaeensis / P / to 32" / yellowish fls / s, e & ec Europe   91
    portlandica / P / to 16" / yellowish fls / w Europe   85
    rigida / P / 12-20" / yellow fls / Sicily, Greece, N. Africa   85
    serrulata / A / to 32" / greenish-yellow fls / sc & w Europe   91
    sikkimensis / P / 2'+ / fls yellow / e Himalayas   85
    wulfenii - see E. characias ssp. wulfenii   91

EURYOPS - Compositae
    acreus / HH Sh / 2' / fls canary-yellow / Basutoland   85
    evansii - see E. acreus   85

EXOCARPUS - Thymelaeaceae
    humifusus / Gh / trailing / apetalous / Australia   45

EXOCHORDA - Rosaceae
    korolkowii / Sh / 12' / white fls / Turkestan   9
    X macrantha 'The Bride' - 4', white fls   (1)
    racemosa / Sh / 10' / pure white fls / China   9

    (1) - MATHIAS - Color for the Landscape. 1973

EWARTIA - Compositae
  nubigena / R / prostrate / "Australian Edelweiss" / New S. Wales   (1)

FALLUGIA - Rosaceae
  paradoxa / Sh / 3' / white fls / California, Utah & s-ward   9

FARSETIA eriocarpa - see FIBIGIA eriocarpa   90

FELICIA - Compositae
  aethiopica - see F. amelloides   85
  amelloides / Gh Sh / 1-2' / sky-blue fls / South Africa   9
  bergeriana / A / 4-6" / deep azure-blue daisies / South Africa   38
  coelestis - see F. amelloides   9
  fragilis - see F. tenella   85
  pappei / HH Sh / 10-12" / clear blue fls / South Africa   43
  tenella / A / 12-15" / pale blue fls / South Africa   95

FENDLERA - Saxifragaceae
  rupicola / Sh / to 6' / fls white or rose-tinged / Texas, New Mexico 69

FERRARIA - Iridaceae
  undulata / C / 4-12" / brownish-purple fls / South Africa   56

FESTUCA - Gramineae
  amethystina / Gr / 20" / dark violet fls / Alps   32
  duriuscula glauca - see F. ovina v. glauca   (2)
  eskia / Gr / mat, stems 1½' / green, gold, purple fls / Pyrenees   85
  gigantea / Gr / tufts, 1½-5' / bright green lvs; purple nodes / Eu.   85
  ovina / Gr / tufted to 2' / useful lawn grass / n temperate zone   85
    "   v. glauca - 9", blue lvs, Europe   42
    "   tenuifolia - see F. tenuifolia   85
  rubra v. pruinosa - coastal dune binder   85
  tenuifolia / Gr / to 1½' / acid soil turf grass / Europe   85

FIBIGIA - Cruciferae
  clypeata / P / 12-30" / fls yellow / Italy, Balkans   90
  eriocarpa - differs but slightly from above, c & s Greece   90

FILIPENDULA - Rosaceae
  hexapetala - see F. vulgaris   91
  palmata 'Nana' - dwarf form of a 2' P, red fls, China   45,(3)
  rubra / P / 2-8' / pink fls / Pennsylvania to Mich. & Kentucky   9
  vulgaris / P / to 32" / fls pale cream & purplish / most of Europe   91

FOENICULUM - Umbelliferae
  vulgare / P / 4-6' / yellow fls / s Europe   42

FORSYTHIA - Oleaceae
  X intermedia 'Beatrix Farrand' - Sh, large canary-yellow fls   42

FOTHERGILLA - Rosaceae
  major / Sh / 9' / white & yellow stamens / Georgia   9

(1) - VALDER in Jour. Royal Hort. Soc. September 1964
(2) - HITCHCOCK - Manual of the Grasses of the United States. 1935
(3) - Iconographia Cormophytorum Sinicorum. Tomus II 1972

FRAGARIA - Rosaceae
  moschata / P / to 16" / edible European Strawberry / c Europe   91
  vesca 'Alpine Yellow' - R, 10", edible yellow strawberries   (1)
    " f. alba - native US woodland strawberry, whitish frs   34
    " leucocarpa - see F. vesca f. alba   *

FRANCOA - Saxifragaceae
  appendiculata / HH P / 2-3' / fls pale rose / Chile   9
  ramosa / HH P / 2' / fls white / Chile   9
  sonchifolia / HH P / 2-3' / fls deep rose / Chile   9

FRANKLINIA - Theaceae
  alatamaha / T / 15-20' / white fls / along Altamaha River, Georgia   13

FRASERA carolinensis - see SWERTIA caroliniensis   34
    " speciosa - see SWERTIA radiata   76

FRAXINUS - Oleaceae
  latifolia / T / to 80' / with stalkless leaflets / w North America   13
  tomentosa / T / 50' / Pumpkin Ash / e & c United States   34

FREMONTIA mexicana - see FREMONTODENDRON mexicanum   13

FREMONTODENDRON - Sterculiaceae
  mexicanum / Gh T / 10-20' / orange-yellow fls / Baja California   13

FRITILLARIA - Liliaceae
  acmopetala / Bb / 1½' / brown & green fls / Asia Minor   42
  agrestis / Bb / 1-2' / greenish-white & brown fls / California   75
  'Antemis' - see F. meleagris 'Antemis'   84
  atropurpurea / Bb / 6-24" / brown, green, purple fls / Oregon   75
  biflora / Bb / 6-18" / greenish to dark purple fls / s California   9
  bithynica / Bb / to 6" / yellow fls / nw & w Asia Minor   84
  bucharica - see RHINOPETALUM bucharicum   54
  camtschatcensis / Bb / 4-20" / fls dark brown-purple / nw N. Am.   60
  citrina / Bb / 8-10" / clear yellow fls / Greece, Taurus   38
  conica / HH Bb / 5" / greenish yellow fls / Greece   56
  crassifolia / Bb / 6" / green & choclate-maroon fls / Lebanon to Iran   56
  davisii / Bb / 6" / deep chocolate fls / Mani Peninsula, Greece   56
  drenovskii / Bb / 8" / purple-brown & yellow fls / Bulgaria   43
  eduardii / Bb / to 2' / bright red fls / c Asia   54
  elwesii / Bb / 18" / green flushed purple fls / Asia Minor   9
  falcata / Bb / 4" / white fls, reddish speckling / California   56
  glauca / Bb / 4" / yellow or brownish yellow fls / Calif., Ore.   56
  gracilis - see F. lanceolata v. gracilis   9
  graeca / Bb / 6" / green fls margined red / Greece   43
    " v. gussichae - 8-16", green fls striped brown   85
    " v. thessalica - vigorous form from n Greece   56
  hispanica / Bb / 8-15" / green fls striped brown or purple / Spain   85
  imperialis / Bb / to 4' / fls yellow to red / India   42
    " 'Aurora' - deep reddish-orange fls, vigorous   84
    " 'Lutea' - deep lemon-yellow fls   84
    " 'Lutea Maxima' - deep lemon-yellow fls, large   84
    " v. raddeana - see F. raddeana   85
    " 'Rubra' - fls bright red   36
  involucrata / Bb / 12-15" / fls pale green, brown markings / Italy   56
  ionica / Bb / to 1' / green & purple fls / nw Greece, Corfu   56

(1) - ROHDE - Uncommon Vegetables and Fruits. 1943

FRITILLARIA, con.
 karadaghensis / Bb / 6" / yellow-green fls, marbled / Iran   43
 karelinii - see RHINOPETALUM karelinii   54
 kurdica / Bb / to 8" / purple fls, yellow banded / Caucasus   54
 lanceolata / Bb / 1-3' / dark purple fls, mottled yellow / Calif.   9
    "   v. gracilis - smaller black-purple fls   9
 latifolia / Bb / to 1' / deep chocolate fls / ne Turkey, Caucasus   56
    "   v. lutea - Caucasian yellow-flowered form   56
 libanotica - see F. persica   56
 liliacea / Bb / 3-12" / whitish fls veined green / California   9
 lusitanica / Bb / 1' / red-maroon & yellow fls / Portugal   56
 meleagris / Bb / 1' / fls reddish-purple & white / Europe   42
    "   'Alba' - all white fls   9
    "   'Aphrodite'-strong-growing, white fls   42
    "   'Artemis' - fls dusky-purple   84
    "   'Charon' - dark purple fls   42
    "   'Pomona' - tall, white fls marked violet-mauve   36
    "   'Poseidon' - soft purplish-rose fls   84
    "   'Saturnus' - fls light reddish-purple   42
 messanensis / Bb / 10" / reddish-blue to brown fls / Crete   43
 michailovskyi / Bb / 4-8" / purple-brown & gold fls / Turkey   85
 montana / Bb / 8-18" / dark red fls / Balkans, e Europe   54
 nigra / Bb / 6" / deep purple-red fls / Medit. region   43
 olivieri / Bb / 15" / yellow fls flushed red-brown / Iran   43
 pallidiflora / Bb / 2' / creamy or greenish-yellow fls / Iran   42
 persica / Bb / 6-40" / fls blackish-plum to straw / Iran, Near East   56
 pinardii / HH Bb / 9" / deep purple & olive-green fls / n Turkey   36
 pluriflora / Bb / 6-12" / rosy-purple fls / California   9
 pontica / Bb / 6" / brown fls, green tipped / sw Europe   4
 pudica / Bb / 2-10" / yellow fls / w North America   9
 pyrenaica / Bb / 1½' / dark maroon-purple fls / Pyrenees   42
 raddeana / Bb / 2½' / pale creamy-yellow fls / Iran, Turkey   85
 recurva / Bb / 1' / scarlet & orange fls / California, Oregon   35
 roderickii / Bb / ? / fls creamy-green / nw North America   (1)
 roylei / Bb / 6-40" / pale green to purplish fls / w Himalayas   56
 ruthenica / Bb / 1-2' / fls livid purple / Caucasus   9
 'Saturnus' - see F. meleagris 'Saturnus'   84
 sewerzowii - see KOROLKOWIA sewerzowii   54
 striata / Bb / 8-15" / pale pink fls, brown veined / California   85
 tenella - see F. nigra   56
 thunbergii - see F. verticillata v. thunbergii   9
 tubiformis / Bb / 2-3" / reddish-purple fls / se France, n Italy   38
    "   delphinensis - a synonym   9
    "   v. moggridgei - yellow fls   56
 tuntasia / Bb / 12" / white & green fls / Altai Mts.   38
 verticillata / Bb / to 2' / cream fls, veined green / Far East   56
    "   v. thunbergii - 1½', fls light yellow, China   60
 whitallii - similar to F. meleagris, w end of Taurus Mts.   (2)

FUCHSIA - Onagraceae
 excorticata / HH T / 36' / dark purple fls / New Zealand   58
 magellanica / HH Sh / 12' / crimson-red & purple fls / Peru   42
    "   pumila - see F. magellanica 'Tom Thumb'   32
    "   'Tom Thumb' - 8-16", red fls   32
 procumbens / HH R / prostrate / dark red fls / New Zealand   85

FUMANA - Cistaceae
 procumbens / Sh / to 16" / yellow fls / wc & s Europe   91

(1) - JESIK in Bull. Am. Rock Garden Soc. 27:3
(2) - BECK - Fritillaries. 1953

FUMARIA africana - see RUPICAPNOS africana   90
   "   procumbens - possibly an error for FUMANA procumbens   *

GAGEA - Liliaceae
   arvensis / HH R / 6" / yellow fls / Spain, North Africa   64
   lutea / R / 6-10" / yellow fls / Far East, Siberia, n Europe   60
   villosa / R / 3" / yellow fls / Caucasus   45

GAILLARDIA - Compositae
   aristata / P / 2' / fls yellow & red / w North America   42
      "   'Goblin' - 1', fls yellow with red tips   44
      "   'Nana Nieske' - 15", yellow & red fls   95
   'Goblin' - see G. aristata 'Goblin'   44
   'Nana Nieske' - see G. aristata 'Nana Nieske'   95
   pinnatifida / P / 6-24" / yellow fls / Utah, Colorado, Oklahoma   76
   suavis / P / ? / sometimes lacking ray fls / Texas   73

GALANTHUS - Amaryllidaceae
   elwesii / Bb / 6"+ / large white fls, green tipped / Jugoslavia   4
   fosteri / HH Bb / 12" / white fls marked green / Lebanon   36
   ikariae / Bb / 6" / white & green fls / Nikaria, island off A. Minor 36
   nivalis / Bb / 6-9" / fls white / Pyrenees to Caucasus   9
      "   olgae - see G. n. ssp. reginae-olgae   84
      "   ssp. reginae-olgae - autumn-flowering, mts. of Greece   84
      "   'Viridipicis' - 3", white fls spotted green   4
   plicatus / Bb / 6" / white & green fls, fragrant / s USSR   36

GALAX - Diapensiaceae
   aphylla / P / 2½' / small white fls / Va., Ga., North Carolina   35

GALEGA - Leguminosae
   orientalis / P / 2½-4' / fls purplish-blue / Caucasus   9

GALEOPSIS - Labiatae
   angustifolia / P / to 16" / fls reddish-pink & yellow / w, c & e Eu. 92

GALIUM - Rubiaceae
   anisophyllum / R / dwarf / pale yellow fls / Europe   21
   purpureum / R / 10" / brownish-red fls / near Lake Como, Italy   33
   verum / P / 1-3' / Yellow Bedstraw / Europe, weedy in US   9

GALTONIA - Liliaceae
   candicans / Bb / to 4' / white fls, bell-shaped / Souyh Africa   42
   princeps - smaller edition of above   9

GARRYA - Garrayaceae
   veatchii / HH Sh / Canyon Tassel-bush / coast & mts. of California   93

GAULTHERIA - Ericaceae
   adenothrix / Sh / to 1' / fls white; frs red / Japan   60
   antipoda / HH Sh / prostrate to 3' / frs red or white / New Zealand 46
   cuneata / Sh / 1' / fls & frs white / w China   35
   depressa / Sh / 8-10" / pink & white fls; scarlet frs / New Zealand 38
   hispida / HH Sh / 6' / fls & frs white / Australia, Tasmania   16
   hispidula / R / creeping / white fls & frs / ne North America   34
   humifusa / Sh / 4" / fls white-pinkish; frs scarlet / British Col.   43
   itoana / HH Sh / creeping / bright red frs / Formosa   46
   miqueliana / Sh / 1' / white fls & frs, pink tinged / Japan   35
   nummularioides / Sh / 1' / white fls; blue-black frs / Himalayas   42
   ovatifolia / Sh / procumbent / fls pink & white / B. C., Oregon   35

GAULTHERIA, con.
4/80 * procumbens / Sh / procumbent / fls white; frs scarlet / e N. Am.   9
watney   rupestris / Sh / 1' / white fls; frs not fleshy / New Zealand   32
          shallon / Sh / 5-6' / pink fls; frs dark purple / w N. America   42
          sinensis / Sh / 3-5" / pink fls; blue frs / w China   38
          trichophylla / Sh / 3-6" / pink fls; blue frs / Himalayas, w China   13

X GAULTHETTYA - Ericaceae
    wisleyensis - Sh, dwarf, fls white, frs purplish   85

GAURA - Onagraceae
    lindheimeri / P / 2-3' / fls white & rosy / Texas, Louisiana   73

GAYLUSSACIA - Ericaceae
    brachycera / Sh / 6-12" / fls white; frs blue / e United States   13

GEISSORRHIZA - Iridaceae
    rochensis / HH C / 4-8" / intense purple-blue fls / sw Cape Province 56
    secunda / HH C / 9" / purple-blue fls / Cape Province   36

GELASINE - Iridaceae
    azurea / HH P / 18" / blue fls / Brazil   45

GENISTA - Leguminosae
    aetnensis / HH Sh / 15' / yellow fls / Sardinia, sicily   91
    anglica / Sh / to 3' / yellow fls / w Europe   91
    dalmatica - see G. sylvestris v. pungens   91
    decumbens - see CYTISUS decumbens   69
    delphinensis - see G. sagittalis ssp. delphinensis   38
    germanica / Sh / 2' / small yellow fls / c & s Europe   9
    hispanica / HH Sh / to 3' / golden yellow fls / Spain, sw Europe   42
        "   'Nana' - the decumbent form   *
    humifusa - see CYTISUS diffusus   69
    pilosa / Sh / to 3' / yellow fls / w & c Europe   91
        "   procumbens - see CYTISUS procumbens   35
    radiata / Sh / 3' / dark yellow fls / s Europe   95
    sagittalis / Sh / 1' / bright yellow fls / c & se Europe   35
        "   ssp. delphinensis - prostrate form, s France   38
    sylvestris v. pungens - 4-6", golden-yellow fls, Dalmatia   13
    tinctoria / Sh / 3' / fls deep yellow / s Europe, Britain   42
        "   v. humifusa - prostrate to 4"   38

GENTIANA - Gentianaceae
    acaulis / R / 2-3" / fls bright blue / Alps, Pyrenees   42
        "   v. alba - good white form   43
        "   v. angustifolia - 4", deep blue fls; narrow lvs, Jura Mts.   43
        "   'Caelestina' - large, vivid sky-blue fls   53
        "   clusii - see G. clusii   9
        "   'Undulatifolia' - medium-blue fls, wavy-edged lvs   53
    affinis / R / 6-18" / fls deep blue, streaked green / Calif., Ore.   75
    algida / R / 4-10" / pale yellow fls, green spots / Japan, Korea   60
        "   f. igarashii - 4", large fls, Hokkaido in high mts.   60
    alpina / R / 2" / bright blue fls / European ranges   38
6/79. andrewsii / P / 2' / blue-purple fls, white tips / e N. America   35
    angulosa / R / 3" / rich deep blue fls, angled calyx-tube / Caucasus   43
    angustifolia / R / 3" / blue fls, spotted green / Alps, Pyrenees   9
W 6/79 asclepiadea / P / 1½-2' / deep blue fls / Europe   42
        "   v. alba - white fls   9
        "   'Nana' - dwarfer form   38

GENTIANA, con.

wd. C/79

asclepiadea 'Phyllis' - light blue fls, reasonably true from seed	(1)
" v. rosea - roseate fls	*
austriaca - see GENTIANELLA austriaca	92
autumnalis / P / to 2' / fls indigo-blue / New Jersey to S. Carol.	34
" f. porphyrio - fls brown-spotted within	34
axillaris - see GENTIANELLA amarella	92
axilliflora - see G. triflora v. japonica	60
baltica - see GENTIANELLA campestris ssp. baltica	92
bavarica / R / to 8" / two-toned blue fls / Alps	92
bellidifolia / R / 4-6" / fls white / New Zealand	38
" v. australe - cream fls, South Alps, N. Z.	(2)
bigelovii / P / 12-16" / fls violet / New Mexico, Arizona, Colorado	74
bisetea / R / 5" / fls blue / inner coastal ranges, Oregon	75
brachyphylla / R / to 2' / deep blue fls / Alps, Pyrenees, Carpath.	92
burseri / P / to 2' / clustered yellow fls, brown spots / sw Alps	92
calycosa / R / 6-12" / deep or pale blue fls / nw North America	75
campestris - see GENTIANELLA campestris	(3)
cashemerica / R / 3-4" / mid-blue fls / Kashmir	32, 38
ciliata / R / 5-10" / fringed pale blue fls / Alps, Apennines	95
clausa / P / 2' / blue to blue-violet fls / ne & ec N. America	82
clusii / R / 3" / deep blue unspotted fls / c & s European mts.	92
concinna / A / 4" / white fls, red streaked / New Zealand	21
corymbifera / R / 12"+ / white fls, dark veined / New Zealand	53
crinita / B / 1-2' / soft blue fls / North America	35
cruciata / R / 10" / bluish to greenish fls / s, c & e Europe	92
" ssp. phlogifolia - corolla twice length of calyx, Carpath.	32
dahurica - see G. olivieri	80
decumbens / R / 2-10" / blue fls / Tibet, Himalayas	9
dendrologii / P / rank, leafy / fls in whitish heads / ?	21
depressa / R / to 2" / greenish-blue fls / Nepal, Sikkim	32
dinarica / R / acaulis type / dark blue fls / Balkans, limy mts.	92
excisa - see G. acaulis	92
farreri / R / 3-5" / bright sky-blue fls / se Tibet, w China	42
fetissowii / P / to 2' / intense dark blue fls / w Siberia	80
" 'Alba' - unrecorded white form	*
fischeri / P / 8-30" / blackish-blue fls, green spotted / w Siberia	80
flavida / P / 1-2' / yellowish fls / c Ontario, c United States	53
freyniana / R / 4-6" / blue fls / Asia Minor, in mts.	32
frigida / R / 2-4" / fls yellowish-white, spotted blue / Carpathians	92
gelida / R / 6-16" / yellow fls / Caucasus	80
germanica - see GENTIANELLA germanica	32
" austriaca alba - see GENTIANELLA austriaca	80
gracilipes / R / 6-9" / clear, rich blue fls / China	32
grayi - see G. linearis ssp. rubricaulis	(3)
X hascombensis - good blue fls, seedlings nearly true	53
jesoana - see G. triflora v. japonica	60
kesselringii - see G. walujewii	80
kochiana - see G. acaulis	92
kurroo / R / to 7" / fls blue, white spotted / Himalayas	9
lagodechiana - see G. septemfida v. lagodechiana	32
linearis / P / 8-20" / blue or roseate-purple fls / ne N. America	(3)
" ssp. rubricaulis - 8-20", cluster of bluisf fls / Gr. Lakes	(3)
loderi - see G. cashemerica	21
lutea / P / to 4' / fls yellow / c & s Europe, in mts.	92
macrophylla / P / 16-28" / blue-violet fls / Siberia to China	80

(1) - HODGKIN in Jour. Royal Hort. Soc. April 1973
(2) - MELVILLE in Jour. Royal Hort. Soc. June 1963
(3) - GILLETT- The Gentians of Canada, Alaska and Greenland. 1963

GENTIANA, con.

makinoi / P / 1-2' / dark blue fls / Honshu in high mt. bogs   60
   "   'Albiflora' - apparently unrecorded white form   *
moorcroftiana / B / 1'+ / skyblue to lavender fls / Kashmir   21
nipponica / R / to 4" / blue fls / alpine Hokkaido & Honshu   60
nivalis / A / 6" / deep blue fls / circumboreal, s in European mts.   96
ochroleuca - see G. villosa   9
olivieri / R / to 1' / blue or blue-violet fls / c Asia   80
orbicularis / R / tufts / sessile deep blue fls / c Europe, in mts.   96
oregana / P / 1-2' / blue fls / nw North America   9
pannonica / P / 2' / fls purple, reddish-black spots / c Europe   92
parryi / R / 9" / purple-blue fls / nw North America   9
phlogifolia / R / 6" / fls intense bluish-violet / Carpathians   33
platypetala / R / 8-10" / brilliant blue fls / Alaska   53
pneumonanthe / R / 6-12" / dark blue fls, striped green / Eu., Asia   95
porphyrio - see G. autumnalis f. porphyrio   34
praecox - see GENTIANELLA praecox   80
procumbens / A / tufted / stems 1-2" long / Nepal   29
prostrata / A or B / to 6" / fls blue / arctic Asia & N. America   63
przewalskii / R / small / violet or blue fls / Koko-Nor, Tibet   33
puberula / P / to 20" / fls pale to dark blue / n & c N. America   (1)
punctata / P / to 2' / fls yellow, maroon spotted / Alps   96
purdomii - "purdomii" of gardens is G. decumbens   21
purpurea / P / to 2' / reddish-purple or coppery fls / c Eu., in mts.   96
quinquefolia / A / 1-3' / fls pale violet / ne United States   72
rostani / R / 3" / light azure-blue fls / Alps, Pyrenees   96
saponaria / P / 16-32" / purplish fls / nc United States   83
saxosa / R / 2-4" / fls white / New Zealand   42
scabra / R / 1'+ / uniformly dark blue fls / e Siberia   80
   "   v. buergeri - the Japanese form, later, handsomer   33
   "   v. saxatilis - procumbent, fls deep blue   53
   "   f. stenophylla - narrow-leaved   60
sceptrum / P / 1-4' / blue fls, marked green / California to B.C.   75
septemfida / R / 6" / deep blue fls, dotted inside / Asia Minor   38
   "   v. lagodechiana - deep blue fls, Caucasus   32
   "   v. latifolia - wider-leaved   33
   "   olivieri - see G. olivieri   9
sikkimensis / R / 6" / one inch blue trumpets / alps of Sikkim   33
simplex / R / 2-8" / deep blue fls / s California to c Oregon   75
sino-ornata / R / mats / gentian-blue fls / se Tibet, w China   42
siphonantha / R / 1' / blue fls / Himalayas   53
stylophora / P / 3'+ / greenish-yellow fls / Asia   21
X 'Susan Jane' - procumbent seedling of 'Inverleith', whitish fls   (2)
terglouensis / R / 3" / sky-blue fls / s & e Alps   96
thunbergii / B / to 6" / blue fls / Japan, Korea, China/ Manchuria   60
tianshanica / P / 8-16" / dark blue fls / c Asia   80
tibetica / P / 2' / greenish to yellowish fls / Tibet   53
triflora / P / 2'+ / dark blue fls / e Siberia, Korea   80
   "   v. japonica - from Japan, Kuriles & Sakhalin   60
   "   v. montana - alpine form, dwarf   60
tubiflora / R / 1' / blue fls / alps of Kashmir & Kumaon   33
utriculosa / A / 4-8" / fls intense blue / c Europe, Balkans   92
verna / R / tufts / variable blue fls / Alps, Asia Minor, Pyrenees   42
   "   angulosa - see G. angulosa   43
villosa / P / 4-24" / greenish-white to purplish fls / ec US   53
walujewii / P / 12-16" / pale yellow fls, blue lined / c Asia   80

(1) - GILLETT - The Gentians of Canada, Alaska & Greenland. 1963
(2) - GORER in Quar. Bull. Alpine Garden Soc. 37:4

GENTIANA, con.
    wilsonii / R / 4" / sea-blue fls / w China   21
    wutaiensis / B / 6"+ / fls dark blue to white / ?   20

GENTIANELLA - Gentianaceae
    amarella / A or B / to 1' / dull purple, blue, white fls / n & c Eu. 92
    austriaca / B / 4-8"+ / purplish or whitish fls / ec Europe   92
    campestris / A or B / 3-10" / bluish-purple fls / n & c Europe   (1)
        "   ssp. baltica - A, low, blue or white fls, s Sweden   92
    detonsa / A or B / 2-8" / dark blue fls / arctic & subarctic Eu.   92
    germanica / B / to 16" / fls violet, pink, whitish / w & c Europe   92
    praecox / B / 6"+ / fls dark blue to white / c Europe   80

GERANIUM - Geraniaceae
    aconitifolium - see G. sylvaticum ssp. rivulare   51
    argenteum / R / 3" / fls pink, darker veins / n & c Italy   91
    candidum / R / decumbent / white fls, rosy center / China   (2)
    cataractum / P / to 16" / fls bright pinkish-purple / sc Spain   91
    chinense / P / 1½' / fls blue to rosy purple / China   (3)
    cinereum / R / 3-6" / fls varying pink shades / Pyrenees   42
        "   'Album' - white fls of purity and brilliance   33
        "   ssp. subcaulescens - deep red-purple fls, Balkans   91
        "   "   'Splendens' - carmine-pink fls   17
    columbinum / A / to 2' / purplish-pink fls / Europe, escaped in US   91
    dalmaticum / R / 6-8" / clean pink fls / Dalmatia   38
    delavayii / R / 8" / black-crimson fls / China   (3)
    dissectum / A / to 2' / purplish-pink fls / most of Europe   91
    endressii / P / 1-1½' / clear pink fls / sw France   91
        "   'Wargrave' - 1½', salmon-rose fls   85
    erianthum / P / 1'+ / bluish-purple fls / n hemisphere   60
    eriostemon / P / 1½' / fls violet-purple / Siberia, China, Korea   9
    farreri - see G. napuligerum   38
    grandiflorum / P / 1-2' / fls lilac, purple veins / n Asia   35
        "   v. alpinum - dwarf, blue fls, alpine Turkestan   33
    grevilleanum / R / creeping / fls deep purple / Himalayas   9
    ibericum / P / 1-1½' / fls deep purple / Caucasus   91
    incanum / Gh / 6" / fls mauve or purple / South Africa   (4)
    macrorrhizum / P / 1-1½' / fls bright red / s Europe   42
    maculatum / P / 1½' / fls pale rose / North America   35
    manescavii - see ERODIUM manescavii   *
    microphyllum / HH R / 1' to prostrate / white fls / New Zealand   2
    napuligerum / R / 6" / pale rose fls / Yunnan   38
    nodosum / P / 8-20" / fls bright pink to violet / s Europe   9
    palmatum / Gh / 15" / fls pale purple / Madeira, Canary Isles   9,85
    pelopenesiacum / P / ? / fls bluish-violet / Albania, s Greece   91
    phaeum / P / 18-28" / fls blackish or brownish-purple / c Europe   91
    platypetalum / P / 6-28" / blue fls / Caucasia, n & nw Iran   26
    pratense / P / 12-32" / fls bright violet-blue / c Europe   91
        "   'Album' - 2', pure white fls, n Europe   42
        "   v. transbaicalicum - 18", bluish-rose recurrent bloom   *
    polyanthes / P / 2'+ / "more ordinary Cranesbill" / Himalayas   21
    psilostemon / P / 1-2' / rich purple fls, black center / Orient   35
    pylzowianum / R / 3" / large clear pink fls / Kansu   38
    pyrenaicum / P / 10-28" / fls purple to lilac / s & w Europe   91
    reflexum / P / 16-28" / fls dull lilac or purple / Balkans   91

    (1) - WEBB - An Irish Flora. 1963
    (2) - STEPHENS in Jour. Royal Hort. Soc. May 1964
    (3) - BECKETT in Gardeners Chronicle 164:3
    (4) - LAWDER in Gardeners Chronicle 164:17

ARG4
SBD

GERANIUM, con.
  renardii / R / 9" / pale lavender fls, veins crimson / Caucasus   17
  richardsonii / P / 1-3' / fls white or pink, red veins / w N. Am.   75
. robertianum / A or B / to 20" / fls bright pink / Eu., N. Am.   91
      "   f. albiflorum - white-flowered   34
      "   album - see G. r. forma albiflorum   34
  sanguineum / P / 18" / fls intense magenta / Europe   42
      "   'Album' - 9", white fls   42
      "   v. lancastriense - see G. s. var. prostratum   32
      "   v. prostratum - 6", clear rose pink fls   32
      "   'Walney Form' - 6-9", fls a deeper rose   (1)
  sessiliflorum 'Nigrum' - 4", white fls; brownish lvs, New Zealand   3
  sibiricum / P / 1-2' / small dingy white fls / Siberia, escape in US   9
  subcaulescens - see G. cinereum ssp. subcaulescens   91
      "   splendens - see G. c. ssp. s. 'Splendens'   17
  sylvaticum / P / to 2' / fls variable in color / most of Europe   91
      "   ssp. rivulare - 1', fls white, red veined, Alps   91
  thunbergii / P / to 20" / pale rose fls, deeper nerves / Japan   60
      "   'Album' - white fls   *
  transbaicalicum - see G. pratense v. transbaicalicum   *
  traversii / HH P / 3-25" / fls pale rose or white / Chatham Isls.   9
      "   'Elegans' - mat, fls pink   20
  wallichianum / R / 1' / fls violet-blue / Himalayas   42
      "   'Buxtons Blue' - fls a deeper shade   42

GERARDIA - Scrophulariaceae
  tenuifolia / A / to 2' / fls light purple, spotted / Maine to La.   34
  virginica / P / to 4' / yellow fls / New Hampshire to Louisiana   83

GERBERA - Compositae
  anandria - see LEIBNITZIA anandria   (2)
  nana - see CREMANTHODIUM nanum   21
  nivea / R / 6" / deep rose-purple fls / Asia   21

GEUM - Rosaceae
  aleppicum / P / to 4½' / orange, deep yellow fls / Eurasia   34
  anemonoides - see G. pentapetalum   60
  X borisii - P, 1', fls orange-scarlet   42
  calthaefolium / R / 6" / yellow fls / nw North America   29
      "   v. nipponicum - to 1', fls yellow, Japanese alps   60
  campanulatum - neater form of G. triflorum; Olympic Peninsula, US   21
  chiloense / P / 1-2' / fls scarlet / Chile   42
      "   v. miniatum - 2-3', two shades lighter color   9
      "   'Mrs. Bradshaw' - see G. X 'Mrs Bradshaw'   44
  coccineum / P / 1-2' / red fls / Balkan Peninsula, in mts.   42
  heldreichii - orange fls, referred to G. montanum   9
  macrophyllum / P / to 3' / bright yellow fls / N. America, Eurasia   34
  montanum / R / 2-4" / fls golden yellow / c & s Europe, in mts.   42
  X 'Mrs. Bradshaw' - 2½-3', semi-double scarlet fls   44
  parviflorum / R / to 1' / fls white / New Zealand, Chile   2
  peckii / R / 6-16" / yellow fls / White Mts., New Hampshire   35
  pentapetalum / Sh / 4-8" / fls white / Japan to Aleutians   60
  X 'Red Wings' - 2', fls brilliant bright scarlet   85
  reptans / R / 6" / fls bright yellow / Alps, Carpathians   91
  X rhaeticum - 4-5", golden yellow fls, natural hybrid in Engadine   38
  rivale / P / 1' / reddish fls, nodding / Europe, including Britain   42
      "   'Album' - creamy-white selection   *
      "   'Leonard' - 1½', salmon, orange tinted fls   42

(1) - C. R. WORTH in corres. 8/7/1974
(2) - VASAK in The Scottish Rock Garden Club Jour. 14:1

GEUM, con.
  rossii / R / 1' / bright yellow fls / Asia to Canadian e arctic   63
  sibiricum - see G. chiloense   32
  triflorum / R / to 1' / yellowish, pink, purple fls / nw N. Am.   9
      "   campanulatum - see G. campanulatum   21
  uniflorum / R / 3" / white fls / New Zealand   33
  'Waights Hybrid' - compact, 6", orange-red fls   3

GEVUINA - Proteaceae
  avellana / HH T / 15' / white fls; red frs / s Chile   46

GILIA - Polemoniaceae
  achilleaefolia / A / 4-24" / blue-violet, white fls / s & c Calif.   75
  aggregata - see IPOMOPSIS aggregata   (1)
  capitata / A / 8-32" / white to blue-violet fls / Calif. to B. C.   75
  longiflora - see IPOMOPSIS lingiflora   (1)
  rigidula / R / 3-10" / fls blue or purple / Col., Kansas, Okla.   76
  rubra - see IPOMOPSIS rubra   (1)

GILLENIA - Rosaceae
  stipulata / P / 2-4' / fls white to pinkish / c & s United States   9
  trifoliata / P / 2-4' / fls white or pinkish / c & s United States   9

GLADIOLUS - Iridaceae
  alatus / HH C / 10" / brick-red fls / Cape Province   36
  atroviolaceus / C / 2' / violet-purple fls / n Turkey   36
  blandus / HH C / 20" / creamy-white fls / Cape Province   36
      "   v. carneus - pale mauvish-pink fls   84
  byzantinus / C / to 2½' / fls bright magenta-pink / e Medit. reg.   42
  carmineus / HH C / 1' / fls deep rose / Cape of Good Hope   70
  carneus - see G. blandus v. carneus   *
  communis / C / 16-32" / rosy purple fls / Spain to Greece   64
  gracilis / HH C / 2' / pink-cream fls / Cape Province   36
  grandis / HH C / 18" / maroon-brown fls / Cape Province   36
  illyricus / C / 1-1½' / purple-red fls / Medit. region   4
  imbricatus / C / to 28" / fls purplish-violet / c Eu., Caucasus   54
  liliaceus - see G. grandis   95
  macowianus / HH C / 2' / cream fls / Cape Province   36
  X nanus - yellow G. tristis x red G. cardinalis, tender   84
  natalensis - see G. psittacinus   84
  orchidiflorus / HH C / 18" / green-brown fls / Natal   36
  palustris / C / 1-2' / purple-red fls / c Europe   32
  papilio / HH C / 2' / cream fls / Cape Province   36
  psittacinus / HH C / 2' / red fls / Natal   36
  segetum / C / 2' / bright purple fls / Mediterranean region   9
  triphyllus / C / small / fls purple & cream-white / Cyprus   37
  tristis / HH C / 2' / yellowish-white fls, dark markings / S.Africa   9
      "   v. concolor - almost white or uniform yellow fls   9
  undulatus - see G. vittatus   9
  viperatus - see G. orchidiflorus   84
  vittatus / HH C / 1' / white fls / South Africa   9

GLAUCIDIUM - Podophyllaceae
  fimbrilligerum - error for GLAUCIUM fimbrilligerum   *
  palmatum / R / 12-16" / pale lilac fls / Japan   42
      "   'Album' - white fls   35

  (1) - INGRAM in Baileya 8:2

GLAUCIUM - Papaveraceae
  corniculatum / A / 12-16" / fls orange or reddish / s Europe   90
  elegans / A / to 1' / fls yellow to red / c Asia, Iran   (1)
  fimbrilligerum / B / 1-2' / fls yellow / c Asia   (1)
  flavum / P gr. as A / 1-3' / yellow or orange fls / eu., N. Africa   42
  grandiflorum / P / 12-20" / fls dark orange to crimson / Greece,Iran 26
  phoeniceum - see G. corniculatum   9

GLEDITSIA - Leguminosae
  japonica / T / 35' / lvs with up to 30 leaflets / Japan   46

GLEHNIA - Umbelliferae
  leiocarpa / R / 4" / white fls / Calif. to Alaska on sandy coasts   75

GLOBULARIA - Globulariaceae
  aphyllanthes - see G. punctata   92
  bellidifolia - see G. meridionalis   92
  cambessedesii / R / 1' / blue fls / ne Spain, in mts.   65
  cordifolia / Sh / to 4" / gray-blue fls / c & s Europe   92
  elongata - see G. punctata   92
  incanescens / R / to 4" / violet-blue fls / Italy   38
  meridionalis / Sh / to 6" / gray-blue fls / se Alps   92
  nana - see G. repens   (2)
  nudicaulis / R / 6" / large medium-blue fls / s Europe   38
  orientalis / Sh / to 10" / lvs in basal rosette / ?   (2)
  punctata / R / to 1' / fls gray-blue / s & c Europe   92
     "   'Alba' - white fls   *
  repens / R / 3" / gray-blue fls / sw Europe, in mts.   42
  spinosa / R / 8" / clear blue fls / se Spain   (2)
  stygia / Sh / dwarf / ice-blue fls / Greece   92
  tricosantha / R / 6-10" / steel-blue fls / e Balkan Peninsula   35
  vulgaris / R / 8" / blue fls / Spain, France, Sweden   9
     "   'Alba' - white fls   *
  wilkommii - see G. punctata   92
     "   'Alba' - see G. punctata 'Alba'   *

GLORIOSA - Liliaceae
  rothschildiana / Gh Cl / tall / crimson fls / tropical Africa   9
  superba / Gh Cl / 5-10' / yellow & red fls / Africa, Asia   9

GNAPHALIUM - Compositae
  dioicum - see ANTENNARIA dioica   51
  norvegicum / R / 4-8" / fls light brownish / Europe   32
  supinum / R / to 4" / brownish fls / Europe & e US, in mts.   32
  trinerve / HH Sh / few inches / pure white fls / New Zealand   20

GODETIA - Onagraceae
  quadrivulnaria / A / ? / lilac or pale crimson fls / Oregon   9

GOMPHOLOBIUM - Leguminosae
  huegelii / HH Sh / 3' / yellow pea fls / New S. Wales, Australia   16

GOODYERA - Orchidaceae
  oblongifolia / P / to 18" / fls white, tinged green / n N. America   23
  pubescens / R / 1' / whitish fls; white-netted lvs / ne N. America   9
  repens / R / 4-8" / white fls; lvs reddish-veined / Europe   23
  tesselata / R / to 1' / white fls / n United States & Canada   9

  (1) - POPOV in Flora USSR Vol. VII 1970(trans.)
  (2) - SCHWARZ in Quar. Bull. Alpine Garden Soc. 35:4

GORDONIA - Theaceae
  lasianthus / HH T / to 60' / white fls / coastal N. Car. to Fla.   9

GREIGIA - Bromeliaceae
  sphacelata / Gh / 3' / rose fls / Chile   9

GREVILLEA - Proteaceae
  lavandulacea / HH Sh / 5' / red fls / Swan River area, Australia   45
  rosmarinifolia / HH Sh / 6-7' / fls deep rosy-red / New S. Wales   13

GRINDELIA - Compositae
  chiloensis / HH Sh / 3-5' / yellow fls; evergreen lvs / Argentina   46
  hirsutula / HH P / 1-3' / yellow fls / coast ranges of c California   75
  squarrosa / P / 8-40" / yellow fls / Washington to South Dakota   76

GROSSHEIMIA macrocephala - see CENTAUREA macrocephala   *

GUNDELIA - Compositae
  tournefortii / HH P / 15" / fls yellow-green / Asia Minor   (1),45

GUNNERA - Haloragidaceae
  chilensis / HH P / 3'+ / fls reddish / Chile   9
  pro-repens / HH R / creeping / red fleshy frs / New Zealand   78

GYMNADENIA - Orchidaceae
  conopsea / P / 8-20" / bright pink fls / Europe, Asia   30
  fragrans - see HABENARIA dilitata   *
  odoratissima / P / to 18" / pale pink fls / c Europe   30

GYMNOCARPIUM - Polypodiaceae
  dryopteris / F / 9" / Oak Fern / Great Britain   50

GYNANDIRIS - Iridaceae
  setifolia / Gh C / 6" / pale blue to lilac & yellow fls / Cape Prov. 56
  sisyrinchium / C / 4-8" / bright blue or mauve fls / Medit. region   42

GYPSOPHILA - Caryophyllaceae
  aretioides / R / cushion / white fls; gray-green lvs / Iran   43
  bungeana - see G. sericea   (2)
  cerastoides / R / 2-3" / fls white, veined purple / Himalayas   38
  dubia / R / 6" / white fls / ?   29
  fastigiata / P / to 3' / fls white or pale purplish / ec Europe   90
  libanotica / P / 4-16" / fls white to pink / e Medit. region   26
  nana / R / to 6" / pale purplish fls / s Greece, in mts.   90
  paniculata 'Rosy Veil' - see G. X 'Rosy Veil'   44
  petraea / R / caespitose / fls white or pale purplish / Carpathians 90
  repens / R / 3-6" / fls lilac-pink to white / Alps   42
    "   'Rosea' - showy pink form   35
    "   'Rosea Minima' - dwarfer   *
  X 'Rosy Veil' - 18", doubled soft pink to white fls   44
  sericea / R / to 1' / white & lilac fls / Siberia, Mongolia   (2)
  silenoides / R / 1' / fls white or pinkish, purple veins / Caucasus 26
  tenuicaulis - error for G. tenuifolia?   *
  tenuifolia / R / to 8" / fls white to pink / Caucasus   35
  viscosa / A / 4-22" / white to pale pink fls / Near East   26

  (1) - TACKHOLM - Student's Flora of Egypt. 1956
  (2) - KOMAROV - Flora of U. S. S. R. Vol. VI

HAASTIA - Compositae
pulvinaris / Sh / dense mound / minute fls / New Zealand — 58
    "   v. minor - smaller in all parts — 2
sinclairii / Sh / fewer branches / shining larger lvs / N. Zealand — 21

HABENARIA - Orchidaceae
bifolia - see PLATANTHERA bifolia — 30
blephariglottis / P / to 3' / fls bright white to creamy / N. Am. — 34
ciliaris / P / to 3' / fls brilliant orange / e United States — 9
dilitata / P / to 4' / fls greenish-white / N. America, in bogs — 9
fimbriata / P / to 3' / pink-purple fls / ne & c North America — 71

HABERLEA - Gesneriaceae
ferdinandi-coburgii / R / 4-6" / pale lilac fls / Balkans — 38
rhodopensis / R / 6-8" / fls pale lilac / Greece — 42
    "   'Virginalis' - white form, less vigorous — 42

HABRANTHUS - Amaryllidaceae
advenus - see HIPPEASTRUM advenum — 84
andersonii / HH Bb / 4-6" / golden-yellow fls / South America — 84
    "   'Cupreus' - fls a dark copper shade — (1)
    "   'Roseus' - pink fls — 56
    "   texanus - see H. texanus — (2)
brachyandrus / HH Bb / to 1' / fls pale rose-pink / South America — 84
citrinus - see ZEPHYRANTHES citrina — *
robustus / HH Bb / to 2' / fls pale rose-pink / Argentina — 41
texanus / Bb / 4-8" / fls yellow to copper / Texas — (2)

HACKELIA - Boraginaceae
brachytuba / P / ? / fls pale to dark blue / Sikkim to Yunnan — (3)
jessicae / P / 12-40" / blue fls / Cascades to Canada — 73

HACQUETIA - Umbelliferae
epipactis / R / 3-4" / yellow fls, ground cover / Europe — 42

HALESIA - Styracaceae
carolina / T / 30'+ / white bells / se United States — 13
monticola / T / 50'+ / white fls / North Carolina to Georgia — 13
    "   v. vestita - young lvs white-woolly — 13

HALIMUM - Cistaceae
atriplicifolium / HH Sh / 3'+ / fls yellow / sw Europe — 91
lasianthum ssp. formosum - 3', spotted yellow fls, s Portugal — 91
umbellatum / HH Sh / 10" / fls white / sw Europe — 91

HAMAMELIS - Hamamelidaceae
japonica / Sh / to 30' / early yellow fls / Japan — 60
    "   'Zuccariniana' - 15', pale lemon-yellow fls — 13
vernalis / Sh / 10' / fls pale yellow to red / c United States — 46
virginiana / Sh / to 25' / bright yellow fls / e & c N. America — 9

HAPLOPAPPUS - Compositae
clementis / R / 4-16" / golden-yellow fls / Wyoming, Col., Utah — 76
coronopifolius / R / mats / yellow fls / Chile — 21
lyallii / R / to 4" / yellow fls / Olympic Mts., Washington — 75
spinulosus / P / 1-2' / yellow fls / Mexico, Texas & n-ward — 74

(1) - LAWRENCE - The Little Bulbs. 1957
(2) - UPHOF in Herbertia Vol. 13
(3) - JOHNSTON in Jour. of the Arnold Arboretum 27:3

HAPLOPHYLLUM - Rutaceae
  boisseranum / R / to 10" / yellow fls; simple lvs / Jugoslavia, Alb. 91
  patavinum / R / to 1' / yellow fls, middle lvs 3-sect. / w Balkans 91

HAQUETIA epipactis - error for HACQUETIA epipactis   *

HARDENBERGIA - Leguminosae
  comptoniana / Gh Cl / to 7' / purplish-blue fls / Australia   41
  violacea / Gh Cl / 6' / purple, pink, white fls / Australia   58
      "   f. rosea - hightwining, pea fls, pink form   16

HARRIMANELLA - Ericaceae
  stelleriana / Sh / mats / white fls / ne Asia, nw N. Am.   85

HARTIA sinensis - see STEWARTIA pteropetiolata   46

HEBE - Scrophulariaceae
  albicans / HH Sh / dwarf / dense, rounded, glaucous lvs / New Zealand46
  armstrongii / HH Sh / to 3' / golden-green whipcord type / N. Zealand 2
  'Autumn Glory' - see H. elliptica 'Autumn Glory'   79
  X balfouriana - dwarf Sh, purple fls, lvs opaque green, purple edged 2
  bidwillii - see PARAHEBE bidwillii   *
  buchananii 'Minor' - 6-8", white fls   13
  'Carl Tescher' - dwarf, violet & white fls, garden hybrid   46
  catarractae - see PARAHEBE catarractae   2
      "   'Rosea' - see PARAHEBE catarractae 'Rosea'   *
  chathamica / HH Sh / prostrate / dark purple fls / coastal N. Z.   2
  ciliolata / HH Sh / to 1' / imbricated lvs / New Zealand, in mts.   2
  colensoi / HH Sh / 1-2' / fls white / North Island, New Zealand   13
  decumbens / HH Sh / 1-3' / white fls / South Island, New Zealand   13
  diffusa - see PARAHEBE catarractae   2
  elliptica / HH Sh / to 6' / white or bluish fls / N. Z., Falklands   2
      "   'Autumn Glory' - 2', purple spikes, late   79
  epacridea / HH Sh / decumbent / white fls / New Zealand   2
  glaucophylla / HH Sh / to 3' / white fls / New Zealand   2
  X guthrieana - 9", fls blue   9
  haastii / HH Sh / prostrate / fls small, white / New Zealand   43
  hookeriana - see PARAHEBE hookeriana   *
  hulkeana / HH Sh / to 5' / pale blue-lilac fls / New Zealand   42
  lavaudiana / HH Sh / 6" / fls rosy pink / South Island, New Zealand 43
  lyallii - see PARAHEBE lyallii   2
  lycopodioides / HH Sh / 1-2' / white fls / South Island, N. Zealand 13
  macrantha / HH Sh / 1-2' / fls white / South Island, New Zealand   85
  X 'McEwanii' - dwarf, erect HH Sh, fls tinged blue   13
  meewanii - error for H. X 'McEwanii'   *
  nivea / HH Sh / tall / white, lilac, pale blue fls / Tasmania, Aus. 21
  pageana - see H. pinguifolia 'Pagei'   13
  parviflora / HH Sh / to 25' / fls in small dense racemes / N. Z.   2
  perfoliata / HH Sh / 1' / blue fls / New South Wales, Australia   45
  pimeleoides / HH Sh / to 1' / fls blue to purple / New Zealand   2
  pinguifolia / HH Sh / decumbent / fls white / New Zealand   69
      "   'Pagei' - 1½', white fls   42
  rakaiensis / HH Sh / dwarf / fls white / New Zealand   46
  raoulii / HH Sh / 9" / pink fls / New Zealand   43
  subalpina - of hort. see H. rakaiensis   46
  X youngii - HH Sh, low, purple fls   81

HEBENSTREITIA - Scrophulariaceae
  dentata / Gh Sh / 1-2' / white fls, flecked yellowish / South Africa 32
  integrifolia / Gh Sh / 1' / white fls / Cape of Good Hope   45

HEDYCHIUM - Zingiberaceae
  gardnerianum / Gh P / 6' / light yellow fls / India   41

HEDYSARUM - Leguminosae
  coronarium / P or B / 2-4' / deep red, fragrant fls / Europe   9
  hedysaroides / P / 16" / red-violet fls / sc Europe, in mts.   91
  obscurum - see H. hedysaroides   91

HELANIOPSIS orientalis - error for HELONIOPSIS orientalis   *

HELENIUM - Compositae
  autumnale / P / 4-6' / yellow fls / e Canada & United States   42
        "   v. pumilum - 1-2' in height   9

HELIANTHEMUM - Cistaceae
  alpestre - see H. oelandicum ssp. alpestre   91
  apenninum / Sh / to 20" / fls white & yellow / s & w Europe   91
  broussonetii / HH Sh / tufted / orange fls / Canary Isls.   20
  canum / R / to 8" / yellow fls / c & s Europe   91
  cinereum / Sh / dwarf / yellow fls / Mediterranean region   91
  ledifolium / A / to 2' / yellow fls / s Europe   91
  lippii / HH Sh / dwarf / yellow fls / N. Africa, Asia Minor   (1)
  lunulatum / R / to 8" / yellow fls, orange base / Maritime Alps   91
  nitidum - see H. nummularium ssp. glabrum   91
  majus - see H. ledifolium   45,91
  nummularium / Sh / to 20" / fls varii-colored / Europe   91
        "   ssp. glabrum - fls yellow, c, s & sw Europe, in mts.   91
        "   ssp. grandiflorum - c, s & sw Europe, in mts.   91
        "   'Jubilee' - double yellow fls   17
        "   'Mutabile' - light rose fls, no longer a botanical var.   9
        "   ssp. obscurum - sepals & lvs pubescent, c Europe   91
  oelandicum / R / to 8" / yellow fls / most of Europe, except n   91
        "   ssp. alpestre - 8", yellow fls, c & s Europe   91
        "   "   'Serpyllifolium' - smaller, prostrate to 2"   38
  ovatum - see H. nummularium ssp. obscurum   91
  pilosum / R / to 1' / white fls, yellow clawed / w Medit. region   91
  tuberaria - see TUBERARIA lignosus   91
  violaceum - see H. pilosum   91
  vulgare - see H. nummularium   91
        "   grandiflorum - see H. nummularium ssp. grandiflorum   91

HELIANTHUS - Compositae
  annuus / A / 1-14' - Yellow Sunflower / Great Plains, US   73
  cordata - see H. mollis v. cordatus   9
  mollis / P / 2-5' / yellow to orange-yellow fls / c US   82
        " v. cordatus - lvs deeply cordate & clasping   34

HELICHRYSUM - Compositae
  alveolatum - see H. splendidum   13
  apiculatum / HH P / 1-2' / orange-yellow fls / Australia   9
  backhousii / HH Sh / small / white fls / Tasmania   (2)
  bellidioides / HH R / 3" / fls white / New Zealand   42
  bracteatum / A / 1½-3' / fls varii-colored / Australia   9
  coralloides / HH Sh / 10" / fls cream / New Zealand   43
  dealbatum / HH P / 1½' / white fls / Tasmania   45
  frigidum / HH Sh / 2-3" / white fls / Corsica   42
  humile / Gh P / low, spreading / rosy involucre / South Africa   9

  (1) - TACKHOLM - Student's Flora of Egypt. 1954
  (2) - GILLANDERS in Bull. Am. Rock Garden Soc. 32:4

HELICHRYSUM, con.
```
  lanatum / HH Sh / 1½-2' / fls bright lemon-yellow / South Africa       42
  marginatum - see H. milfordiae                                        85
  microphyllum / HH Sh / to 32" / yellow fls / New Zealand              78
  milliganii / A / 6" / bracts colored as H. bracteatum / Australia     21
  milfordiae / HH R / 4" / silvery-white & yellow fls / Basutoland      42
  orientale / Sh / 10-12" / clear yellow fls / Medit. region            38
  petiolatum / HH P / 2-3' / woolly lvs; fls cream-white / S. Africa 9,32
  plicatum / R / 6" / deep, vivid yellow fls / Medit. region            21
  rosmarinifolium - see OZOTHAMNUS thyrsoideus                          46
  scorpoides / HH P / 2' / fls yellow / s Australia                     16
  selago / Sh / 8" / fls creamy-white, white-felted stems / N. Zealand 43
      "  v. tumidum - tomentum loose, sometimes scanty                   2
  semi-papposum / A / to 3' / smaller fls / Australia                   21
  splendidum / Sh / 3' / white-woolly lvs; yellow fls / Africa, in mts.13
  stoechas / HH R / 1' / yellow fls / Spain, Italy, N. Africa           64
  tumidum - see H. selago v. tumidum                                    2
  virgineum / Sh / 8-10" / silvery-pink fls / Balkans                   38
```

HELICTOTRICHON - Gramineae
```
  sempervirens / P Gr / 1-4' / yellow & purple fls / sw Europe          85
```

HELIOPHILA - Cruciferae
```
  longifolia / A / 1-1½' / blue & white or yellow fls / South Africa    42
```

HELIOPSIS - Compositae
```
  helianthoides / P / to 4½' / yellow fls / e & c North America         34
```

HELIOSPERMA albanicum - see SILENE albanica   *
```
     "       alpestre - see SILENE alpestris                           90
     "       alpina - see SILENE vulgaris ssp. prostrata               90
     "       quadridentata - see SILENE pusilla                        90
     "       quadrifidum - see SILENE pusilla                          90
```

HELIPTERUM - Compositae
```
  albicans / HH R / to 9" / white & yellow fls / alps of s Australia    16
  alpinum - see H. incanum v. alpinum                                   *
  anethemoides / HH P / to 18" / white bracts / s Australia, Tasmania   16
  incanum / HH P / ? / colored bracts / Tasmania                        21
      "  v. alpinum - HH R, 4-6", white fls, N. S. Wales, Australia    (1)
```

HELLEBORUS - Ranunculaceae
```
  abschasicus / P / 2' / carmine-red fls / Caucasus                    (2)
  'Appleblossom' - pale pink flowered Lenten Rose                      (3)
  atrorubens - see H. dumetorum ssp. atrorubens                        90
  caucasicus / P / 2' / fls pale greenish to yellowish-brown / Caucas.(2)
  corsicus - see H. lividus ssp. corsicus                              90
  cyclophyllus / P / 2' / fls light glaucous-green / Balkans           90
         "     odorus - see H. odorus                                  90
  dumetorum ssp. atrorubens - 1½', fls violet, Jugoslavia              90
  foetidus / P / 8-32" / fls green, purple margins / sw Europe         90
  guttatus / P / 2' / fls white, red spotted, purple margins / Caucas.(2)
  lividus / P / to 32" / fls pale green / Balearic Isls.               90
      "    ssp. corsicus - with spinier lvs, Corsica, Sardinia         90
  niger / R / to 1' / fls white or pink tinged / e Alps                90
      "  'Potters Wheel' - 1-1½', pure white fls with broad petals     42
  odorus / P / 2' / scented green fls / e, c & s Europe                90
```

```
  (1) - VALDER in Jour. Royal Hort. Soc.  Sept. 1964
  (2) - KRASHKENINNIKOV in Flora USSR.  Vol. VII  1970(trans.)
  (3) - FISH in Bull. Hardy Plant Soc.  1:7
```

HELLEBORUS, con.
    orientalis / P / 2' / varii-colored fls / Greece, Asia Minor   42
        "   atrorubens - see H. dumetorum ssp. atrorubens   *
        "   'Peach Blossom' - cream-pink fls   (1)
    'Prince Rupert' - pale green fls, heavily spotted maroon   (1)
    purpurascens / P / 14" / fls purplish-violet / ec Europe, Ukraine   90
    'Rupert' - see H. 'Prince Rupert'   (1)
    X sternii - variable strain of the Corsican clan   85
    viridis / P / 9-18" / fls yellowish-green / c Europe, Maritime Alps   90
        "   ssp. occidentalis - lvs glabrous, w Europe   90

HELONIAS - Liliaceae
    bullata / P / 12-18" / fls clear pink / coastal bogs, N. J. & s-ward 35

HELONIOPSIS - Liliaceae
    breviscapa - see H. orientalis v. breviscapa   60
    japonica - see H. orientalis   60
    orientalis / P / to 2' / fls rose-purple / Far East   60
        "   alba - see H. orientalis v. flavida   60
        "   v. breviscapa - 1', fls white to pale rose, Japan   60
        "   v. flavida - 1'+, fls white, Honshu   60

HEMEROCALLIS - Liliaceae
9.79   dumortieri / P / to 20" / orange-yellow fls / Japan, Siberia   60
    esculenta - see H. middendorffii v. esculenta   60
    flava / P / 2'+ / fls yellow / Europe, Asia   9
    middendorffii / P / to 28" / orange-yellow fls / Far East   60
        "   v. esculenta - longer-petalled fls, Honshu   60
    minor / P / 18" / fls golden yellow / n & e Asia   9
    'Pink Damask' - 34", old rose fls, yellow throated   95
    thunbergii - see H. vespertina   60
    vespertina / P / 3'+ / fragrant lemon-yellow fls / Japan, Korea   60
    yezoensis / P / 17-34" / fls greenish- yellow / Hokkaido   (2)

HEMITELIA smithii - see CYATHEA smithii   2

HEPATICA - Ranunculaceae
    acutiloba / R / 6" / white, blue, pink fls / e United States   35
    americana / R / 4" / deep blue to white fls / e North America   35
        "   f. rhodantha - the rosy-pink variant   34
    angulosa alba - see H. transsylvanica 'Alba'   *
        "   rosea - see H. transsylvanica 'Rosea'   *
    nobilis / R / 6" / white, blue, pink fls / most of Europe   90
        "   'Alba' - the selected white   *
        "   v. glabrata - glabrous forms not botanically significant   *
        "   v. japonica - from the Far East   60
    transsylvanica / R / 5" / fls mauve-blue / c Roumania   90
        "   'Alba' - white fls   *
        "   'Rosea' - pink fls   *
    triloba - of Europe see H. nobilis; of America see H. americana   *
        "   alba - white fls on H. nobilis or H. americana   *
        "   asiatica - presumably see H. nobilis v. japonica   *
        "   rosea - if H. americana see H. H. a. forma rhodantha   *
        "   rubra - reddish form of either Eu. or Am. round-lobed sp.   *

(1) - FISH in Bull. Hardy Plant Soc. 1:7
(2) - HU in American Horticultural Magazine 47:2

HERACLEUM - Umbelliferae
  dissectum - see H. sphondylium ssp. montanum   91
  lanatum / P / 4-8' / bold plant; white umbels / N. Am., w Asia   9
  mantegazzianum / B or P / 6-16' / white or pink umbels / w Asia   91
  minimum 'Roseum' - R, 1', pink umbels, se France in mts.   91
  sphondylium / B or P / 4'+ / white umbels / c Europe   91
       "   ssp. montanum - ternately-divided lvs, European mts. 91
  stevenii / B or P / 3'+ / lvs white beneath; white fls / Caucasus 91
  villosum - see H. stevenii   91

HERBERTIA - Iridaceae
  drummondiana - see ALOPHA drummondii   72
       "   louisiana - provenance only   *
  platensis / C / 2'+ / light porcelain-blue fls / LaPlata, Argentina 9
  pulchella / C / 6-12" / pale blue-purple fls / South America   84

HERMODACTYLUS - Iridaceae
  tuberosus / Tu / 1' / purple-black fls / e Mediterranean region   42

HERTIA - Compositae
  cheirifolia / Gh P / trailing / yellow fls / Algeria, Tunisia   32

HESPERALOE - Liliaceae
  parviflora v. engelmannii - HH P, 3-4', rosy bell-shaped fls, Texas 9

HESPERANTHA - Iridaceae
  buchrii / HH C / 9" / white & pale pink fls / Natal   36
  falcata / HH C / to 1' / claret-red fls / South Africa   9
  montana / HH C / 4" / white fls, purple flushed / South Africa   37
  standfordiae / HH C / 18" / pale yellow fls / Cape Province   36

HESPERIS - Cruciferae
  matronalis / B / 1-4' / fls purple to white / c & s Europe   90
       "   'Nana Candidissima' - pure white garden selection   9

HESPEROCHIRON - Hydrophyllaceae
  californicus / R / 3-4" / white fls, veined / California   38
  pumilus / R / 2-3" / fls white, blue veins / Oregon   35

HETEROPAPPUS - Compositae
  hispidus / B / to 3' / blue-purple to white fls / Far East   60

HEUCHERA - Saxifragaceae
  bracteata / R / 4-6" / fls in dense panicles / Colorado, s Wyoming 9
  cylindrica / P / 10-24" / grown for colored lvs / B. C. to Idaho   9
      "   v. ovalifolia - lvs dark green to red-brown   (1)
  'Greenfinch' - 2½', fls greenish-white   (2)
  grossularifolia / P / 18" / white fls / along Columbia River   75
      "   v. tenuifolia - 2½'+, Idaho, Oregon, Washington 47
  longiflora / P / 2'+ / plant mostly glabrous / W. Virginia to Ala. 34
  maxima - see H. sanguinea 'Maxima'   9
  micrantha / P / 1-2' / whitish fls / California to British Columbia 9
      "   'Erubescens' - of gardens belongs here   9
  ovalifolia - see H. cylindrica v. ovalifolia   (1)
      "   alpina - not separated in latest botanical treatment   (1)
  'Pleuie de Feu' - see H. sanguinaria 'Pleuie de Feu'   57

(1) - CALDER & SAVILLE in Brittonia 11:2
(2) - BLOOM - Perennials for Your Garden. 1971

HEUCHERA, con.
  racemosa - see ELMERA racemosa   35
  richardsonii / R / 1'+ / greenish fls / c North America   34
     "   v. hispidior - more hispid, Wisconsin to Colorado   34
  sanguinea / P / 1½-2' / fls deep, bright red / Mexico, Arizona   42
     "   'Bressingham Hybrids' to 2', white, pink, coral-red fls   44
     "   'Maxima' - dark crimson fls   9
     "   'Pluie de Feu' - 18", cherry-red fls   44
  villosa / P / 1-3' / fls pinkish / Virginia to Tennessee   9

HEXAGLOTTIS - Iridaceae
  flexuosa / HH C / 15" / yellow fls / Cape Province   36
  virgata / HH C / 12" / yellow fls / Cape of Good Hope   45

HIBISCUS - Malvaceae
  cameronii / HH P / tall / pink fls, dark basal blotch / Madagascar   (1)
  huegelii / HH Sh / 3-6' / fls lilac, purplish-red / s & w Australia   (1)
  militaris / P / 4-6' / fls white to pale rose / Pa.-Minn., & s-ward   9
  moscheutos / P / 3-8' / fls white, pink, rose / Virginia & s-ward   9
     "   ssp. palustris - the northern race, Mass. to Mich.   (1)
  palustris peckii - see H. m. ssp. palustris, white fls   (1)
  syriacus / Sh / 6-12' / fls rose, purple, white / Asia   9
  trionum / A / 1½' / fls creamy-white & purple-black / tropics   42

HIERACEUM - Compositae
  alpinum / R / 6" / bright yellow fls / Europe & Asia, in mts.   9
  amplexicaule / P / 18" / yellow fls / Pyrenees   45
  aurantiacum / R / 6-8" / orange-red fls / Eu., weedy in US   38
  bombycinum / R / 10" / silvery lvs, yellow fls / ?   17
  cynoglossoides / P / 1-4' / fls yellow / nw North America   76
  gronovii / P / to 3'+ / yellow fls / e & c United States   34
  intybaceum / R / to 10" / light yellow fls / e & c Alps   32
  japonicum / R / to 1' / deep yellow fls / Honshu   60
  lanatum / P / to 20" / bright golden fls / w Alps   32
  maculatum / P / 1½' / yellow fls / Bulgaria   20
  X pamphilii - yellow fls; H. lanatum X villosum   (2)
  paniculatum / P / to 4' / yellow fls / open woods, e N. America   34
  pratense / P / to 2' / yellow fls; aggressive King Devil / Europe   34
  rubrum / P / 1½' / densely woolly plant / ec Europe   10
  scouleri / P / 1-1½' / orange fls / California to Canada   75
  umbellatum / P / 3'+ / dark brown infloresence / N. Am., Eu., Asia   34
  venosum / P / 1-3' / bright yellow fls / Maine to Nebraska, weedy   9
  villosum / R / 1' / bright yellow fls / c Europe   42
  waldsteinii - see H. lanatum   51

HIMANTOGLOSSUM - Orchidaceae
  longibracteatum / P / to 20" / red & pink-violet fls / Med. reg.   30

HIPPEASTRUM - Amaryllidaceae
  advenum / Gh Bb / 1' / fls crimson-scarlet / South America   84
  elwesii / Gh Bb / 10" / fls pale yellow / Argentina   20

HIPPOCREPIS - Leguminosae
  comosa / R / mat / yellow fls / c & s Europe   35

HOHERIA - Malvaceae
  glabrata / HH T / 30' / white fls / New Zealand   32
  lyallii glabrata - see H. glabrata   32

  (1) - BATES in Baileya 16:3
  (2) - RUFFIER-LANCHE in Bull. Am. Rock Garden Soc. 22:2

HOLODISCUS - Rosaceae
  discolor / Sh / to 20' / creamy-white fls / B. C. to Montana   9

HOMALOCEPHALA texensis - see ECHINOCACTUS texensis   (1)

HOMERIA - Iridaceae
  breyniana / HH C / 6-18" / yellow or salmon fls / Cape Peninsula   (2)
  collina / HH C / 18" / bright scarlet to creamy-white fls / S. Afr.   84
     " v. ochroleuca - taller, yellow fls   84
  comptonii / HH C / 30" / flame-red & yellow fls / South Africa   37
  miniata / HH C / 24" / salmon fls / Cape Province   36

HOMOGYNE - Compositae
  alpina / R / 6" / light purple fls / c Europe   9

HONKENYA - Tiliaceae
  peploides / R / trailing / greenish-white fls / n & w Eu., coastal   90

HORDEUM - Gramineae
  jubatum / A Gr / 1-1½' / silvery-gray seed-heads / N. & S. America   42

HORKELIA - Rosaceae
  sericata / R / 6-12" / white or pink fls / nw Calif., sw Oregon   75

HORMATOPHYLLA reverchonii - see PTILOTRICHUM reverchonii   90

HORMINIUM - Labiatae
  pyrenaicum / R / 6-8" / bluish-purple fls / Pyrenees to Tyrols   38

HOSTA - Liliaceae
  albomarginata / P / to 18" / pale purple fls / Japan   85
     "   v. alba - all green lvs; white fls   85
  atropurpurea / P / 18-24" / fls deep purple / mts. of Hokkaido   60
  clavata / P / 18" / fls white to pale purplish / mts. of Honshu   60
  coerulea - see H. ventricosa   85
  crispula / P / 1½-2½' / fls violet; lvs white-margined / Japan   42
  decorata / P / to 22" / light purple fls; wh.-margined lvs / Honshu   85
     "   f. normalis - lvs green, Honshu native   60
     "   minor alba - this name not associated with H. decorata   *
     "   'Thomas Hogg' - an obsolete synonym of the sp.   48
  elata / P / to 3' / fls light bluish-violet / Japan   85
  fortunei / P / 1½-2' / deep violet fls / garden clones   85
     "   v. albo-picta - 1½', lilac fls; lvs yellow & green   48
     "   v. aureomarginata - lvs narrowly yellow-margined   48
     "   gigantea - see H. elata   85
     "   robusta - see H. sieboldiana; v. elegans   48
     "   v. variegata - green & white lvs   95
  'Frances Williams' - sieboldiana seedling, yellow-edged lvs   (3)
  glauca - see H. sieboldiana   85
  lancifolia / P / 12-16" / dark violet fls / Honshu   85
     "   albomarginata - see H. albomarginata   85
     "   fortis - see H. undulata v. erromena   48
     "   'Hogan Gold' - see H. l. 'Wogan's Gold   (4)
     "   tardiflora - see H. tardiflora   85
     "   'Wogan's Gold' - yellow-leaved form   (4)
  longipes / R / 12" / fls pale purple / Honshu, Kyushu   60

(1) - HUTCHINSON - The Genera of Flowering Plants. Vol. II 1967
(2) - KIDD - Wild Flowers of the Cape Peninsula. 1950
(3) - WISTER in Am. Horticultural Magazine 50:3
(4) - MULLOY in corres.

HOSTA, con.
```
longissima / P / 20" / fls pale rose-purple / Honshu              60
    "        v. brevifolia - purplish fls, Honshu                 60
'Louisa' - 14", pure white fls, lvs edged white                 (1)
minor alba - see H. albomarginata v. alba                        48
montana - see H. elata                                           85
nakaiana / P / 1-1½' / purple fls / Honshu, Kyushu               60
    "     minor - included in the type                          (1)
plantaginea / P / 16-26" / waxy white fls / China                60
    "        'Grandiflora' - 1½-2', long white fls               42
rectifolia / P / to 32" / fls whitish / Japan, Kuriles           60
sieboldiana / P / 1½-2' / fls pale lilac / Japan                 42
    "        aureomarginata - see H. fortunei v. aureomarginata  85
    "        v. elegans - fls white and shorter                  85
    "        v. fortunei - smaller plant, orbicular lvs          60
    "        v. hypophylla - larher lvs, shorter scapes, fls darker  60
'Snowflake' - seedling of H. albomarginata v. alba              (1)
tardiflora / R / 6-12" / late pale purple fls / Japan            85
'Tinker Bell' - seedling of H. albomarginata v. alba            (1)
tokudama / P / 1-1½' / fls white to pale purple / Honshu         60
undulata v. erromena - 3', fls light violet, Japanese clone      48
ventricosa / P / 3' / fls dark violet / e Asia                   85
    "        'Variegata' - yellow-variegated lvs                 (2)
venusta / R / 8-12" / pale lilac fls / Korea, Japan              85
```

HOUSTONIA - Rubiaceae
```
caerulea / R / 3-6" tufts / light blue fls / ne United States    35
longifolia / R / to 1' / purplish fls / nc North America         35
tenuifolia / R / to 1' / purple fls / Mexico to Pennsylvania     35
```

HOUTTUYNIA - Saururaceae
```
cordata / HH P / 1½-3' / fls white / Far East                     9
```

HUDSONIA - Cistaceae
```
tomentosa / Sh / 6" / frosty gray lvs; yellow fls / e United States  35
```

HUMEA - Compositae
```
elegans / Gh Sh / 6' / aromatic lvs; red fls / Australia         41
```

HUTCHINSIA - Cruciferae
```
alpina / R / 4" / fls white / c & s Europe, in mts.              90
    "   ssp. auerswaldii - to 6", stems flexuous, n Spain        90
    "   ssp. brevicaulis - 2", petals narrower                   90
auerswaldii - see H. alpina ssp. auerswaldii                     90
brevicaulis - see H. alpina ssp. brevicaulis                     90
```

HYACINTHELLA - Liliaceae
```
azurea / Bb / 3-6" / clear azure-blue fls / Asia Minor, in mts.  85
    "  'Alba' - 6", white fls                                     4
dalmatica / Bb / 4" / fls in dense spikes, blue / Jugoslavia     56
```

HYACINTHUS - Liliaceae
```
amethystinus - see BRIMEURA amethystina                          85
    "        alba - see BRIMEURA amethystina 'Alba'              85
azureus - see HYACINTHELLA azurea                                85
    "    alba - see HYACINTHELLA azurea 'Alba'                   85
ciliatus - see BELLEVALIA ciliata                                85
```

(1) - WISTER in Am. Horticultural Magazine 50:3
(2) - BLOOM - Perennials for Your Garden. 1971

HYACINTHUS, con.
  dubius - see BELLEVALIA dubia   55
  fastigiatus - see BRIMEURA fastigiata   56
  orientalis / Bb / 1' / white to mauve-purple fls / c & e Medit. reg. 84
  romanus - see BELLEVALIA romana   86
  spicatus - see STRANGWEIA spicata   56

HYDRANGEA - Hydrangeaceae
  paniculata / Sh / 12-20' / fls white, aging purplish / Far East   13
  quercifolia / Sh / 3-6' / fls white / se United States   85

HYDRASTIS - Ranunculaceae
  canadensis / R / 1' / white fls, crimson frs / e North America   35

HYDROPHYLLUM - Hydrophyllaceae
  appendiculatum / P / 1-2' / fls pale violet / c & n North America (1)
  canadense / P / 1-2½' / fls green, white, purple / e North America 9
  macrophyllum / P / 2-3' / violet or purple fls / Va., W. Va.   83

HYLOMECON - Papaveraceae
  japonicum / R / 1' / golden yellow fls / Japan   42
  vernalis / R / 8-16" / yellow fls / Manchuria   (2)

HYMENANTHERA - Violaceae
  alpina / HH Sh / 1-2' / coriaceous lvs / alps of Canterbury, N. Z. 2
  crassifolia / HH Sh / 2-4' / insignificant white fls / N. Zealand   9

HYMENOSPERMUM flavum - error for HYMENOSPORUM flavum   *

HYMENOSPORUM - Pittosporaceae
  flavum / HH T / to 40' / cream & yellow fls / Australia   16

HYMENOXIS - Compositae
  grandiflora / R / 6-14" / yellow fls / Rocky Mts.   (3)
  richardsonii / R / 2-18" / yellow or orange fls / N. Mex. to Can. 74
  scaposa / R / 6-12" / yellow fls / Colorado to Kansas & s-ward   (3)

HYOSCYAMUS - Solanaceae
  niger / A or B / 1-2½' / fls greenish-yellow / Europe, Asia   9

HYPERICUM - Hypericaceae
  aegypticum / HH Sh / low / yellow fls / Mediterranean islands   91
  androsaemum / Sh / 2-3' / light yellow fls / w Europe, Balkans   13
  annulatum / P / to 2' / sulphur-yellow fls / Balkan Peninsula   91
  ascyron / P / to 32" / fls yellowish to reddish / n temperate zone 60
  balearicum / HH Sh / to 4' / yellow fls / Balearic Isls.   91
  buckleyi / Sh 1' / yellow fls / North Carolina, Georgia, in high mts. 9
  bupleuroides / P / 18-32" / yellow fls / Russian Armenia   26
  calycinum / HH Sh / 10-15" / rich yellow fls / se Eu., Asia Minor 95
  canariense / HH Sh / 2' / yellow fls / Canary Isls.   29
  chinense / HH Sh / to 3' / golden fls / China, Formosa   46
  coris / P / 18" / yellow fls / n & c Italy, Switzerland   91
  cuneatum - see H. pallens   26
  degenii - see H. annulatum   91
  drummondii / A / to 32" / small yellow fls / s & sc United States 34

  (1) - STEVENS - Kansas Wild Flowers. 1948
  (2) - POPOV in Flora USSR Vol. VII 1970(trans.)
  (3) - DRESS in Baileya 8:2

HYPERICUM, con.
```
elatum - see H. X inodorum                                          46
   "   'Elstead' - see H. X inodorum 'Elstead'                      46
empetrifolium / HH Sh / 12-15' / pale golden fls / Greece           13
   "        v. oliganthum - procumbent, Crete, in mts.              13
   "            prostratum - see H. e. var. oliganthum              13
fragile / R / to 4" / fls yellow, red tinged / Greece               91
frondosum / Sh / 3'+ / bright yellow fls / s & se United States     46
gramineum / HH R / 1' / grassy plant / New Caledonia                29
haplophylloides / Sh / 10" / yellow fls / s Albania                 91
hirsutum / P / 1-3½' / yellow fls, yellow veined / Europe           91
hookerianum / HH Sh / 2-5' / deep to pale yellow fls / Himalayas    13
X inodorum - HH Sh, to 4½', small pale yellow fls                   46
   "     'Elstead' - selection for salmon-red frs                   46
japonicum / A or P / 8-20" / yellow fls / Far East                  60
kalmianum / Sh / 2-3' / small yellow fls / ne North America          9
kamtschaticum v. senanense - R, 1', yellow fls, alps of Honshu      60
kelleri / HH R / procumbent / yellow fls / w Crete                  91
kouytchense / HH Sh / 2-4' / rich yellow fls / w China              13
lanuginosum / HH P / to 2½' / yellow fls; whitish lvs / Near East   26
   "     v. gracile - 6-12", woolly-coated plant, coast of Syria    33
linarioides / R / 7" / yellow fls, red tinged / c Balkans           91
lydium / P / 4-30" / yellow fls, rarely red-veined / n Iraq         26
maculatum / P / 3-40" / yellow fls, black-dotted / most of Europe   91
montanum / P / 10-28" / yellow fls / w & c Europe                   91
mutilum / A or P / 1-3' / yellow fls / e & ec United States         34
olympicum / P / 4-20" / large yellow fls / Balkan Peninsula         91
   "     'Citrinum' - fls pale yellow                               38
   "     f. minor - included in the sp., which has variable heights (1)
orientale / R or P / 2½-18" / yellow fls / Turkey                   26
pallens / HH Sh / to 10" / yellow fls / e Mediterranean region      26
patulum 'Hidcote' - HH Sh, to 3', large yellow fls                  42
perforatum / P / 4-40" / fls yellow / all of Europe                 91
polyphyllum / R / 6-12" / deep yellow fls / sw Asia Minor           42
   "        'Sulphureum' - paler fls                                38
pseudopetiolatum v. yakusimanum - 2", tiny yellow fls, Japan        52
ptarmicaefolium - see H. orientale                                  26
pulchrum / P / 4-36" / fls yellow, red tinged / nw Europe           91
repens - see H. linarioides                                         91
reptans / R / prostrate / golden fls / Sikkim                       38
rhodopeum / R / 6" / pale golden fls / se Europe, Asia Minor        42
tomentosum / P / decumbent to 3' / yellow fls / sw Europe           91
trichocaulon / R / 10" / yellow fls / w & s Crete                   91
yakusimanum - see H. pseudopetiolatum v. yakusimanum               52
```

HYPOCHOERIS - Compositae
```
lanata / R / ? / silvery lvs / Andes Mts.                           21
radicata / P / 1-3' / yellow fls / much of US, introduced from Eu.  76
uniflora / P / 6-20" / yellow fls / Europe, in mts.                 96
```

HYPOPITYS monotropa - see MONOTROPA hypopitys   (2)

HYPOXIS - Amaryllidaceae
```
hirsuta / P / 4-24" / starry yellow fls / e & c United States       35
hygrometrica / R / 6" / yellow fls / Australia                      10
```

(1) - ROBSON in Notes from the Royal Bot. Gard., Edinburgh 27:2
(2) - WHERRY in Bull. Am. Rock Garden Soc. 32:3

HYSSOPUS, con.
    officinalis / P / 8-24" / brilliant blue-violet fls / Eu., Asia   96
          "   'Albus' - white fls   *
          "   v. aristatus - 1-2' , fls blue, Israel   42
          "   'Roseus' - rosy fls   *

HYSTRIX - Gramineae
    patula / P Gr / 2-4' / decorative spikes / North America   85

IBERIS - Cruciferae
    amara v. coronia - A, 1', large white fls   9
     " 'Little Gem' - presumably I. sempervirens 'Little Gem'   *
    attica / A / to 1' / fls rose or white / e Medit. region   26
    candolleana - see I. pruitii   90
    conferta - see TEESDALIOPSIS conferta   90
    gibraltarica / HH R / to 1' / reddish-lilac to white fls / Gibralter 90
    jordanii - see I. pruitii   90
    jucunda - see AETHIONEMA coridifolium   9
    'Little Gem' - see I. sempervirens 'Little Gem'   17
    procumbens / HH R / 4-12" / lilac fls, rarely white / Portugal   90
    pruitii / A or P / 6" / white to lilac fls / Mediterranean mts.   90
    saxatilis / R / 4-6" / fls white / s Europe, Pyrenees   42
    semperflorens / HH Sh / to 32" / fls white, evergreen lvs / w Italy 90
    sempervirens / Sh / 10" / white fls / high mts. of Medit. region   90
          "   'Compacta' - dwarf form   10
          "   'Little Gem' - free-flowering selection   17
    simplex / A or P / to 1' / fls white to pale purple / s Russia   90
    spathulata / R / to 4" / fls purplish to white / Pyrenees   90
    taurica - see I. simplex   90
    tenoreana - see I. pruitii   90
    umbellata / A / 9-15" / fls in purple shades / s Europe   42
          "   'Rose Cardinal' - rosy-carmine fls   85

ILEX - Aquifoliaceae
    cornuta / HH Sh / 8-10' / spiny-leaved evergreen / China, Korea   13
    fargesii / HH T / to 20' / frs red, globose / w China   13
    montana / Sh / to 36' / red frs, deciduous / New York & s in uplands 83
    opaca / T / to 40' / red frs, evergreen lvs / e & c United States   13
    paraguariensis / Gh Sh / to 20' / frs reddish-brown / Brazil   9
    rugosa / Sh / creeping / white fls; red frs / n Japan, Kuriles   60
    verticillata / Sh / 9' / bright red frs / e & c North America   9

ILIAMNI - Malvaceae
    corei / P / 3' / rose fls / Giles County, Virginia   83

ILLICIUM - Magnoliaceae
    floridanum / HH Sh / 6-10' / dark crimson to purple fls / Fla., La.   9

IMPATIENS - Balsamaceae
    biflora - see I. capensis   34
    capensis / A / 2-3' / orange fls, spotted / North America   34
    cristata / A / 2' / yellow fls / China   45
    glandulifera / A / 3-7' / purple to wine-red fls / Himalayas   32
    pallida / A / 3-6' / fls lemon-yellow / ne & nc North America   71

INCARVILLEA - Bignoniaceae
    bonvalottii - see I. compacta   (1)
    compacta / R / 6" / purple fls / nw China   85

    (1) - GRIERSON in Notes from the Royal Bot. Gard., Edinburgh 23:3

INCARVILLEA, con.
  delavayi / P / 1-1½' / fls rosy / w China   42
    "   'Bees Pink' - soft pink fls   42
  grandiflora - see I. mairei v. grandiflora   85
    "   brevipes - see I. mairei   85
    "   'Frank Ludlow' - see I. mairei 'F. L.'   85
  mairei / R / to 1' / fls crimson-purple / Tibet, China   85
    "   'Frank Ludlow' - rich deep pink fls, Bhutan   85
    "   v. grandiflora - solitary crimson flower   85
    "   'Nyoto Sama' - light pink fls, se Tibet   85
  variabilis / P / 1-2' / rose fls / e Tibet   32

INDIGOFERA - Leguminosae
  decora / HH Sh / 18" / reddish-purple fls / Japan, China   60
  gerardiana - see I. heterantha   13
  heterantha / HH Sh / 2-4' / rosy-purple fls / nw Himalayas   13
  incarnata - see I. decora   60

INULA - Compositae
  acaulis / R / 1½" / stemless golden daisies / Asia Minor   38
  ensifolia / R / 12" / yellow daisies / Europe, n Asia   35
    "   'Compacta' - 9", golden daisies   17
  glandulosa / P / 2-3' / orange-yellow fls / Caucasus   85
  helenium / P / tall / yellow fls / Eurasia, naturalized in N. Am.   9
  hirta / P / 12-15" / yellow fls / Europe, n Asia   9
  hookeri / P / 1-2' / bright yellow fls / Himalayas   9
  orientalis - see H. glandulosa   85
  rhizocephala / R / low / yellow fls / Iran, Afghanistan   32
  royleana / P / 20" / orange-yellow fls / Himalayas   9
  viscosa / HH P / 18" / yellow fls; sticky lvs / sw Europe   65

IONOPSIDIUM - Cruciferae
  acaule / A / 2-3" / fls white fading lilac / North Africa   9

IPHEION - Amaryllidaceae
  uniflorum / Bb / 6" / white or pale lilac-mauve fls / South America   42
    "   'Violaceum' - light blue fls   4
    "   'Wisley Blue' - 2", fls deepest blue   36

IPOMOEA - Convolvulaceae
  coerulea - see I. nil   45
  dissecta - see MERREMIA dissecta   (1)
  nil / HH Cl / twining / blue fls / Africa, naturalized in s US   45,(1)
  purpurea / A Cl / 6' / purple fls / American tropics   45,(1)

IPOMOPSIS - Polemoniaceae
  aggregata / P / 1-3' / bright red fls / nw Coast Ranges & e-ward   75
  longiflora / P / 4-16" / fls white or pink / Nebraska to Utah   74

IRIS - Iridaceae
  albomarginata / Bb / 15" / fls bright lilac / Turkestan   85
  aphylla / P / 6-16" / red-purple fls / Balkans & e-ward   66
  arenaria / R / wee / golden fls / Balkans   33
  attica / R / 2-4" / fls varii-colored / Greece   9
  aucheri / Bb / 6-22" / pale lilac-blue fls / Mesopotamia   42
  aurea - see I. crocea   85
  bloudowii / R / 3" / bright yellow fls / Altai Mts., e Europe   43
  bracteata / P / 18" / fls cream with purple veins / w N. Am.   35

(1) - GOULD - Texas Plants. 1962

IRIS, con.
```
  bucharica / Bb / 1½' / fls creamy white / Turkestan                           84
     "     orchioides - synonym of the sp.                                      54
  bulleyana / P / variable / does not come true from seed                       66
  caucasica / P / 4-8" / yellow fls / n Iran, Asia Minor                        54
  carthaliniae- see I. violacea                                                 66
  cengialtii / P / 12" / bright lilac fls / s Tyrole:                            9
  chamaeiris / R / 1-6" / blue & yellow fls / Maritime Alps                     43
     "     v. campbellii - 8", deep purple fls                                  10
  X chrysofor - I. chrysographes X forrestii                                    43
  chrysographes / R / 12" / deep blue fls, gold markings / w China              35
     "     'Rubella' - 10", maroon with dark falls, China                        6
  chrysophylla / R / 9" / creamy yellow fls / Oregon                            85
  clarkei / P / 2' / blue to purple fls / Himalayas                             66
  clavissima - probable error for I. flavissima                                  *
  cretica / HH R / stalkless fls / blue-lilac fls / e Medit. region             64
  cristata / R / 6" / pale mauve fls / e United States                          38
  crocea / P / 3-3½' fls bright yellow / Himalayas                              85
  cypriana / HH P / 3' / reddish-lilac fls / Cyprus                              9
  danfordiae / Bb / 3" / yellow fls / Caucasus                                  36
  darwasica / R / 1' / green & purple fls / Bokhara                              9
  decora / HH Tu / 20" / fls bright lavender / sw China, Himalayas              32
  delavayi / P / 3-4' / fls violet-blue / China                                 42
  dichotoma / P / 2' / fls white & light purple / Russia, China                  9
  douglasiana / R / 6-12" / purplish fls / nw United States                     42
     "     'Agnes James' - collected albino                                    (1)
     "     'Alba' - white fls                                                    *
     "     'Pegasus' - selected white-flowered                                 (2)
  dykesii / P / 20" / fls dark blue-purple / China                              20
  ensata / P / 1-3' / fls bright blue or lilac / Russia, Japan                   9
  fernaldii / P / 18" / cream-yellow fls / c California                         75
  filifolia / Bb / 1½' / rich red-purple fls / s Spain, N. Africa               84
  flavissima / R / 3-6" / golden fls / Hungary, ne Asia                         35
  foetidissima / P / 1-2' / fls yellowish-green & lilac / Europe                42
  forrestii / P / 12-18" / yellow fls / Asia                                    35
  fulva / P / 2-3' / reddish-brown fls / Illinois, Georgia, Texas                9
  germanica / P / 3' / purple fls / c Europe                                    36
  giganticoerulea / P / 4' / fls violet-blue / s Louisiana                      10
  gormanii - see I. tenax                                                       66
  gracilipes / R / to 9" / pinkish-mauve fls / Japan                            43
  graebneriana / R / 4-8" / fls mauve, variable markings / Turkestan            85
  graminea / P / 15-36" / fls bright lilac / c & s Europe                        9
  halophila / P / 2-3' / fls yellow / Caucasus, c Asia                          54
  hispanica - see I. xiphium                                                     9
  histrio v. aintabensis - 4", pale blue fls, n Syria                           84
  histrioides 'Major' - Bb, 4", blue fls, gold & white markings                42
  hoogiana / P / to 2' / lilac-violet or white fls / c Asia                     54
  hookeri / P / to 2' / fls deep to pale blue / ne North America                34
  iberica / R / 6" / brownish fls / Caucasus, Iran                               9
  imbricata / P / 12-20" / fls greenish-yellow / Transcaucasia, Iran             9
  innominata / R / 8" / fls in shades of yellow / Oregon                        42
  juncea / HH Bb / 12" / yellow fls / s Spain                                   36
  kaempferi - see I. laevigata                                                  60
     "     'Rose Queen' - see I. laevigata 'Rose Queen'                          *
  kamaonensis / R / 6" / purple fls / w Himalayas                              (3)
  kerneriana / P / 1-1½' / yellow fls / Armenia, Asiatic Turkey                 85
```

(1) - DAVIDSON in Bull. Am. Rock Garden Soc. 23:3
(2) - KLABER in Bull. Am. Rock Garden Soc. 23:1
(3) - RAU - Illustrations of West Himalayan Plants. 1963

IRIS, con.
  koreana / R / 10" / yellow fls / Korea   10
  kumaonensis - see I. kamaonensis   85
  lactea chinensis - see I. ensata   (1)
  lacustris / R / 2-4" / fls pale lilac-blue / Great Lakes region   42
  laevigata / P / 2'+ / fls blue-purple or white / Far East   60
      "   'Variegata' - leaf variegation   *
  lusitanica / P / 1-2' / fls yellow / Spain   9
  lutescens - see I. chamaeiris   9
  macrosiphon / P / 16" / yellow, purple or lavender fls / c & n Calif.   75
  magnifica / Bb / 1½-2' / pale violet fls / c Asia   85
      "   'Alba' - the white form in cult.   85
  mellita / R / 3-4" / pale smoky-brown fls / Malta, se Europe   38
      "   'Aurea' - smoky-yellow fls   66
      "   rubromarginata - see I. rubromarginata   66
  microglossa / Bb / 6" / pale mauve & white fls / c Afghanistan   85
  milesii / P / 2-3' / fls bright lilac / Himalayas   9
  minuta - see I. minutoaurea   43
  minutoaurea / R / 4" / golden yellow & brown fls / Japan   43
  missouriensis / P / 8-20" / pale or deep blue fls / nw United States   75
      "   'Alba' - white fls   *
  monnieri / P / 2-3' / lemon-yellow fls / unknown origin   9
  munzii / HH P / 2½' / pale lavender & darker fls / California   85
  musulmanica / P / 2'+ / yellow fls / Caucasus   54
  nepalensis - see I. decora   85
  ochroleuca - an undetermined sp. of I. spuria group   66
  orchioides / Bb / 1' / golden yellow fls / Turkestan   84
  orientalis - see I. sanguinea   66
  palestina / Gh / 6" yellow to blue-green fls in winter / Syria   20
  paradoxa / R / 6" / fls in purple shades or white / n Iran   20
  persica / R / dwarf / grayish-blue fls, but variable / Near East   56
  planifolia / HH Bb / 8-12" / fls bright lilac-blue / Sicily, N. Afr.   56
      "   'Alba' - recorded white form   56
  prismatica / P / 1-2' / fls bright lilac / e North America   9
  pseudacorus / P / 2-3' / fls deep golden-yellow / n Europe   42
      "   v. bastardii - lemon-yellow fls   42
      "   'Variegata' - lvs striped creamy-yellow   9
  pseudocaucasica / Bb / 4" / fls azure blue / Caucasus   54
  pseudocyparus - see I. graminea   (1)
  pumila / R / 4-5" / stemless varii-colored fls / Eu., Asia Minor   38
      "   attica - see I. attica   66
  purdyi / R / 6-12" / fls white or pale lavender / n California   75
  reticulata / Bb / 6-8" / deep bluish-mauve fls / Asia Minor, Iran   42
      "   'J. S. Dijit' - reddish-purple fls   84
      "   'Springtime' - blue & white fls   85
  rubromarginata - like I. mellita, red-edged lvs   66
  ruthenica / R / 6" / deep blue fls / Siberia, China   38
  sanguinea / P / 18" / bright lilac fls / Far East   9
  scorpioides - see I. planifolia   66
  setosa / P / 2'+ / fls blue-purple / Far East   60
      "   canadensis - see I. hookeri   34
      "   hookeri - see I. hookeri   34
  shrevei - see I. virginica v. shrevei   34
  sibirica / P / 2'+ / fls bright lilac-blue / c & e Eu., Siberia   9
      "   alba - see I. s. var. flexuosa   9
      "   v. flexuosa - fls white   9
      "   'Helen Astor' - 2½', rosy red fls   85
      "   'Perrys Blue' - 3½', sky blue fls   85
      "   'Tycoon' - 3½', rich violet fls   85

(1) - DYKES - The Genus Iris. 1913

IRIS, con.
  sintensii / R / 9" / blue fls, white veined / s Europe   17
  sogdiana / P / 3'+ / fls azure with darker veins / c Asia   54
  songarica / P / 12-18" / fls bluish but variable / Iran, w China   85
  spuria / P / 2-4' / cream, yellow, blue fls / c & s Europe   42
     "   sogdiana - see I. sogdiana   *
  spathacea - see MORAEA spathacea   51
  stolonifera / P / 1-2' / fls bright blue / Turkestan   9
  subbiflora / HH P / 8-16" / deep purple fls / s Portugal, s Spain   65
  sulphurea - color form of I. pumila   9
ATGG
S'80 tectorum / R / 1' / fls light blue streaked dark / Japan   42
     "   'Alba' - frosty white fls   35
  tenax / R / 6-12" / fls varii-colored / sw Oregon, Washington   75
  tenuis / R / 1' / fls white or cream, veined purple / n Oregon   75
  tenuissima / P / ? / fls white or cream, purple veins / California   75
  X thompsonii - I. innominata X douglasiana   66
  tingitana / HH Bb / 2' / pale purplish-blue fls / nw Africa   84
  unguicularis / R / 6-8" / lilac-mauve fls / s & e Medit. region   42
     "   'Alba' - white form, streaked yellow   42
     "   cretensis - see I. cretica   64
  urmiensis / R / to 1' / lemon-yellow fls / Iran   85
  verna / R / 6" / violet fls / Maryland, Virginia & s to Florida   71
  versicolor / P / 1½-2' / violet-blue fls / n North America   9
     "   'Kermesiana' - deep reddish-purple fls   42
  vicaria / Bb / 8-16" / fls violet with darker veins / c Asia   54
  violacea / P / to 3' / sky-blue fls, veined dark blue / Caucasus   54
  virginica / P / 2' / fls in shades of blue / Va., Fla. & Texas   71
     "   v. shrevei - lvs firmer, flower-stem erect, mainly c US   34
  watsoniana - see I. douglasiana   32
  wilsonii / P / to 2' / pale yellow fls / w China   9
  winogradowii / Bb / 4" / clear pale yellow fls / w Caucasus   43
  xiphioides / Bb / 1' / fls dark violet-purple / Pyrenees   9
  xiphium / HH Bb / 2' / purple fls / s Spain   36

ISOPOGON - Proteaceae
  cuneatus / HH Sh / 4-8' / fls pale purple / w Australia   20

ISOPYRUM - Ranunculaceae
  nipponicum / R / 10" / pale greenish-yellow fls / Honshu   60
  stipitatum / R / 2-3" / white or pinkish fls / n Calif., Oregon   35

ISOTOMA - Campanulaceae
  axillaris / HH R / 6-12" / fls bluish-purple / Australia   9
  longiflora / HH P / 2' / fls pure white / Mid- & S. America   32

ISOTRIA - Orchidaceae
  verticillata / R / to 1' / purple & yellow-green fls / e US   34

ITEA - Iteaceae
  illicifolia / HH Sh / 6' / greenish-white fls, fragrant / c China   46

IXIA - Iridaceae
  maculata / HH C / 15" / yellow fls / Cape Province   36
  polystachya / HH C / 6-12" / white fls / Cape of Good Hope   9
  viridiflora / HH C / 12" / green fls shaded Prussian blue / Cape Pr.   36

IXIOLIRION - Amaryllidaceae
  ledebourii - see I. tataricum v. ledebourii   54
  montanum / Bb / 1½' / fls lavender-blue to blue / c Asia   84
     "   v. pallasii - fls rose-purple, Caspian region   84

IXIOLIRION, con.
  pallasii - see I. montanum v. pallasii   84
  pallescens - could it be an error for I. pallasii?   *
  tataricum / Bb / 8-18" / light blue to dark violet fls / c Asia   54
     "   v. ledebourii - of slight botanical variation   54

IXODA - Compositae
  achilleoides / HH Sh / 1-3' / fls yellow, bracts white / s Australia 20

JACARANDA - Bignoniaceae
  mimosifolia / Gh Sh / 10'+ / blue fls / Brazil   41
  ovalifolia - see J. mimosifolia   41

JASIONE - Campanulaceae
  humilis / R / 4". / blue fls / Pyrenees   35
  jankae / R / 12" / blue fls / Hungary   35
  montana / A or B / 1' / pale blue fls / Europe   9
  perennis / R / 10" / bright blue fls / w Europe   38
     "   ssp. carpetana - presumably dwarfer, Spain   21
  tuberosa - see JASONIA tuberosa   *

JASMINUM - Oleaceae
  humile 'Revolutum' - HH Sh, 3-6', fragrant yellow fls   85
  parkeri / HH Sh / 1' / clear yellow fls / nw India   38
  revolutum - see J. humile 'Revolutum'   85

JASONIA - Compositae
  tuberosa / P / 15" / yellow spiked fls / s Europe   33,51

JEFFERSONIA - Berberidaceae
  diphylla / R / 10" / white fls / ne United States   35
  dubia / R / 6" / pale lavender-blue fls / Manchuria   42
  manschuriensis - see J. dubia   (1)

JOVELLANA - Scrophulariaceae
  sinclairii / Gh / 3' / white fls, purple spotted / New Zealand   2

JOVIBARBA - Crassulaceae
  heuffelii / R / 4-8" / pale yellow fls / se Europe   85
  hirta / R / 4-6" / pale to yellowish-brown fls / e Alps, Hungary 85
  kopaonikense / R / 6" / gray-green lvs / Serbia, Bulgaria   32
  simonkiana - near J. hirta, Carpathians   21
  sobolifera / R / 4-8" / greenish-yellow fls / n Europe, Asia 85

JUNCUS - Juncaceae
  alpinus / R / 2-20" / black or brownish infloresence / n Europe 63

JUNIPERUS - Pinaceae
  communis v. depressa - 4', broadly spreading evergreen, e N. Am. 9
     "   v. hemisphaerica - 3', mts. of s Europe   (2)
     "   v. montana - mats, mts. of n Europe   (2)
     "   "   hemisphaerica - see J. c. var. hemisphaerica *
     "   v. saxatilis - see J. c. var. hemisphaerica   (2)
  chinensis v. procumbens - low Sh, needles with white bands, Japan 60
  horizontalis / Sh / procumbent / bluish needles / ne North America 28
  nana - see J. communis v. montana   (2)
  occidentalis / HH T / 35' / grayish-green needles / w United States 28

  (1) - FEDCHENKO in Flora USSR Vol. VII 1970(trans.)
  (2) - HUNT & WELCH in Taxon 17:5

[handwritten left margin: c/79. Emerald Sea? ARGS. P.Sale 6/2/79]

JUNIPERUS, con.
   oxycedrus / HH T / 30' / red or brown frs / Mediterranean region   28
   procumbens - see J. chinensis v. procumbens   60
   saxatilis - see J. communis v. hemisphaerica   (1)
   virginiana / T / 35'+ / brownish-violet frs / N. Am., e of Rockies   28

JURINEA - Compositae
   arachnoidea - see J. mollis ssp. arachnoidea   (2)
   mollis / B or P / 2' / fls rose-purple / s Europe   10
      " ssp. arachnoidea - webbing somewhere   *

KALMIA - Ericaceae
   angustifolia / Sh / to 6' / purple or crimson fls / e N. America   9
      "   alba - see K. a. var. candida   34
      "   v. candida - white fls   9
      "   v. pumila - few inches high   43
      "   v. rubra - crimson fls   9
      "   " 'Nana' - red-flowered dwarf   *
   cuneata / HH Sh / to 5' / fls creamy-white, red banded / Carolinas   9
   glauca - see K. polifolia   69
   latifolia / Sh / 6'+ / fls pale to deep rose-pink / e N. America   42
      " v. rubra - fls deep pink   9
   microphylla / Sh / to 2' / rose-purple to pink fls / w N. America   (3)
      "   'Nana' - 2-6", matting high mountain form   (3)
   polifolia / Sh / 2' / rose or purplish fls / mid-n N. America   9
      " v. microphylla - see K. microphylla   (3)
      "   " 'Nana' - see K. microphylla 'Nana'   (3)

KALMIOPSIS - Ericaceae
   leachiana / Sh / 1' / rose-purple fls / Oregon   38
      "   'Curry Co. Form' - rose-purple fls   (4)
      "   'M. LePiniec' - designating an early collected plant   (4)
      "   'Umpqua Form' - trailer with good bloom   81

KENNEDYA - Leguminosae
   eximia / Gh Sh / prostrate / scarlet fls / w Australia   20
   prostrata / HH Sh / prostrate / scarlet fls / Australia   9
   rubicunda / Gh / twining / purplish fls / Australia   16

KENTRANTHUS - Valerianaceae
   ruber / P / 2-3' / fls red / Europe   42

KERNERA - Cruciferae
   saxatilis / R / to 1' / white fls / s & c Europe, in mts.   90

KIRENGESHOMA - Hydrangeaceae
   palmata / P / 3' / fls bright yellow / Japan   95

KLEINIA repens - see SENECIO repens   32

KNAUTIA - Dipsacaceae
   arvensis / P / 12-32" / lilac-blue fls / n Europe, Siberia   32
   drymeia / P / 3½' / fls reddish-violet to purple / Balkans   10
   macedonica / P / 2' / fls dark red / Macedonia   32
   sylvatica / P / 3' / violet fls / Europe   10

(1) - HUNT & WELCH in Taxon 17:5
(2) - STOYANOFF & STEFANOFF - Flora of Bulgaria. 1943
(3) - EBINGER in JAYNES - The Laurel Book. 1975
(4) - DAVIDSON in Bull. Am. Rock Garden Soc. 25:3

KNIPHOFIA - Liliaceae
caulescens / HH P / 4½' / pink fls suffused greenish-yellow / S. Afr.95
galpinii / HH P / 2-2½' / orange-flame fls / Transvaal   42
pumila / HH P / 2' / fls red or yellow / South Africa   9
snowdenii / HH P / 5' / fls orange-yellow / Mt. Eglon, Uganda   20
tuckii / P / 4' / yellow fls, tipped red / c S. Africa   9
uvaria / P / 2-3' / red & yellow fls / Cape region   9

KOCHIA - Chenopodiaceae
prostrata / Sh / 2'+ / green fls / s Europe to sc Russia   90

KOELERIA - Gramineae
cristata / P Gr / 1-1½' / open, dry ground plant / prairies, N. Am.   9
vallesiana / P Gr / silvery-green or purplish fls / sw Europe   85

KOELREUTERIA - Sapindaceae
paniculata / T / 30' / fls yellow / Korea, China   60

KOHLERIA cristata - error for KOELERIA cristata   *

KOHLRAUSCHIA prolifera - see PETRORHAGIA prolifera   90

KOROLKOWII - Liliaceae
sewerzowii / Bb / 8-20" / brownish-violet fls / c Asia   54

KRIGIA - Compositae
biflora / P / 8-28" / yellow fls / e & c North America   34
montana / R / 9-12" / yellow dandelions / Carolinas & Georgia   9
virginica / A / 12" / yellow dandelions / Maine, Florida, Texas   72

KUNZEA - Myrtaceae
ambigua / HH Sh to small T / ? / white stamens / Australia   16
ericifolia / HH Sh / 8-12' / fls yellow / Queensland, Australia   20
peduncularis / HH Sh / tall / fls white / Australia   10

LABURNUM - Leguminosae
alpinum / T / 15'+ / fls yellow / sc Europe, in mts.   91
   "   v. watereri - see L. X watereri   46
anagyroides / T / 15'+ / yellow fls / c & s Europe   46
X watereri - small tree with glossy lvs   46

LACHENALIA - Liliaceae
bachmannii / HH Bb / 10" / fls white, ridged red / South Africa   (1)
bulbifera / HH Bb / 1' / varii-colored fls / South Africa   84
glaucina / HH Bb / 1' / blue-lilac fls / Cape Province   36
   "   v. pallida - light yellow fls   70
juncifolia / HH Bb / 6" / fls white tinged red / South Africa   (1)
liliflora / HH Bb / 1' / white fls / South Africa   32
pallida - see L. glaucina v. pallida   70
purpureo-coerulea / HH Bb / 6-8" / reddish-purple fls / S. Africa   32

LACTUCA - Compositae
perennis / P / 1-2' / lilac or blue fls / s, c & e Spain; s France   65
tenerrima / R / bushy clump / sprays of blue fls / s Europe   33

LAGENIFERA pumila - error for LAGENOPHORA pumila   *

(1) - INGRAM in Baileya 14:3

LAGENOPHORA - Compositae
pinnatifida / HH R / to 10" / white to purple fls / New Zealand   2
pumila / HH R / 6"+ / white to purple fls / New Zealand   2

LAGERSTROEMIA - Lythraceae
indica / HH T / 10-35' / fls usually bright pink / China   9

LAGURUS - Gramineae
ovatus / A Gr / 1' / soft white-woolly heads / Medit. region   9

LAMARCKIA - Gramineae
aurea / A Gr / 6-12" / golden yellow panicles / Medit. reg.; Afghan.   9

LAMIUM - Labiatae
galeobdolen / P / to 18" / fls yellow / Europe, w Asia   9
    "   'Variegatum' - 6", fls yellow; lvs silver & green   42
orvala / P / 20-40" / pink to dark purple fls / n Italy, Jugoslavia 42

LAPAGERIA - Liliaceae
rosea / Gh / twiner / rose to rose-crimson fls / Chile   41

LAPEIROUSIA - Iridaceae
cruenta - see L. laxa   (1)
    "   'Alba' - see L. laxa 'Alba'   (1)
erythrantha / HH C / to 16" / bluish, white or reddish fls / Africa 56
laxa / C / 1' / fls bright carmine / Transvaal   (1)
    " 'Alba' - white fls   4
    " ssp. grandiflora - larger fls   56
rhodesiana - see L. erythrantha   56
sandersonii - see L. erythrantha   56
schimperi / HH C / to 1' / white fls / Ethiopia, s & sw Africa   56

LARIX - Pinaceae
laricina / T / to 60' / light bluish green needles / ec North America 9

LASERPITIUM - Umbelliferae
gallicum / P / 4' / white or pink fls / s Europe, in mts.   91

LASTHENIA - Compositae
chrysotoma / R / to 16" / golden fls / Calif., Oregon, Arizona   75
macrantha / R / 4-16" / yellow fls / coastal California, Oregon   75

LATHRAEA - Orobanchaceae
clandestina - pale gray-purple fls; plant parasitic on willow, Eu.   9

LATHYRUS - Leguminosae
albus - see L. pannonicus   91
aurantius - see VICIA crocea   (2)
aureus / P / to 2' / fls brown or orange-yellow / Black Sea region 91
cyaneus - see L. digitatus   91
digitatus / R / 4-16" / fls bright reddish-purple / se Europe   91
drummondii - see L. rotundifolius   20
filiformis / P / 6-20" / fls red-purple / n Italy to e Spain   91
inermis - see L. laxiflorus   91
japonicus ssp. maritimus - 3', fls purple, w Europe   91
laevigatus / P / 8-24" / fls yellow / ec & e Europe   91

(1) - LAWRENCE in Baileya 3:3
(2) - SHISHKIN & BOBROV Flora USSR Vol. XIII 1972(trans.)

LATHYRUS, con.
```
  latifolius / P / 2'+ / fls purple-pink / c &s Europe                   91
      "      'Alboroseus' - two-color fls                                 *
      "      'Albus' - white fls                                          9
      "      'Pallidus' - light pink fls                                  *
  laxiflorus / P / 8-20" / fls blue-violet / se Europe                   91
  luteus aureus - see L. laevigatus                                      32
  maritimus - see L. japonicus ssp. maritimus                           91
  niger / P / to 3' / fls purple turning blue / Europe                  91
  nissolia / A / to 3' / fls crimson / w, c & s Europe & England        91
  odoratus / A Cl / to 8' / fls in wide range of color / Sicily         42
  pannonicus / P / 6-20" / pale cream fls / ec Europe                   91
  pubescens 'Albus' - Gh Sh, white fls , South America                   9
  roseus / P / to 5' / pink fls / Anatolia, Caucasus                    91
      "   'Plenus' - doubled fls                                        85
  rotundifolius / P Cl, by tendrils / fls deep rose / e Russia          (1)
  sativus / A / 3' / fls white, pink, blue / fodder plant in Europe     91
  sphaericus / A / 4-20" / fls orange-red / s Europe, n to Sweden       91
  sylvestris / P Cl / 2-6' / fls purple-pink / most of Europe           91
  tingitanus / A / 2-4' / bright purple fls / se Iberian Peninsula      91
  tuberosus / P / 1-4' / fls bright red-purple / Europe, intro. e US    91
  variegatus - see L. venetus                                           91
  venetus / P / 8-16" / fls reddish-purple / se & ec Europe             91
  vernus / P / 8-16" / fls reddish-purple / Europe                      91
      "  'Albus' - white form                                            9
      "  'Alboroseus' - two-color form                                   *
```

LAURENTIA - Campanulaceae
```
  casparrini - error for L. gasparrini                                   *
  gasparrini / A / 4" / tiny lilac fls / Portugal, w & n Spain          65
  minuta / R / to 4" / china-blue fls / s Europe, in bogs            32,33
  tenella - see L. minuta                                               32
```

LAVANDULA - Labiatae
```
  lanata / HH Sh / 1-2' / very woolly plant / Spain                    (2)
  officinalis - see L. spica                                           (2)
      "       v. compacta - see L. spica v. angustifolia              (2)
      "       nana-alba - see L. spica 'Nana-alba'                     (2)
  pedunculata - see L. stoechas ssp. pedunculata                       92
  spica / HH Sh / to 4' / dark mauve fls / Mediterranean region        42
      "  v. angustifolia - includes most dwarf cultivars               (2)
      "  'Munstead Dwarf' - 1', mound of flower spikes                 (3)
      "  'Nana' - dwarf                                                 20
      "  'Nana-alba' - 1', white fls                                   13
  stoechas / HH Sh / 1' / fls dark purple / s Europe                   42
      "     'Munstead Dwarf' - see L. spica 'M. D.'                     *
      "     ssp. pedunculata - longer peduncle, c Spain                92
```

LAVATERA - Malvaceae
```
  arborea / HH P / to 10' / fls purple-pink veined darker / s Europe   95
  cachemiriana / P / 5' / pale rose fls / Kashmir                      89
  olbia / Gh Sh / 6' / pink to reddish-pink fls / s France            46
  plebeia / Gh / 2' / pale fls / Australia                            45
  thuringiaca / P / 2-5'+ / fls purplish-pink / c & se Europe          91
  trimestris / A / to 4' / fls bright pink / Medit. region, Portugal   91
```

```
  (1) - HALLEY in corres.
  (2) - De WOLF in Baileya 3:1
  (3) - NEUGEBAUER in American Herb Grower 3:7
```

LEDEBOURIA - Liliaceae
  socialis / Gh Bb / 4" / gray blotched lvs; fls greenish / S. Afr.   56

LEDUM - Ericaceae
  columbianum / Sh / 3' / white fls / Washington, Oregon   9
  groenlandicum / Sh / 1-3' / fls white / mid-n North America   9
        "   'Compactum' - the dwarf cultivar   32
        "   nanum - see L. g. 'Compactum'   32
  hypoleucum - see L. palustre v. diversipilosum   60
  palustre / Sh / 1-2' / white fls / northern hemisphere   9
     "   v. diversipilosum - the far eastern variety   60
     "   japonicum - see L. p. var. diversipilosum   60
     "   yesoense - see L. p. var. diversipilosum   60

LEGOUSIA - Campanulaceae
  speculum-veneris / A / 8-18" / fls violet-blue to white / Eurasia   32
        "   'Grandiflora' - 9", blue fls   89

LEIBNITZIA - Compositae
  anandina - error for L. anandrina   *
  anandrina / R / to 8" / white & red-purple fls / Far East   60

LEIOPHYLLUM - Ericaceae
  buxifolium / Sh / to 3' / fls white / New Jersey to Florida   9
     "   v. prostratum - dense tufts, North Carolina & Tennessee   9

LEMBOTROPIS - Leguminosae
  nigricans / Sh / to 3' / fls golden-yellow / sc Europe & Italy   91

LEONTICE chrysogonum - see BONGARDIA chrysogonum   64

LEONTOPODIUM - Compositae
  alpinum / R / 4-6" / silvery-white bracts / European Alps   42
     " v. nivale - see L. nivale   32
  calocephalum / R / to 16" / white or yellowish fls / Tibet   32
  campestre - see L. leontopodioides   32
  discolor / R / to 1' / bracts brown / Hokkaido, Sakhalin   60
  fauriei / R / 6" / white & brown bracts / Honshu   60
  hayachinense / R / to 8" / white woolly bracts / Honshu   60
  japonicum / P / 10-22" / yellowish bracts / Far East   60
  leontopodioides / R / to 1' / white bracts / Altai & Himalaya Mts.   32
  X lindavicum - hybrid of L. alpinum X L. japonicum   10
  nivale / R / 4" / white woolly bracts / Bulgaria   32
  palibinianum / R / 4" / free-flowering / Mongolia, Siberia   32
  sibiricum - see L. palibinianum   32
  souliei / R / 6" / grayish-white fls / w China   17,32
  stracheyi / P / to 20" / silvery-gray bracts / sw China   32

LEOPOLDIA - Liliaceae
  comosa / Bb / greenish-brown fls / Medit. reg., w Asia   56
    " 'Alba' - the white form   56
    " v. plumosa - mauve sterile fls only   56
  tenuiflora / Bb / to 14" / fls bright bluish-violet / c Asia   54

LEPACHYS columnifera - see RATIBIDA columnifera   82

LEPTARRHENA - Saxifragaceae
  pyrolifolia / R / 8-16" / small white fls / Alaska to Washington   9

LEPTOLEPIA - Dennstaedtiaceae
  novae-zelandiae / Gh F / to 1½' / 3-pinnate frond / New Zealand   2

LEPTOPTERIS superba - see TODEA superba   2

LEPTOSPERMUM - Myrtaceae
  humifusum / HH Sh / prostrate / small white fls / Tasmania   46
  laevigatum / HH Sh / 20'+ / fls white / Australia   9
  lanigerum / HH Sh / 5'+ / silvery lvs / Australia, Tasmania   46
  pubescens / HH T / small / fls white / Australia   9
  scoparium / HH Sh / 12' / fls white / New Zealand   9
     "   'Nanum' - 4-6", lvs heather-like   42
     "   'Nicholsii Nanum' - 4", red fls   43
     "   'Nicholsii Pygmeum' - see L. s. 'Nicholsii Nanum'   43
     "   'Prostratum' - see L. humifusum   46

LEPTOTAENIA dissecta - see LOMATIUM dissectum   59

LESPEDEZA - Leguminosae
  capitata / P / 18-38" / fls creamy-white / e & c United States   34

LESQUERELLA - Cruciferae
  engelmannii ssp. ovalifolia - R, 5", yellow fls, Col. Kan. to Texas   (1)
  fendleri / R / 4" / golden-yellow fls / Kansas, Colorado, Utah   76
  kingii / R / 3-8" / yellow fls, gray lvs / Oregon, Calif., Utah   76
  occidentalis / R / S-curved stems / yellow fls / n Calif. & e-ward   75
  ovalifolia - see L. engelmannii ssp. ovalifolia   (1)
  tumulosa / R / congested dome / yellow fls / Utah   (2)

LESSINGIA - Compositae
  leptoclada / P / 1-3' / lavender or bluish fls / s Sierra Nevadas   75

LEUCANTHEMUM catananche - see CHRYSANTHEMUM catananche   43
     "   hosmariense - see CHRYSANTHEMUM hosmariense   43

LEUCOCORYNE - Liliaceae
  ixioides f. odorata - Bb, 16", cobalt-blue fls, Chile   36
  odorata - see L. ixioides f. odorata   *
  purpurea / HH Bb / 1' / fls lavender & crimson-maroon / Chile   20

LEUCOGENES - Compositae
  grandiceps / Sh / 4" / light yellow & silver fls / New Zealand   43
  leontopodium / R / 3-6" / silvery white fls / New Zealand   42

LEUCOJUM - Amaryllidaceae
  aestivum / Bb / 1½-2' / white fls / Europe, Asia Minor   42
     "   'Gravetye Giant' - tall with large fls   56
     "   v. pulchellum - little variation from type   56
  autumnale / Bb / 4-6" / fls white tinged pink / sw Europe   42
  hiemale - see L. nicaeense   (3)
  longifolium / Bb / 8" / small white fls / Corsica   56
  nicaeensis / HH Bb / 6" / white fls / sw Europe   (3)
  roseum / HH Bb / 4" / pinkish fls / Corsica, Sardinia   84
  tricophyllum / HH Bb / 10" / white fls / sw Europe   84
  vernum / Bb / 8" / fls white / Europe   84
     "   v. carpathicum - greenish-yellow tipped, Poland, Roumania   42
     "   v. vagneri - robust form from Hungary   84

(1) - CLARK in Brittonia 27:3
(2) - RIPLEY in Quar. Bull. Alpine Garden Soc. 40:3
(3) - NUTT in Quar. Bull. Alpine Garden Soc. 36:1

LEUCOPOGON fraseri - see CYATHODES fraseri   2

LEUCOTHANEUM hosmariense - error for LEUCANTHEMUM hosmariense   *

LEUCOTHOE - Ericaceae
  catesbaei - see L. fontanesiana   (1)
  davisiae / Sh / 5' / white fls / Oregon, California   69
  fontanesiana / Sh / 6' / white fls / Virginia to Georgia   (1)
  keiskei / Sh / declining branches / white fls / Honshu   60
  recurva / Sh / 3-9' / white fls / Virginia to Alabama   83

LEWISIA - Portulacaceae
  bernardina - see L. nevadensis   31
RW C/79 Seeds   brachycalyx / R / rosette / white fls / nw North America   38
  columbianum / R / 8-10" / white to light pink fls / Washington, B.C.   35
      "   'Rosea' - deep rose-red fls   43
      "   v. rupicola - intermediate in size, Oregon   31
      "   v. wallowensis - smaller in all parts   31
  cotyledon / R / 9" / variable pink fls / California   43
      "   'Alba' - white fls   81
      "   v. finchae - included in the sp.   31
      "   v. heckneri - lvs fringed deep rose   38
      "   v. howellii - lvs fluted, Siskiyous   31
      "   'Jean Turner' - photograph in the reference   31
      "   'Millardii' - toothed lvs   21
  finchae - see L. cotyledon   31
  'Jean Turner' - see L. cotyledon 'Jean Turner'   31
  heckneri - see L. cotyledon v. heckneri   31
  howellii - see L. cotyledon v. howellii   31
  leana / R / 9" / white or light pink fls / Siskiyou Mts.   35
  millardii - see L. cotyledon 'Millardii'   21
RW C/79 Seeds   nevadensis / R / rosette / small white fls / Nevada   38
  oppositifolia / R / 6" / white fls / Oregon   43
  pygmaea / R / dense rosette / silvery-pink fls / Rocky Mts.   38
    "   ssp. longipetala - rose-red fls, California   31
  rediviva / R / tufts / pink fls / Montana & w-ward   35
    "   'Alba' - white fls   35
  rupicola - see L. columbianum v. rupicola   31
  sierrae / R / tufts / pink or rose fls / California   31
  stebbinsii / R / to 7" / white & rose fls / Mendocino Co., Calif.   (2)
  triphylla / R / 2-4" / white or pink fls / nw United States   31
  tweedyi / R / 4" / flesh pink & pale apricot fls / Washington   43
    "   'Alba' - white fls   *
    "   'Rosea' - rose-pink fls, yellow centres   6

LIATRIS - Compositae
  aspera / P / 4'+ / purple fls / c North America   (3)
    "   'White Spire' - white-flowered clone   (3)
  borealis - see L. novae-angliae   (3)
  cylindracea / P / 8-24" / purplish fls / New York to Arkansas   71
  elegans / P / to 5' / purple or white fls / S. Carolina, Fla., Tex.   (3)
  graminifolia / P / 2'+ / rose-purple fls / coastal plain, N.J. & s   34
  gracilis / P / 1-3' / purple fls / Georgia, Alabama, Florida   9
  novae-angliae / P / to 3' / fls rose-purple or white / N. Y., N. Eng.   (3)
  punctata / P / 10-30" / purple fls / Wisconsin to New Mexico   9

(1) - INGRAM in Baileya 9:2
(2) - WHEELER in Bull. Am. Rock Garden Soc. 27:4
(3) - DRESS in Baileya 7:1

LIATRIS, con.
  pycnostachya / P / 3-5' / purplish fls / Illinois to Texas   9
       "   alba - see L. p. forma hubrichtii   82
       "   f. hubrichtii - white fls   82
       "   'White Spires' - belongs to L. aspera   *
  secunda / P / to 32" / rose-purple fls / Florida to North Carolina   (1)
  spicata / P / to 5' / fls reddish-purple / New York to Mich. & s   (2)
      " 'Kobold' - 2', deep purple fls   89
      " f. montana - shorter flower spike, Va. & Ga. in mts.   (2)
  squarrosa / P / 6-20" / fls bright purple / e & c United States   9

LIBERTIA - Iridaceae
  coerulescens / HH P / 1-2' / blue fls / Chile   9
  formosa / HH P / 2-3' / fls white / Chile   9
  grandiflora / HH P / 2-3' / fls white / New Zealand   9
  ixioides / HH P / 1-2' / fls white / New Zealand   9
  pulchella / HH P / to 1' / fls white / s Australia, Tasmania, N. Z.   9

LIGULARIA - Compositae
  clivorum - see L. dentata   (3)
      " 'Desdemona' - see L. dentata 'Desdemona'   85
  dentata / P / 3-5' / orange-yellow fls / China, Japan   43
      " 'Desdemona' - 3-4½', bright orange-red fls   85
  hodgesonii / P / 3' or less / yellow to orange fls / Japan   (3)
  japonica / P / to 3' / orange-yellow fls / Far East   (3)
  przewalskii / P / to 6' / yellow fls; deeply lobed lvs / n China   85
  sibirica / P / 3' / bright yellow fls / Europe, Asia   (3)

LIGUSTICUM - Umbelliferae
  scoticum / P / to 3' / dark green lvs; fls white / coasts of n Eu.   91

LIGUSTRUM - Oleaceae
  lucidum / HH Sh / to 20' / fls white / Japan, China   9
  scoticum - error for LIGUSTICUM scoticum   *
  sinense / Sh / 10'+ / fls white; black-purple frs / China   46

LILIUM - Liliaceae
  amabile / Bb / 2-3' / orange-red fls / Korea   84
  auratum v. platyphyllum - 6', white fls heavily spotted   36
  'Backhouse Hyb.' - 5-6', cream, pink,wine or yellow fls, spotted   85
  'Bellingham Hyb.' - 4-7', yellow, orange, red fls, spotted   85
  'Black Beauty' - dark crimson-maroon fls   85
  'Black Dragon' - 5-8', pure white fls, purple-brown reverse   85
  bolanderi / Bb / 1-3' / deep reddish-purple fls / California   9
  'Bright Star' - Aurelian Hybrid, 4', ivory-white fls   85
  brownii / Bb / 3-4' / white & purple fls / wc China   36
  bulbiferum / Bb / to 3' / orange-red fls / w & c Europe   84
       "   v. croceum - light orange fls, 1-4', w & c Alps   84
  canadense / Bb / 4-6' / yellow fls spotted maroon / e N. America   43
       "   v. editorum - slender red fls, Pennsylvania to Alabama   34
       "   v. flavum - lemon-yellow fls, brown spotted   9
       "   f. rubrum - red form in the range of the sp.   34
  candidum / Bb / 3-5' / white fls / n Greece   43
  carniolicum / Bb / 4' / bright red fls / n Jugoslavia   84
      "   v. jankae - bright lemon-yellow fls, Balkans   84
  carolinianum - see L. michauxii   34

(1) - SMALL - Manual of the Southeastern Flora. 1933
(2) - DRESS in Baileya 7:1
(3) - DRESS in Baileya 10:2

LILIUM, con.
  centifolium 'Olympic Hyb.' - see 'Olympic Hybrids   85
  cernuum / Bb / 3' / rosy-lilac fls, purple spots / Korea, Manchuria   84
  chalcedonicum / Bb / 3-4' / scarlet fls / Asia Minor   36
  'Cinnabar' - Asiatic Hybrid, 2', cinnabar-red fls   36
  columbianum / Bb / 4'+ / yellowish-orange fls / nw North America   84
  concolor / Bb / 1-1½' / bright crimson-scarlet fls / Japan   9
  cordatum - see CARDIOCRINUM cordatum   85
  'Creelman Hybrid' - see L. X imperiale 'George C. Creelman'   *
  X dalhansonii - fls deep reddish-maroon   84
  davidii 'Maxwill' - 7', orange-red fls   84
     "   v. willmottiae - 7', deep orange fls, dark spots   84
  duchartrei / Bb / to 4' / white fls, purple spotted / w China   84
  'Enchantment' - 2-3', nasturtium-red fls   85
  formosanum / HH Bb / 3-4' / white fls / Formosa   84
     "   v. pricei - hardier mt. strain, fls flushed purple   84
  giganteum - see CARDIOCRINUM giganteum   85
  'Golden Clarion Strain' - Aurelian Hybrid, fls yellow, gold & lemon   (1)
  grayii / Bb / 2-4' / orange-yellow & dull red fls / Va. to N. C.   34
  'Green Mountain Strain' - 5-7', fls white with green throat   85
  'Harlequin Hybrids' - 3-5', pink to tangerine reflexed fls   85
  henryi / Bb / to 8' / bright orange fls / China   43
     "   'Black Beauty' - see L. 'Black Beauty'   85
  humboldtii / Bb / to 6' / orange-red fls / Sierra Nevadas, Calif.   84
  'Imperial Silver Strain' - 5-6', white fls spotted vermilion   85
  X imperiale 'George C. Creelman' - regale X sargentiae hybrid   85
  kelleyanum / Bb / 2-3' / orange to yellow fls / California   85
  kelloggii / Bb / 2-4' / pink fls spotted dark purple / nw Calif.   9
  kesselringianum / Bb / 2' / fls yellow / Caucasus   54
  lankongense / Bb / 2-3' / white fls, dark spotted / Yunnan   (2)
  leichtlinii / Bb / 3' / lemon-yellow fls, wine spotted / Japan   36
     "   v. maximowiczii - 2', orange fls   36
  leucanthemum v. centifolium - to 9', white fls, s Kansu   84
  'Limelight' - Aurelian Hybrid, 3-5', lime-yellow fls   85
  mackliniae / HH Bb / 2½' / white fls, flushed pink / Manipur   84
  maculatum / Bb / 8-32" / orange-red to yellow fls / Honshu, Shikoku   60
  X 'Marhan' - 4-7', rich orange fls, brown spotted   85
  maritimum / Bb / 2' / crimson fls / w United States   36
  martagon / Bb / to 6' / light purple to deep maroon fls / n Europe   43
     "   v. album - 5', clean white fls   84
     "   v. cattaniae - 7', deep wine to maroon fls, Balkans   84
     "   v. dalmaticum - see L. m. var. cattaniae   9
     "   v. hirsutum - stems densely pubescent   9
     "   v. sanguinco-purpureum - spotted fls, Balkans   84
  medeoloides / Bb / 16" / fls apricot & red / Japan   36
  michiganense / Bb / 5' / orange-red fls, spotted / e & c N. America   84
  monadelphum / Bb / to 5' / waxy pale yellow fls / Caucasus   84
  nanum / Bb / 6" / lilac fls speckled purple / Sikkim, Tibet   43
  nevadense / Bb / to 6' / orange-red fls / Sierra Nevadas, Calif.   84
  occidentale / Bb / 3-4' / orange-red fls / w United States   36
  'Olympic Hybrids' - 5-6', pale ivory to sulphur fls   85
  oxypetalum / Bb / 8" / greenish or bronzy-yellow fls / nw Himalayas   84
  pardalinum / Bb / to 8' / orange fls spotted red / w N. America   43
  parryi / Bb / 5-6' / fls orange-red / w United States   36
  parviflorum / Bb / 6' / small orange-red fls / coastal, w N. Am.   9
  parvum / Bb / 3' / yellow fls / w United States   36
  'Perfection', pink strain - see L. X 'Pink Perfection'   *

(1) - FELDMAIER - Lilies. 1970(trans.)
(2) - FINDLAY in RHS The Lily Yearbook 1967

LILIUM, con.
```
  philadelphicum / Bb / 1-4' / orange to orange-red fls / e US       84
        "      v. andinum - red-scarlet fls, nc North America        34
  philippense v. formosanum - see L. formosanum                      84
  X 'Pink Perfection' - 5', fls in orchid shades                     85
  pitkinense / Bb / 3-6' / grenadine red, purple spots / California  85
  pomponium / Bb / to 2½' / scarlet-red fls / Maritime Alps          84
  pumilum / Bb / 1-2' / bright red fls / n China, Manchuria          84
       "   'Red Star' - 2', scarlet fls, comes true from seed       (1)
  pyrenaicum / Bb / 2-4' / lemon-yellow fls / Pyrenees               43
        "     v. aureum - deeper golden yellow fls                    9
        "     v. rubrum - orange-red fls spotted maroon              84
  'Red Star' - see L. pumilum 'Red Star'                              *
  'Redstart' - 3', mahogany-red fls, spotted                         85
  regale / Bb / 6' / white fls, yellow throat / w China              84
      "  'Album' - completely white fls                              36
      "  'Creelman' - see L. X imperiale 'George C. Creelman'         *
      "  'Pink Perfection' - see L. X 'Pink Perfection'               *
      "  'Sentinal Strain' - see L. 'Sentinal Strain'                85
  rubellum / Bb / 2½' / deep pink fls / Japan                        43
  sargentiae / Bb / 3-4' / white fls, yellow throat / w China        36
  'Sentinal Strain' - 3-5', white fls, golden throat                 85
  shastense / Bb / 4' / dark yellowish-orange fls / California       84
  speciosum 'Album' - 4', white fls with green band                  36
  superbum / Bb / to 8' / deep yellow & orange-red fls / e & c US    84
       "   'Rubrum' - pure red form collected by Mrs. Henry          (2)
  'Sutton Court' - 5-6', yellow fls, spotted purple                  85
  szovitsianum / Bb / 5' / deep yellow fls / s Caucasus              43
  tigrinum / Bb / 6' / orange-red fls, dark spots / Japan, e China   84
       "    v. splendens - deeper reddish-orange fls                 84
  tsingtauense / Bb / 3' / fiery orange fls / e China, Korea         84
  vollmeri / Bb / 3' / yellow to reddish-orange fls / California     75
  wardii / Bb / 5' / pinkish-purple fls / se Tibet                   84
  washingtonianum / Bb / 2-7' / white fls / Washington, Oregon, Calif. 75
       "          v. purpurascens - pinkish-purple fls, vigorous     84
  wigginsii / Bb / 3' / yellow fls, purple spots / Siskiyous         84
```

LIMNANTHES - Limnanthaceae
```
  douglasii 'Sulphurea' - A, 6", yellowish fls, California            9
```

LIMONIUM - Plumbaginaceae
```
  bellidifolium / R / to 1' / pale violet fls / Europe, saline soils  92
  cosyrense / R / 4" / lavender fls / s Europe                       43
  diffusum / HH P / to 16" / pale violet fls / s Portugal, sw Spain  92
  globulariifolium - see L. ramosissimum                             92
  gougetianum / R / 6-10" / lavender fls / Italy                     38
  incanum nanum - see L. tataricum v. nanum                           9
  latifolium / P / 20-32" / fls pale violet / se Europe, Balkans     92
  minutum / R / 6-9" / reddish-purple fls / se France                35
  ramosissimum / P / 8-20" / pale pink fls / salt marshes of Medit.  92
  spathulatum / HH P / 24-32" / violet fls / North Africa            92
  tataricum / P / 1' / ruby-red fls / s Europe to Siberia             9
       "     v. nanum - dwarf strain                                  9
  tetragonum / Gh P / 2' / red fls / Cape of Good Hope               45
  tomentellum / R / to 1' / pinkish fls / se Russia                  92
```

```
(1) - WOODSTOCK & STEARN - Lilies of the World  1950
(2) - FELDMAIER - Lilies  1970(trans.)
```

LINANTHUS - Polemoniaceae
  nuttallii ssp. floribunda - P, to 28", whitish fls, filiform lvs, Ca.59

LINARIA - Scrophulariaceae
  alpina / R / 6" / blue & orange fls / Alps   9
    " v. rosea - pink & yellow fls   43
  amethystea / A / 1'+ / fls bluish-violet / Spain, Portugal   92
  angustissima / P / 2'+ / fls pale yellow / s & ec Europe   92
  anticaria / HH P / to 18" / fls grayish-lilac / s Spain   92
  bipartita - see L. incarnata   92
  broussonetii - see L. amethystea   92
  caesia / A, B, P / 4-28" / fls yellow, brown striped / w Iberian Pen.92
  'Canon J. Went ' - see L. purpurea 'Canon J. Went'   *
  cuartanensis / R / ? / bluish-lavender fls / s Spain   (1)
  cymbalaria alba-compacta - see CYMBALARIA muralis 'Alba-compacta' *
       "   globosa alba - see CYMBALARIA muralis 'Globosa Alba'   *
  dalmatica - see L. genistifolia ssp. dalmatica   92
  faucicola / R / semi-prostrate / blue-violet fls / Spain   43
  genistifolia ssp. dalmatica - 3'+, yellow fls, Balkans   92
  glareosa - see CHAENORHINUM glareosum   92
  globosa rosea - see CYMBALARIA muralis 'Globosa Rosea'   *
  incarnata / A / to 2' / violet to red-purple fls / Spain   92
  italica - see L. angustissima   92
  japonica / P / 6-28" / fls pale yellow / Far East   60
  lilacina / HH P / to 18" / orange & yellow & lilac fls / se Spain 92
  macedonica - included in L. genistifolia ssp. dalmatica   92
  maroccana / A / 9-15" / violet-purple & yellow fls / Morocco   43
  nevadensis / R / 8" / fls yellow & brown / Sierra Nevada, Spain 92
  origanifolia - see CHAENORHINUM origanifolium   92
  pallida - see CYMBALARIA pallida   92
  purpurea / P / 1-3' / fls bright purple / s Europe   9
    "   'Canon J. Went' - pale pink fls, true from seed   89
  repens / P / 1-2' / fls white, purple striped / Europe   9
  supina / R / 6" / fls pale to deep yellow / Majorca   43
    "   nevadensis - see L. nevadensis   92
  triornithophora / P / 2-3' / white, orange, purple fls / Portugal 9
  triphylla / A / to 1½' / white, orange, violet fls / se & ec Europe 92
  tristis / P / to 3' / yellow & brown fls / s Spain, s Portugal (2)
    "   'Lurida' - scree plant, creamy-gray & heather fls, Atlas Mts. 21
    "   nevadensis - see L. nevadensis   92
  villosa - see CHAENORHINUM villosum   92
  vulgaris / P / 3'+ / bright yellow & orange fls / N. Am., Europe 68

LINDELOFIA - Boraginaceae
  longiflora / P / 2' / fls deep blue / Himalayas   9
  pterocarpa - high mt. race of L. stylosa in Pamirs, c Asia; red fls (3)
  spectabilis - see L. longiflora   9

LINDERA - Lauraceae
  benzoin / Sh / 15' / early greenish-yellow fls / Maine to Texas 69
    "   aestivalis - delete aestivalis   69

LINNAEA - Caprifoliaceae
  borealis / R / 2" / pink fls / n Europe, n Asia / N. America   9

LINOSYRIS vulgaris - see ASTER linosyris   51

  (1) - RIPLEY in Quar. Bull. Alpine Garden Soc. 41:2
  (2) - INGRAM in Baileya 4:3
  (3) - POPOV - Flora USSR Vol. 19

LINUM - Linaceae
  alpinum - see L. perenne ssp. alpinum   91
  altaicum / P / to 2' / lilac-blue fls / w Siberia, c Asia   (1)
  anglicum - see L. perenne ssp. anglicum   91
  angustifolium - see L. bienne   91
  aquilinum / R / dwarf tuft / yellow fls, red tinged / Chile   21
  arboreum / Sh / 1' / golden yellow fls / Crete   43
  bienne / B or P / to 2' / blue fls / w & s Europe   91
  capitatum / R / to 14" / fls yellow / Balkans, Italy   91
  catharticum / A / 6" / white fls, yellow claw / Europe   91
  dolomiticum / R / 6" / yellow fls / on dolomite in Hungary   91
  extraaxillare - see L. perenne ssp. extraaxillare   91
  flavum / P / to 2' / fls yellow / c & se Europe   91
    " 'Compactum' - 6", large bright yellow fls   89
  grandiflorum 'Rubrum' - A, 1-1½', red fls, North Africa   42
  hirsutum / P / 1½' / fls blue / ec & e Europe, CZ, Russia   91
  lewisii / P / 4-30" / fls blue / Wisconsin s- & w-ward   75
  macraei / R / ? / fls yellow / Chile   21
  monogynum / P / 1-2' / fls white / New Zealand   9
  narbonense / P / 1½' / fls clear blue / c & e Europe   42
    " 'Gentianoides' - garden selection   17
    " 'Heavenly Blue' - 1½', ultramarine-blue fls   85
  olympicum / HH Sh / 4-6" / fls violet / Bithyrian Olympus   33
  perenne / P / to 2' / blue fls / c & e Europe   91
    " ssp. anglicum - stems decumbent or ascending, Britain   91
    " ssp. alpinum - 2-6", Pyrenees & Alps   91
    " ssp. extraaxillare - like ssp. anglicum, Carpathians   91
    " lewisii - see L. lewisii   9
  salsoloides - see L. suffruticosum ssp. salsoloides   91
    " nanum - see L. s. ssp. salsoloides 'Nanum'   57
  suffruticosum ssp. salsoloides - 10", fls white, sw Europe   91
    " " 'Nanum' - 2" replica   57
  sulcatum / A / 2½' / fls yellow / e North America   10
  tenuifolium / P / 8-18" / pink or white fls / c & s Europe   91
  viscosum / P / 2' / fls pink / s & sc Europe, in mts.   91

LIPARIS - Orchidaceae
  lilifolia / R / to 10" / fls madder-purple / e & c US, China   23
  loeselii / R / 2-8" / greenish fls / North America, Europe   9

LIRIODENDRON - Magnoliaceae
  tulipifera / T / 100' / green & orange fls / e North America   42

LIRIOPE - Liliaceae
  spicata / P / 16-18" / pale lavender fls / Japan   (2)

LITHODORA - Boraginaceae
  oleifolia / Sh / 1' / fls pale pink turning blue / Pyrenees   92

LITHOSPERMUM - Boraginaceae
  angustifolium - see L. incisum   (3)
  buglossoides purpureo-caeruleum - see BUGLOSSOIDES p.-c.   92
  canescens / P / 4-18" / orange-yellow fls / N. Dakota to Oklahoma   76
  croceum - differs but slightly from L. canescens, Oklahoma   76
  diffusum 'Grace Ward' - large pale blue fls, prostrate shrub   13
  doerfleri - see MOLTKIA doerfleri   (3)

  (1) - YUZEPCHUK in Flora USSR Vol. 10
  (2) - SKINNER in Jour. Royal Hort. Soc. August 1971
  (3) - INGRAM in Baileya 6:2

LITHOSPERMUM, con.
    graminifolium - see MOLTKIA suffruticosa   13
    incisum / P / 4-20" / yellow fls / North America   (1)
    oleifolium - see LITHODORA oleifolia   (1)
    prostratum 'Grace Ward' - see L. diffusum 'Grace Ward'   13
    purpureo-caeruleum - see BUGLOSSOIDES purpureocaerulea   92

LITTONIA - Liliaceae
    modesta / Gh Cl / 6' / orange-red fls / Natal, n Transvaal   84

LLOYDIA - Liliaceae
    graeca / HH Bb / 3-8" / fls white, purple striped / e Medit. reg.   85
    serotina / Bb / 3-6" / fls whitish / Colorado, Europe, Asia   9

LOASA - Loasaceae
    laterita - see CAJOPHORA laterita   32
    nana / R / dwarf / yellow fls / Valdivian Andes   21
    sigmoides / R / mass of small bristly lvs / fls orange-yellow / S.Am. 21
    vulcanica / HH P / 20-40" / white fls, streaks / Ecuador   32

LOBELIA - Campanulaceae
    cardinalis / P / 2-4' / fls intense red / e North America   9
    georgiana / P / to 3' / fls pale blue / Virginia to Florida   34
    kalmii / P / to 2' / blue fls, white-eyed / e & c North America   34
    linnaeoides / R / 3" / blue & white fls / New Zealand   33
    sessilifolia / P / 20-40" / blue-purple fls / Far East   60
    siphilitica / P / 2-3' / fls blue or purplish / e United States   34
        "   'Alba' - nearly white fls   9
        "   'Rosea' - pinkish fls   *
        "   vedrariense - see L. X vedrariense   85
    tupa / HH P / 4-7' / blood-red fls / Chile   9
    X vedrariense - not too hardy, deep purple fls   85

LOISELEURIA - Ericaceae
    procumbens / Sh / tufts / rose-colored fls / mts. of n hemisphere   60

LOMATIA - Proteaceae
    ferruginea / HH T / to 30' / fls tawny-yellow & red / Chile   13

LOMATIUM - Umbelliferae
    angustatum flavum - see L. martindalei v. flavum   47
    columbianum / P / to 2' / fls purple / nw United States   47
    cous / R / to 1' / fls yellow; lvs sparse / Montana   21
    dissectum / P / 3-5' / yellow or red fls / California to B. C.   75
    grayi / P / 8-25" / fls yellow; lvs dissected / Colorado to Wash.   76
    martindalei / R / 2-14" / fls white or cream / nw North America   75
        "   v. flavum - fls yellow   47
    nudicaule / P / 12-16" / yellow fls / California, B. C., Idaho   9
    suksdorfii / R / 2-8" / fls yellow / Klickitat Co., Washington   47
    triternatum / P / to 2½' / fls deep yellow / California, B. C.   9
    utriculatum / P / 4-20" / yellow fls / nw United States   75

LONICERA - Caprifoliaceae
    alpigena / Sh / 4-8' / yellow fls, tinged red / c & s Europe   13
    X americana - Cl, yellow fls suffused reddish-purple, s & se Eu.   13
    ciliosa / Cl / twining / fls yellow or orange-scarlet / w N. Am.   13
    demissa / Sh / 12' / whitish fls; scarlet frs / Japan   69

(1) - INGRAM in Baileya 6:2

LONICERA, con.
  X purpusii - Sh, 10', white fls, fragrant   13
    sempervirens / Cl / vigorous / orange-scarlet fls / Conn. to Texas   13
    standishii / Sh / 6-8' / fragrant white fls; red frs / China   13
    syringantha / Sh / to 9' / fls pale rosy-lilac / w China   9

LOPEZIA - Onagraceae
    coronata / A / to 3' / fls pale lilac, red marked / Mexico   9,32

LOROPETALUM - Hamamelidaceae
    chinense / HH Sh / to 12' / whitish fls / c & se China   9

LOTUS - Leguminosae
    corniculatus / R / procumbent / yellow fls, turning orange / Europe 42
         "   v. japonicus - fewer yellow fls   60
    creticus / HH P / to 20" / yellow & purple fls / Medit. region   91
    tenuifolius - see L. tenuis   91
    tenuis / P / to 3' / yellow fls / Europe   91

LUDWIGIA - Onagraceae
    alternifolia / Sh / 2-3' / yellow fls / e US in wet places   9

LUETKEA - Rosaceae
    pectinata / Sh / prostrate to 6" / small white fls / Alaska to Cal.   9

LUFFA - Cucurbitaceae
    cylindrica / A Cl / high / Dish-cloth Gourd / Old World tropics   9

LUINA - Compositae
    hypoleuca / R / 6-16" / straw-yellow fls / nw United States   75

LUNARIA - Cruciferae
    annua / B / 1½-2' / violet-lilac to purple fls / Sweden   42
      " 'Alba' - white fls   9
      " 'Variegata' - with variegated lvs   42
    rediviva / P / 3' / fls deep mauve / Europe   42

LUPINUS - Leguminosae
    angustifolius / A / 8-32" / blue fls / s Europe   91
    arboreus / HH Sh / 4-10' / fls sulphur-yellow / California   9
    argenteus stenophyllus - see L. argenteus v. tenellus   (1)
         "   v. tenellus - 16-28", blue fls, Great Basin area, N. Am. (1)
    breweri / R / prostrate mats / fls violet & white / Oregon   75
    caespitosus / R / 3-6" / pale blue fls; silvery lvs / w N. America 33
    diffusus / HH P / 1-3' / fls blue / Florida to North Carolina   72
    latifolius / P / 1-4' / fls blue or purplish / w North America   75
         "   v. thompsonianus - 12", fls not hairy, Wash., Oregon   47
    lepidus / R / 6" / purple-blue fls / w North America   38
       "   v. lobbii - prostrate mats, sub-alpine   47
    littoralis / P / to 2' / fls blue or lilac / n Calif. to B. C.   75
    lyallii / R / mats / fls blue / s Sierra Nevada Mts., Calif.   75
    microcarpus / A/? / blue-purple fls / South America   21
    palaestinus / A / 16" / purple or lilac & cream fls / Israel, Egypt (2)
    perennis / P / 1-2' / fls blue to white / Canada to Florida   9
    pilosus / A / to 3' / fls rose & red / s Europe   9
    polyphyllus / P / 2½-4' / fls varii-colored / Washington to Calif. 42
         "   'Roseus' - selection for pink fls   *

  (1) DUNN & GILLETT - The Lupines of Canada and Alaska. 1966
  (2) BENJAMIN in Bull. Am. Rock Garden Society 29:1

LUPINUS, con.
  sericeus / P / 1-2' / blue fls / British Columbia to Texas   (1)
  succulentus / HH P / 4-24" / fls deep purplish-blue / coastal Calif. 74

LUZULA - Juncaceae
  glabrata / R / tufted / brown fls / Calif. to B.C., Rocky Mts.   59
  luzuloides / P / 2' / whitish fls / Europe   32
  maxima - see L. sylvatica   32
  multiflora / R / to 1' / brownish fls / e & c North America   34
  spicata / R / 1'+ / dense brown panicles / alpine areas, N. America 34
  sylvatica / P / 18" / bracted panicles / Europe   9

LUZURIAGA - Philesiaceae
  erecta / HH Cl / 18" / white fls / Chile   20
  radicans / HH Sh / creeping / white fls; orange frs / Tasmania   46

LYCHNIS - Caryophyllaceae
  'Abbotswood Rose' - see L. coronaria 'Abbotswood Rose'   42
  alba - see SILENE alba   90
  alpestris - see SILENE alpestris   51
  alpina / R / 2-6" / fls pale purple / Alps, Pyrenees   90
      "   'Alba' - white fls   *
      "   'Rosea' - pink fls   *
  apetala - see SILENE wahlbergella   90
  X arkwrightii - 9", orange-scarlet fls   17
  chalcedonica / P / 2-3' / brilliant scarlet fls / s Russia   42
  coronaria / P / 1-3' / fls purplish / Europe   90
      "   'Abbotswood Rose' - 1½', vivid pink fls   42
      "   'Alba' - white fls, true from seed   *
      "   'Atrosanguinea' - 2½', dark crimson fls   89
  coronata / B / 1½' / fls brick-red to salmon / Far East   9
  dioica - see SILENE dioica   90
  flos-cuculi / P / to 3' / fls pale purplish / Europe   90
  flos-jovis / P / 1-2' / fls purple or scarlet / c Alps   42
      "   'Alba' - white fls   *
      "   'Horts Var.' - 6-12", bright pink fls; gray lvs   85
      "   'Milkmaid' - selection for soft pink fls, dwarf   *
  forrestii / R / fairly tall / ragged white fls / ?   21
  X haageana - P, 1', fls scarlet to salmon shades   42
  'Milkmaid' - see L. flos-jovis 'Milkmaid'   *
  sartorii - see L. viscaria ssp. atropurpurea   90
  senno / P / 2' / fls scarlet, white / China, cult. in Japan   10,90
  viscaria / P / to 3' / fls dark or pinkish-purple / Europe   90
      "   'Alba' - white fls on 9" spikes   44
      "   ssp. atropurpurea - 18", purplish fls, Balkans   90
  vulgaris - see L. viscaria   *

LYCOPODIUM - Lycopodiaceae
  annotinum / R / trailing, branches 6-8" / evergreen / n temperate z. 9
  clavatum / R / trailing / Common Club-moss / n temperate zone   9
  complanatum / R / trailing / evergreen / n hemisphere   9
  obscurum / R / trailing / Common Ground-pine / N. America, Japan   9

LYGODESMA - Compositae
  aphylla texana - see L. texana   73
  texana / R / ? / fls pale lavender or purplish / Texas   73

LYGODIUM - Schizaceae
  palmatum / F / twining to 2' / Hartford Fern / Mass. to Florida   9

  (1) - DUNN & GILLETT - The Lupines of Canada and Alaska. 1966

LYONIA - Ericaceae
  ligustrina / Sh / 3-8' / fls dull white / e North America   13
  lucida / HH Sh / 6' / fls white to pink / Va. to Fla. & la.   69
  mariana / Sh / to 6' / white or pinkish fls / e & s United States 13

LYSICHITUM - Araceae
  americanum / P / 2-3' / yellow spathes / w North America   42

LYSIMACHIA - Primulaceae
  clethroides / P / 3' / fls white / China, Japan   9
  ephemerum / P / 3' / fls white tinged purple / sw Europe   42
  japonica v. minutissima - small yellow fls, creeper   (1)
  mauritiana / B / 4-16" / fls white to pinkish / Far Eastern shores 60
  punctata / P / 3'+ / yellow fls / Europe, Asia   9
  quadrifolia / P / 1-3' / yellow fls / e United States   9
  thymiflora / P / 1-2' / yellow fls / n hemisphere   60

LYTHRUM - Lythraceae
  salicaria / P / 2-3' / purple fls / n temperate zone   9

MAACKIA - Leguminosae
  amurensis / T / 40' / fls whitish / Manchuria   9

MACHERANTHERA - Compositae
  bigelovii / P / 8-40" / purple or violet fls / New Mexico, Colorado 74
  tanacetifolia / R / 4-16" / fls bright red-violet / Montana to Kan. 76

MAGNOLIA - Magnoliaceae
  denudata / T / 30' / pure white fls / China   13
  grandiflora / HH T / to 80' / fls white; evergreen lvs / se US   42
  X highdownensis - HHT, 15', pendulous white fls   42
  kobus / T / 18'+ / fragrant white fls / Japan   46
  macrophylla / T / 45-65' / large white fls / s Ohio & s-ward   46
  obovata / T / to 100' / white fls / China, Japan, in mts.   60
  salicifolia / T / 20'+ / white fls; aromatic lvs / Japan   46
  sieboldii / Sh / 10' / waxy white fls / Japan   42
  sinensis / Sh / 15' / pendulous white fls / w China   46
  X soulangeana 'Lennei' - 20'+, fls rose-purple-white within   13
  tripetala / T / 40' / white fls / Pennsylvania to Alabama & Arkansas 9
  wilsonii / Sh / 10'+ / white fls / w China   46

MAHONIA - Berberidaceae
  aquifolium / Sh / 4' / yellow fls / nw North America   42
     "   'Heterophylla' - narrow, wavy-edged leaflets   46
  'Charity' - HH Sh, to 10', yellow fls   46
  japonica / Sh / 7' / lemon-yellow fls in long racemes / China   42
  nervosa / Sh / 2' / yellow fls / British Columbia to California   35
  piperiana / Sh / ? / lvs lustrous green above, gray below / Oregon 1
  pumila / Sh 1' / yellow fls / w North America   35
  repens / Sh 1' / yellow fls / British Columbia to New Mexico   35

MAIANTHEMUM - Liliaceae
  bifolium / R / 9" / white fls / Eurasia   35
  canadense / R / 5" / starry white fls / e North America   35
  dilitatum / R / 4-10" / white fls / Far East, w N. America   60

MAITENUS boaria - see MAYTENUS boaria   45

  (1) - KITAMURI, MURATA & HORI - Colored Illus. of Herb. Plants. 1964

MALESHERBIA - Malesherbiaceae
  linearifolia / HH A / 18" / purple or black fls / Chile   45

MALUS - Rosaceae
  florentina / T / 12' / white fls; red frs / Italy, Jugoslavia   92
  floribunda / T / 10'+ / crimson buds; white fls / Japan   46
  fusca / T / 35' / fls white or pinkish / Alaska to California   69
  sargentii / Sh / 6' / pure white fls; frs dark red / Japan   69

MALVA - Malvaceae
  alcea / P / 1-4' / fls bright pink / most of Europe   91
    " 'Fastigiata' - 3', fls deep pink   42
  moschata / P / 1-2' / fls rose or white / Europe   9
    " 'Alba' - white fls   9
  sylvestris / B / 2-3' / fls purple-rose / Europe, tropical Asia   9
  trimestris - see LAVATERA trimestris   *

MALVASTRUM - Malvaceae
  coccineum / R / to 1' / bright scarlet fls / mid North America   38
  lateritum / HH R / prostrate to 6" / brick-red fls / South America   9

MALVUS florentina - error for MALUS florentina   *

MAMMILLARIA - Cactaceae
  multiceps / Gh / ? / pale yellow fls / Mexico   32

MANDEVILLA - Apocynaceae
  laxa / HH Cl / 12'+ / fls white / Argentina, Bolivia   32

MANDRAGORA - Solanaceae
  officinarum / P / rosette / purple fls / Medit. reg.   9

MANFREDA virginica - see AGAVE virginica   34

MARGYRICARPUS - Rosaceae
  setosus / Sh / 6-8" / green fls; white frs / Andes Mts.   38

MARRUBIUM - Labiatae
  incanum / P / to 20" / white fls; white, woolly lvs / Italy, w Balk. 92
  libanoticum / R / 1' / fls pale pink / Asia Minor   10

MARSHALLIA - Compositae
  caespitosa / R / 6-16" / white fls / Louisiana, Texas, n to Missouri 73
  grandiflora / P / 1-3' / pink or white fls / Pa., N. Carolina, Ken. 72

MATRICARIA - Compositae
  tchihatchewii / R / 4-10" / small white daisies / Asia Minor   32

MATTEUCCIA - Polypodiaceae
  pensylvanica / f / 3-5' / Ostrich Fern / North America   50
  struthiopteris / F / to 5' / moist soil / Eurasia   26

MATTHIOLA - Cruciferae
  fruticosa ssp. vallesiaca - error fro M. fruticulosa ssp. v.   *
  fruticulosa ssp. perennis - P, 2', fls yellow to purple-red, s Eu. 90
     " ssp. valesiaca - low, fls yellow to red, s Europe 90
  perennis auremerica - see M. fruticulosa ssp. perennis   90
  scapigera / R / close tufts / fls cream to deep purple / Atlas Mts. 21

MAURANDIA - Scrophulariaceae
barclaiana / Gh Cl / 10' / fls deep purple / Mexico   9
erubescens / Gh Cl / 10' / rosy-pink fls / Mexico   41
lophospermum / Gh Cl / 10' / rosy-purple fls / Mexico   9
scandens / Gh Cl / 10' / lavender, lilac or red fls / Mexico   41

MAYTENUS - Celastraceae
boaria / HH Sh or T / 20'+ / greenish-white fls, evergreen / Chile   13

MAZUS - Scrophulariaceae
japonicus / R / to 6" / fls white to purplish & yellow / Far East   60
radicans / R / creeper / white & gold fls / New Zealand, Australia   38
reptans / R / prostrate / blue-purple & gold fls / Himalayas   38
rugosus - see M. japonicus   60

MECONOPSIS - Papaveraceae
aculeata / P / 1-2' / blue-purple fls / w Himalayas   9
X beamishii - to 4', fls yellow, purple blotched   88
betonicifolia / P / 2-5' / rich sky-blue fls / Tibet, Yunnan   42
       "   'Alba' - white fls   *
       "   f. baileyi - only slightly differing   (1)
cambrica / R / 1' / fls yellow or orange / w Europe   42
   "   'Aurantiaca' - has the orange fls   *
'Crewdson Hybrid' - similar to M. X sheldonii   (2)
dhwojii / B / 2-2½' / yellow fls / Nepal   95
grandis / P / to 3' / fls deep blue / Nepal, Tibet   42
   "   'Alba' - white fls   *
   "   'Branklyn' - a rich blue form   42
horridula / B / 3' / purple or wine-red fls / c Asia   95
integrifolia / monocarpic / 1½' / fls yellow / Tibet   42
latifolia / monocarpic / 3-5' / pale blue fls / n Kashmir   88
napaulensis / monocarpic / to 8' / red, purple, blue fls / Nepal   88
paniculata / monocarpic / to 6' / fls yellow / Nepal, Assam   88
   "   'Alba' - white fls   *
punicea / P / 2½' / pendulous red fls / ne Tibet, w China   88
quintuplinervia / P / 1-1½' / fls lavender-blue / Tibet   42
regia / mnoncarpic / 4-5' / fls yellow / Nepal   42
X sarsonsii - P, 3', fls sulphur-yellow   88
X sheldonii - P, 3', fls deep blue   85
simplicifolia / A / 18" / blue or violet-blue fls / c Asia   95
superba / monocarpic / to 3½' / white fls / Tibet, Bhutan   88
villosa / P / 15-24" / yellow fls / Nepal, Sikkim, Bhutan   88

MEDEOLA - Liliaceae
virginiana / P / 1-3' / pale greenish-yellow fls / e North America   9

MEDICAGO - Leguminosae
orbicularis / A / 8-36" / small yellow fls / s Europe   91
sativa / P / 1-3' / green & purple fls: Alfalfa / Europe   9

MEGACARPAEA - Cruciferae
polyandra / R / ? / white fls / Himalayas   33

MELALEUCA - Myrtaceae
fulgens / HH Sh / 4' / red fls / w Australia   16
hypericifolia / HH Sh / 15' / stamens rich red / Australia   (3)
wilsonii / HH Sh / to 4' / mauve to crimson fls / s Australia   16

(1) - GREY-WILSON in Gardeners Chronicle 165:14
(2) - LYALL in Bull. Hardy Plant Soc. 1:6
(3) - ENARI - Ornamental Shrubs of California. 1962

MELAMPYRUM - Scrophulariaceae
  nemerosum / P / 6-20" / bright yellow fls / n & c Europe   92

MELANDRIUM album - see SILENE alba   90
     "   apetalum - see SILENE wahlbergella   90
     "   diurnum - see SILENE dioica   90
     "   keiskeii - see SILENE keiskeii   35
     "   rubrum - see SILENE dioica   90
     "   zawadskyii - see SILENE zawadskyii   90

MELASPHAERULEA - Iridaceae
  graminea / HH C / 1'+ / fls yellowish-green / South Africa   9

MELICA - Gramineae
  ciliata / Gr / 8-30" / panicles purplish or whitish / Eurasia   85

MELISSA - Labiatae
  officinalis / P / to 3' / Lemon Balm, yellowish fls / Europe   92

MELITTIS - Labiatae
  melissophyllum / P / 8-28" / fls white, pink, purple / w, s & c Eu. 92

MENTHA - Labiatae
  arvensis / P / to 2' / lilac to white fls, sickly scent / Europe 92
     "   v. canadensis - see M. a. var. villosa   34
     "   v. villosa - more pubescent, Nfld. to Alaska, s to US   34
  requienii / HH R / creeping / pale lilac fls, pungently minty / Cors. 92
  X rotundifolia - M. longifolia X M. suavolens, variable   92

MENTZELIA - Loasaceae
  decapetala / B or P / 2'+ / fls white / mid-United States   9
  laevicaulis / P / to 3' / fls pale yellow / California   95
  pumila / P / ? / yellow fls / Wyoming to Mexico   74

MENYANTHES - Gentianaceae
  trifoliata / Aq P / 8-18" / white or purplish fls / Eurasia, N. Am. 9

MENZIESIA - Ericaceae
  ciliicalyx / Sh / to 3' / fls pale yellow / Honshu   60
     "   v. purpurea - fls purple   60
  ferruginea / Sh / 6' / fls white, tinged pink / Alaska to Oregon 13
  pilosa / Sh / 2-6' / yellowish fls tinged red / Pa. to Georgia   9
  purpurea / Sh / to 8' / fls rose-purple / Kyushu   60
  tubiflora - see M. ciliicalyx   60

MERENDERA - Liliaceae
  montana / C / 4" / purplish-pink fls / Pyrenees, Alps   38
  sobolifera / C / 3" / pale rosy-lilac to white fls / Asia Minor   84

MERREMIA - Convolvulaceae
  dissecta / Cl / ? / white funnel, red throat / Texas to Florida   73

MERTENSIA - Boraginaceae
  bella / P / 4-28" / blue fls / w Oregon, Idaho   75
  ciliata / P / 1-3' / fls bright blue / Rocky Mts., w-&n-ward   9
  echioides / R / 1' / fls deep blue / Himalayas   9
  maritima / R / mats / turquoise & mauve fls / n seashores   38
  petrocopta - error for M. pterocarpa?   *
  primuloides / R / 4-6" / violet-blue fls / Himalayas   38
  pterocarpa / R / 9"+ / sky-blue fls / Far East   17

MERTENSIA, con.
  virginica / P / 2' / fls purplish-blue / e United States   42
      "   'Alba' - white fls   34

MESEMBRYANTHEMUM - cooperi - see DELOSPERMA cooperi   20

METANARTHECIUM - Liliaceae
  luteoviride / R / 8-16" / yellow-green fls / Japan, in mt. meadows   60

MEUM - Umbelliferae
  athamanticum / P / to 2' / white or purplish fls / w&c Eu., in mts.   91

MIBORA - Gramineae
  minima / A Gr / 2" / recommended association plant / Alps   38
  verna - see A. minima   *

MICROMERIA - Labiatae
  croatica / Sh / to 8" / purplish fls / Jugoslavia   92
  dalmatica / P / to 20" / fls pale lilac / Balkan Peninsula   92
  juliana / HH Sh / 4-16" / purplish fls / c Portugal, Medit. reg.   92
  rupestris - see M. thymifolia   92
  teneriffae / HH Sh / 6-12" / fls small, purple / Teneriffe   29
  thymifolia / P / to 20" / fls white & violet / w Balkans   92

MICROSERIS alpestris - see NOTHOCALAIS alpestris   59
     "   troximoides - see NOTHOCALAIS troximoides   59

MICROSORIUM scandens - see PHYMATODES scandens   2

MILIUM - Gramineae
  effusum 'Aureum' - P Gr, 3', yellow-leaved   85

MILLA - Liliaceae
  biflora / HH Bb / fls waxy white / s Arizona, New Mexico & s-ward   9

MIMULUS - Scrophulariaceae
  alsinioides / R / 2-12" / yellow & red fls / n California to Canada   75
  aurantiacus / HH/P / 2-7' orange fls / coastal California   75
  'Bonfire' - P gr. as A, 9", orange-scarlet fls   89
  X burnetii - 9-12", yellow & bronze fls   42
  cardinalis / R / 1' / scarlet & yellow fls / Oregon to Arizona   35
  coccineus / A / to 7" / red-purple fls / California   59
  cupreus / R / 8-10" / yellow fls ageing to copper / Chile   38
     "   'Red Emperor' - bright crimson-scarlet fls, compact   89
     "   'Whitecroft Scarlet' - 4", vermilion fls   42
  douglasii / R / 3" / purple fls / n California, s Oregon   75
  glutinosus / HH Sh / to 3½' / fls salmon-yellow / c & s California   95
     "   aurantiacus - see M. aurantiacus   *
  guttatus / P / 2-36" / yellow fls, spotted red / w North America   75
  langsdorfii - see M. guttatus   34
  lewisii / P / 1-1½' / bright yellow fls / B. C., Calif., Utah   35
     "   guttatus - see M. guttatus   75
  nanus / R / 2-6" / purple, yellow, white fls / ne California   75
  nasutus / P / 4-30" / yellow fls / California, Arizona, Mexico   74
  primuloides / R / mat to 5" / yellow fls / California, Oregon   75
     "   f. linearifolius - linear lvs, Siskiyou Mts.   59
  ringens / P / 2½-3½' / violet fls / e North America   95
  tilingii / R / 8" / yellow & red fls / Baja California to B. C.   75

MINUARTIA - Caryophyllaceae
  austriaca / R / to 8" / white fls / e Alps   90
  caucasica - see M. circassica   26
  circassica / R / to 8" / white fls / Caucasia   26
  gerardii - see M. verna   90
  imbricata / R / mats to 4" / white fls / w & c Caucasia   26
  juniperina / R / to 10" / white fls / s & w Greece   90
  laricifolia / R / to 1' / white fls / c Spain to Carpathians   90
        "   ssp. kitabelii - robust form, e Austrian Alps   90
  recurva / R / 4" / white fls / Portugal to s Carpathians   90
  rosanii / R / 1-2" / fls white / Italy   9
  rubella / R / caespitose / high montane variant of M. verna / Eu.   90
  sedoides / R / cushion / solitary white fls / Pyrenees, Alps   90
  stricta kitabelii - see M. laricifolia ssp. kitabelii   90
  verna / R / to 8" / white fls / s, w & c Europe   90
    " 'Caespitosa' - denser form   *
    " 'Caespitosa Aurea' - a dense yellow moss in effect   35

MIRABILIS - Nyctaginaceae
  jalapa / HH A / 1½-3' / varii-colored fls / C. America to Peru   95

MITCHELLA - Rubiaceae
  repens / R / creeping / pinkish fls / Nova Scotia to Mexico   35

MITELLA - Saxifragaceae
  breweri / R / 1' / greenish-yellow fls / Sierra Nevada Mts.; Montana 75
  caulescens / R / 4-16" / greenish fls / California, B. C., Montana   75
  diphylla / R / 8" / lacy white fls / ne N. Am. to Missouri   9
  ovalis / R / 6-12" / creamy fls / Oregon, Washington, B. Columbia   75
  pentandra / R / 4-12" / greenish-yellow fls / Calif., Alaska, Col.   75
  trifida / R / 6-14" / white fls, tinged purple / Cascades to Rockies 75

MITRARIA - Gesneriaceae
  coccinea / Gh Sh / scandent / bright scarlet fls / Chile   9

MOEHRINGIA - Caryophyllaceae
  glaucovirens / R / 6" / white fls / s Alps   90

MOLTKIA - Boraginaceae
  X intermedia - Sh, to 15", violet-blue fls   43
  petraea / Sh / 6" / pinkish-blue fls which darken / Greece   38
  suffruticosa / Sh / trailing to 10" / blue fls / n Italy, in mts.   92

MOLUCELLA - Labiatae
  laevis / A / 1½' / small white fls; large green calyces / Syria   42

MOMORDICA - Cucurbitaceae
  charantia / A Cl / to 10' / yellow fls / tropical Africa, se Asia   41

MONARDA - Labiatae
  'Adam' - 3', cerise-red fls   85
  didyma / P / 2-3' / scarlet fls / New York to Michigan & Georgia   42
  fistulosa / P / to 4' / lilac or pinkish fls / e North America   34

MONARDELLA - Labiatae
  odoratissima / R / 9-12" / bracts whitish to purplish / w US   9
       "   v. discolor - lvs densely hairy beneath   47

MONESES - Pyrolaceae
  uniflora / R / 2-6" / fls white or rosy / n hemisphere   60

MONOTROPA - Pyrolaceae
  hypopitys / R / to 8" / yellowish saprophyte / Europe, N. America   92
  uniflora / R / to 1' / white saprophyte / Asia, North America   60

MONTBRETIA - Iridaceae
  solfaterre - see M. 'Solfatare'   85
  'Solfatare' - HH C, 1½-3', apricot-yellow fls, bronze lvs   85

MONTIA - Portulacaceae
  parviflora - error for M. parvifolia   *
  parvifolia / R / to 1' / fls rose to white / B. Columbia to Montana   9
  saxosa / R / dense tufts / pink fls / n coast ranges of California   75
  sibirica / P / to 20" / white or pink fls / Alaska to Idaho, Calif.   27

MORAEA - Iridaceae
  catenulata / HH C / 15" / fls white tinged blue / Mauritius   10
  framesii / HH C / 6-9" / white fls / South Africa   37
  grandiflora - see LIBERTIA grandiflora   *
  iridioides / HH C / ? / white fls, yellow & brown spots / S. Africa   41
  irioides - see DIETES vegeta   32
  ixioides - see LIBERTIA ixioides   51
  natalensis / HH C / 12-18" / lilac fls / Natal   37
  papilionacea / HH C / 2' / yellow-brown fls / Cape Province   36
  polystachya / HH C / 2-3½' / bright lilac fls / South Africa   (1)
  ramosa - see M. ramossisima   36
  ramosissima / HH C / to 5' / yellow fls / South Africa   70
  spathacea - see M. spathulata   84
  spathulata / HH C / 2' / fls bright yellow / South Africa   84
  stricta / HH C / to 6" / purple fls / e Cape, Lesotho   56
  tricuspis / HH C / 1-2' / fls whitish-lilac, purple spotted / Cape   9
        "   'Lutea' - yellowish fls   *

MORINA - Dipsaceae
  longifolia / P / 2-3' / white fls, aging crimson / Nepal   42

MORUS - Moraceae
  alba / T / 30-45' / white or pinkish frs / China   13

MUILLA - Liliaceae
  transmontana / R / 4-20" / white fls / ne Calif., Nevada   76

MUSCARI - Liliaceae
  ambroisiacum - see MUSCARIMA ambroisiacum   56
  argaei f. album - 4", neat white fls, Asia Minor   4
  armeniacum / Bb / 4-8" / bright blue fls / Armenia   42
      "   'Album' - 6", white fls, Turkey   4
      "   'Cambridge Blue' - probably same as 'Cantab'   *
      "   'Cantab' - 6", clear Cambridge blue fls   4
      "   'Early Giant' - like 'Heavenly Blue' but earlier   84
      "   'Heavenly Blue' - blue selection   85
      "   v. szovitsianum - purple-blue fls   85
  atlanticum - see M. neglectum   32
  atropatanum - see M. tenuifolium   85
  aucheri / Bb / to 6" / sky-blue, globose fls / Anatolia   85
  azureum - see HYACINTHELLA azurea   85
      "   album - see HYACINTHELLA azurea 'Alba'   85

(1) - BAILEY - Manual of Cultivated Plants. 1949

MUSCARI, con.
```
  botryoides / Bb / 6-9" / fls sky-blue / c & s Europe              85
      "        'Album' - white fls                                   85
      "        'Heavenly Blue' - see M. armeniacum 'H. B.'           85
      "        v. heldreichii - inflorescence dense, Balkan mts.     85
      "        v. kerneri - inflorescence loose, linear lvs          85
      "        'Pallidum' - pale blue fls                            85
  bourgaei / Bb / 6" / brilliant blue & white fls / Anatolian alps   85
  caucasicum / Bb / to 14" / brown & buff fls / Turkey, Iran         85
  colchicum - see M. armeniacum                                      85
  commutatum / Bb / 6" / deep blackish-blue fls / Italy to Balkans   85
  comosum - see LEOPOLDIA comosa                                     56
      "    'Album' - see LEOPOLDIA comosa 'Alba'                     56
      "    v. plumosum - see LEOPOLDIA comosa v. plumosa             56
      "    'Monstrosum' - see LEOPOLDIA comosa v. plumosa            56
  conicum / Bb / 9" / blue fls / Iran                                36
  dolychanthum / Bb / 1' / bluish-violet fls / Caucasus             54
  'Early Giant' - see M. armeniacum 'E. G.'                          84
  graecum - see M. comosum                                           85
  grossheimii - see M. armeniacum                                    85
  heldreichii - see M. botryoides v. heldreichii                     85
  holzmannii - see M. comosum                                        85
  kerneri - see M. botryoides v. kerneri                             85
  latifolium / Bb / 1' / fls dark dusky-blue / Asia Minor            42
  leucostemon - see M. neglectum                                     85
  macrocarpum - see MUSCARIMA macrocarpum                            56
  moschatum - see MUSCARIMA moschatum                                56
      "    minor - see MUSCARIMA moschatum 'Minor'                    *
  muscarima - see MUSCARIMA moschatum                                 *
  neglectum / Bb / to 1' / fls deep blue / Europe, N. Africa, Orient 85
      "    v. pulchellum - 6", without offsets, Greece               85
  pallens / Bb / to 10" / fls light blue / Caucasus, Turkey          85
  paradoxum - see BELLEVALIA paradoxa                                85
  plumosum - see LEOPOLDIA comosa v. plumosa                         56
  polyanthum - see M. armeniacum                                     85
      "    'Album' - see M. armeniacum 'Album'                        4
  pulchellum - see M. neglectum v. pulchellum                        85
  racemosum - see M. neglectum                                       85
  sosnovskyi - see M. armeniacum                                     85
  steupii / Bb / 1'+ / violet-azure fls / Caucasus                  54
  steurii - error for M. steupii?                                     *
  szovitsianum - see M. armeniacum v. szovitsianum                   85
  tenuiflorum / Bb / to 10" / fls violet / c Europe, Ukraine         85
  tubergenianum / Bb / 4-6" / fls dark & light blue / nw Iran        42
  turkewiczii / Bb / to 4" / brownish fls / ne Turkey                85
  woronowii / Bb / to 16" / bluish-violet fls / c Asia, Iran        54
```

MUSCARIMA - Liliaceae
```
  macrocarpum / Bb / 6-8" / fls yellow & brown / Greece, Turkey      56
  moschatum / Bb / 4-6" / purplish fls, aging yellow / w Turkey      56
```

MUSINEON - Umbelliferae
```
  tenuifolium / R / stemless / yellow fls / Rocky Mts.               22
```

MUTISIA - Compositae
```
  illicifolia / HH Cl / to 10' / fls bright pink or mauve / Chile    41
  retusa / HH Cl / 10-20' / pink fls / Chile                         20
```

MYOSITIDIUM - Boraginaceae
```
  hortensia / HH P / 2' / azure-blue fls / Chatham Isls.             32
```

MYOSOTIS - Boraginaceae
  alpestris / R / 6" / light blue fls, yellow eye / se Europe   43
  alpina / R / mat / bright blue fls / Pyrenees   65
  australis / R / 6" / yellow fls / New Zealand   38
     "   v. conspicuus - 5", fls bright yellow or white, N. Z.   6
  eximia / R / to 10" / white fls / limestone cliffs, New Zealand   2
  macrantha / R / 1'+ / fls tawny orange / South Island, N. Zealand   33
  rakiura / HH R / to 1' / white fls / coastal, New Zealand   2
  rupestris - see ERITRICHIUM rupestre   (1)
  rupicola / R / 2-3" / sky-blue fls, yellow eye / European Alps   35
  sylvatica / A or B / 8-20" / pale blue fls / Eu., escape in US   34

MYRCENGENIA apiculata - error fro MYRCEUGENIA apiculata   *

MYRCEUGENIA apiculata - see MYRTUS luma   32

MYRICA - Myricaceae
  gale / Sh / 1-5' / brownish catkins / Maryland to Florida   9
  pensylvanica / Sh / to 6' / white or waxy-gray frs / e North America 34

MYRIOCEPHALUS - Compositae
  stuartii / A / 6" / yellow & white fls / Australia   16

MYRRHIS - Umbelliferae
  odorata / P / 2-3' / fls whitish, small / Europe   91

MYRSINE - Myrsinaceae
  nummularia / HH Sh / prostrate / minute fls; bluish-purple frs / NZ 2

MYRTUS - Myrtaceae
  communis / HH Sh / 10-12" / white fls / Levant, originally   13
  luma / HH Sh / 20'+ / white fls / Chile   32
  nummularia / Sh / 1-2" / white fls; pink frs / Falkland Isls.   38
  ugni / HH Sh / 4'+ / white fls; purple frs / Chile   9

NANDINA - Berberidaceae
  domestica / HH Sh / 8' / white fls; red frs / China   46

NARCISSUS - Amaryllidaceae
  asturiensis / Bb / 3-5" / deep gold fls / nw Spain, in mts.   42
  atlanticus / Bb / 12" / creamy-white fls / Atlas Mts., Morocco   (2)
  'Baby Moon' - Jonquil, 9", rich buttercup-yellow fls   36
  bulbocodium / Bb / 2-5" / light yellow fls / Spain, Portugal   42
     "   ssp. albidus - fls whitish-yellow, Morocco   (2)
     "   "   "   v. zaianicus - whitish fls, Morocco   (2)
     "   v. citrinus - 6", pale lemon-yellow fls   84
     "   v. conspicuus - deep yellow fls   42
     "   v. mesatlanticus - see N. b. ssp. romieuxii var. m.   84
     "   v. monophyllus - see N. cantabricus ssp. monophyllus   (2)
     "   v. nivalis - 2½-3", fls pale yellow   56
     "   ssp. obesus - fls rich, deep yellow, robust   84
     "   obvallaris - see N. pseudo-narcissus ssp. obvallaris   (2)
     "   petunoides - see N. cantabricus v. petunoides   (2)
     "   ssp. romieuxii - lemon-yellow fls in winter, N. Africa   42
     "   "   "   v. mesatlanticus - deeper yellow fls   84
     "   ssp. tananicus - nearly white fls, Morocco   84

(1) - POPOV in Flora USSR. Vol. 19
(2) - MEYER in American Horticultural Magazine Jan. 1966

NARCISSUS, con.
```
  calcicola / Bb / 5-6" / fls bright yellow / Portugal              (1)
  cantabricus / Bb / nearly sessile fls / fragrant, white fls / Spain (1)
        "      v. foliosus - lvs erect                               (1)
        "      ssp. monophyllus - white fls, s Spain, N. Africa      (1)
        "      v. petunoides - corolla widely expanded               (1)
  cyclamineus / Bb / 4-8" / deep yellow fls / Spain, Portugal        42
        "      'February Gold' - see N. 'February Gold'               *
        "      'Woodcock' - see N. 'Woodcock'                         *
  'February Gold' - Cyclamineus Hybrid, larger earlier fls           (2)
  fernandesii / Bb / 4" / yellow, 2-flowered / Portugal              85
  gaditanus / Bb / 5-8" / bright yellow, fragrant fls / s Spain, Port.(1)
  hedraeanthus / Bb / horizontal scape / pale yellow fls / se Spain  (1)
  jonquilla / Bb / 6-12" / fls yellow with small cup / s Europe      42
        "      'Baby Moon' - see N. 'Baby Moon'                       *
        "      v. henriquesii - longer fls, orange-yellow, Portugal  (1)
  juncifolius / Bb / to 6" / deep yellow fls / Spain, Portugal       42
        "      calcicola - see N. calcicola                          (1)
  'Little Beauty' - hybrid bicolor trumpet, dwarf                    (2)
  'Little Gem' - selected form of N. minor                           (2)
  lobularis - see N. pseudo-narcissus ssp. obvallaris               84
  longispathus - see N. pseudo-narcissus ssp. longispathus           (1)
  marvieri - see N. rupicola v. marvieri                             (1)
  minor / Bb / to 8" / variable bicolor trumpet / Portugal           84
    "  v. pumilus - 6", solid yellow fls                             (2)
  minutiflorus / Bb / 5-8" / uniform yellow fls / Spain, Portugal    (1)
  nevadensis - see N. pseudo-narcissus ssp. nevadensis               (1)
  nobilis - see N. pseudo-narcissus ssp. nobilis                     (1)
  obvallaris - see N. pseudo-narcissus ssp. obvallaris               (1)
  pachybolus - see N. tazetta ssp. pachybolus                        (1)
  pallidiflorus - see N. pseudo-narcissus ssp. pallidiflorus         (1)
  panizzianus - see N. tazetta ssp. panizzianus                      (1)
  papyraceus - see N, tazetta ssp. papyraceus                        (1)
  poeticus / Bb / 1' / white fls / s Europe                          36
  pseudo-narcissus / Bb / 1' / yellow fls / British Isles            36
        "        ssp. longispathus - longer spathes & pedicels, Spain(1)
        "        ssp. nevadensis - 6"+, fls yellow & golden          (1)
        "        ssp. nobilis - larger plant, yellow & gold fls      (1)
        "        ssp. obvallaris - 12", golden yellow fls            (1)
        "        ssp. pallidiflorus - creamy fls, w Pyrenees         (1)
  pumilus - see N. minor v. pumilus                                  (2)
  rupicola / Bb / 6" / deep rich yellow fls / Spain, Portugal        84
    "   v. marvieri - fls soft yellow, Atlas Mts.                    84
    "   v. minutiflorus - see N. minutiflorus                        (1)
  scaberulus / Bb / 6" / deep yellow & orange fls / Portugal         (1)
  serotinus / Bb / 8" / white & yellow fls in fall / Medit. region   84
  tazetta ssp. pachylobus - Gh Bb, large bulbs, white fls, Algeria   (1)
    "      "    panizzianus - white fls, Italian Riviera             (1)
    "      "    papyraceus - old cultivated form                     (1)
  triandrus / Bb / 4-6" / creamy-white fls / nw Spain, Portugal      42
    "    v. albus - 1', white to cream fls, Spain, in mts.           84
    "    v. cernuus - yellow bicolor, Portugal, Spain                (1)
    "    v. concolor - pale golden-yellow fls                        84
    "       "    'Aurantiacus' - darker fls, earlier                 (2)
    "    v. loiseleurii - fls white or light cream, Glenan Is.       84
  watieri / Bb / 3" / ice-white fls / North Africa                   43
  'Wee Bee' - soft yellow fls                                        (2)
  'Woodcock' - yellow cyclamineus hybrid                             (2)
```

(1) - MEYER in American Horticultural Magazine Jan. 1966
(2) - LEE in American Horticultural Magazine Jan. 1966

NARTHECIUM - Liliaceae
  californicum / P / 18-20" / yellowish-green fls / California   9
  ossifragum / R / 6-12" / bright yellow fls / Ireland, e Europe   (1)

NASSAUVIA - Compositae
  aculeata / R / 8" / creamy white fls; spiny lvs / Andes Mts.   21
  araucana / R / slender / white fls / Andes Mts.   21
  lagascae / R / tufts / white fls; woolly lvs / Andes Mts.   21

NECTAROSCORDUM siculum - see ALLIUM siculum   56

NEMASTYLIS - Iridaceae
  acuta / Bb / 6" / fls bright blue or purple / Texas, Mo., Tenn.   9
  geminiflora / Bb / 1-2' / blue fls / Texas, Tenn., Kansas   73

NEMOPANTHUS - Aquifoliaceae
  mucronata / Sh / to 10' / fls white; frs red / ne N. America   9

NEMOPHILA - Hydrophyllaceae
  maculata / R / trailing / fls white, blotched purple / California   75

NENOTHERA argillicola - see OENOTHERA argillicola   *

NEOMARICA - Iridaceae
  caerulea / Gh / 2-3' / fls blue or lilac / Brazil   32

NEOTTIA - Orchidaceae
  nidus-avis / P / 8-30" / fls brownish-yellow / Europe, Asia   30

NEPETA - Labiatae
  cataria / P / to 3' / fls whitish, purple dotted / Europe   34
  cranica - see N. ucranica   92
  mussinii / R / 12" / blue fls / Caucasus, Iran   (2)
     "   'Six Hills Giant' - see N. 'Six Hills Giant'   44
  nervosa / P / 1-2' / clear blue fls / Kashmir   62
  'Six Hills Giant' - 2-2½', fls violet-blue   85
  ucranica / P / to 20" / fls bluish-violet / Balkans, Russia   92

NERINE - Amaryllidaceae
  bowdenii / HH Bb / 2' / fls in shades of pink / South Africa   42

NERTERA - Rubiaceae
  depressa - see N. granadensis
    "   granadensis - see N. granadensis
  granadensis / R / mat / fls greenish; frs orange / Andes Mts.; N. Z. 38

NICANDRA - Solanaceae
  physaloides / A / 2-3' / blue fls / Peru   42

NICOTIANA - Solanaceae
  glauca / HH Sh / 18' / yellow fls / Argentina, Bolivia   92
  sylvestris / HH P / tall / white fls / Argentina   9

NIEREMBERGIA - Solanaceae
  caerulea 'Purple Robe' - 6", purple fls, pot plant   42

  (1) - WEBB - An Irish Flora. 1963
  (2) - De WOLF in Baileya 3:2

NIGELLA - Ranunculaceae

NIVENIA - Iridaceae

NOMOCHARIS - Liliaceae

NOTHOCALAIS - Compositae

NOTHOCHELONE nemerosa - see PENSTEMON nemerosus   (1)

NOTHOFAGUS - Fagaceae

NOTHOLAENA - Polypodiaceae

NOTHOLIRION - Liliaceae

NOTHOSCORDUM / Liliaceae

NOTOSPARTIUM - Leguminosae

NOTOTHLASPI - Cruciferae

NUPHAR - Nymphaeaceae

NYSSA - Nyssaceae

OAKESIELLA sessilifolia - see UVULARIA sessilifolia   34

ODONTOSPERMUM - Compositae

    (1) - LODEWICK in corres.
    (2) - TRAUB in Plant Life. Vol. X 1954

ODONSTOMUM - Liliaceae
  hartwegii / HH P / 1-3½' / yellowish or white fls / California   75

OENOTHERA - Onagraceae
  acaulis / P or B / stemless / white fls, fading pink / Chile   35
      "   v. aurea - yellow fls   38
      "   lutea - see C. acaulis v. aurea   38
      "   taraxifolia - included in the sp.   32
  albicaulis / A or B / to 1' / white fls aging rose / mid-US & w-ward   9
  argillicola / P / 2-5' / fls bright yellow / e Alleghenies   83
  argophylla - see O. missouriensis v. incana   21
  biennis / B / 3-4' / large yellow fls / Europe   9
  brachycarpa / R / stemless / fls purplish / Montana, Kan., w&s-ward   9
  caespitosa / R / 2-4" / white to pink fls / mid-western US   35
  deltoides / R / 2-10" / fls white, aging pink / Oregon to Nevada   76
  drummondii / A / 1-2' / fls bright yellow / Texas coast   9
  erythrosepala / B / 1-5' / yellow fls; red calyx / w & c Europe   91
  'Fireworks' - see C. tetragona 'Fireworks'   42
  flava / R / tufted / yellow fls / New Mexico, Arizona, Mexico   74
  fraseri - see C. tetragona v. fraseri   32
  fremontii / R / 2-6" / yellow fls / Kansas & Nebraska   76
  fruticosa / P / 1-3' / yellow fls / Nova Scotia, s & w-wards   9
  glabra - an impoverished O. caespitosa   21
  glauca fraseri - see O. tetragona v. fraseri   32
  heterantha / R / tufted / yellow fls / Sierra Nevada Mts.   75
  hookeri / P / 1-4' / pale yellow fls / w United States   75
  kunthiana / R / to 8" / pink fls / Texas, Mexico   82
  longissima / P / 4-10' / pale yellow fls, aging reddish / Cal., Col.   76
  mexicana - see O. kunthiana   82
      "   childsii - see O. kunthiana   82
      "   rosea - see O. kunthiana   82
  missouriensis / R / 6-9" / lemon-yellow fls / sc United States   42
      "   v. incana - bright yellow fls 3' across   (1)
  mutica / R / rosette / white or pink fls / Chile   (2)
  odorata / P / 1½' / yellow fls, aging red / s North America   62
  pallida / P / 4-20" / fls white / Texas, South Dakota, Washington   74
  perennis / R / 6" / small yellow fls / e North America   38
      "   pumila - a synonym of the sp.   34
      "   v. rectipilis - local e Canadian with different hairs   34
  pumila - see O. perennis   38
  riparia - see O. tetragona 'Riparia'   42
  serrulata / B or P / yellow fls / Minnesota, w & s-ward   9
  speciosa / P / 2' / white, pink, lavender fls / Missouri & s-ward   73
      "   childsii - see O. kunthiana   82
  subacaulis - see O. heterantha   77
  taraxifolia - see O. acaulis   38
  tetragona / P / 2' / yellow fls / New York, Illinois, Georgia   34
      "   'Fireworks' - 18", fls yellow, red in bud   42
      "   v. fraseri - glaucous plant of higher elevations   34
      "   'Riparia' - 18", long-flowering, bright yellow fls   42
  triloba / B / rosette / fls pale yellow to roseate / W. Va., Texas   34
      "   flava - superfluous; involved synonymy here   77

OLEARIA - Compositae
  alpina / HH Sh / 3' / white fls; glossy lvs / Tasmania   (3)
  cymbifolia - see O. nummularifolia f. cymbifolia   46

  (1) - COLE in Bull. Am. Rock Garden Soc. 28:2
  (2) - MODIC in Bull. Am. Rock Garden Soc. 19:2
  (3) - TALBOT in Jour. Royal Hort. Soc. May, 1964

OLEARIA, con.

gunniana - see O. phlogopappa	46
haastii / HH Sh / 9' / evergreen, fls white, small / N. Zealand	42
illicifolia / HH Sh / 6-10' / white fls; lvs white-felted / N. Z.	46
insignis - see PACHYSTEGIA insignis	46
" minor - see PACHYSTEGIA 'Minor'	46
lyrata / HH Sh / 9' / evergreen; white fls / Australia, Tasmania	(1)
macrodonta / HH Sh / 15' / white & yellow fls / New Zealand	42
nummularifolia / HH Sh / 6-10' / creamy-white fls / New Zealand	46
" f. cymbifolia - lvs strongly revolute	46
X oleifolia - HH Sh, 6-10', white daisies	46
pannosa / HH Sh / 4' / lvs tomentose beneath / Australia	10
phlogopappa / HH Sh / 6-10' / white daisies / Tasmania, se Australia	46
" v. subrepanda - denser habit	46
" 'White Form' - descriptive of the sp.	*
semidentata / HH Sh / 1-3' / light to violet-purple fls / Chatham Is.	32

OLYMPOSCIADUM - Umbelliferae

caespitosum / R / to 1' / white fls / Turkey	26

OMPHALODES - Boraginaceae

'Anthea Bloom' - see O. cappadocica 'Anthea Bloom'	(2)
cappadocica / R / 6-8" / sky-blue fls / Asia Minor, Turkey	42
" 'Anthea Bloom' - 8", fls intense blue	(2)
linifolia / A / 16" / fls white or bluish / sw Europe	92
" 'Alba' - selection for white fls	*
luciliae / R / 6-8" / pale china-blue fls / Greece, Asia Minor	42

OMPHALOGRAMMA - Primulaceae

minus / R / 4" / fls purple / China	(3)
soulei / R / to 8" / violet-purple fls / w China	32
vinciflorum / R / 6-8" / strong blue-violet fls / w China	42

ONCIDIUM - Orchidaceae

bifolium / Gh P / ? / fls yellow, barred brown / Argentina	9

ONOBRYCHIS - Leguminosae

arenaria / P / 4-32" / pink fls, veined purple / c, e & se Europe	91
montana / P / to 20" / pink fls, usually purple veins / s Eu., in mts	91
saxatilis / R / caespitose / pale yellow fls, pink veins / w Medit.	91
viciifolia / P / 1-2' / fls whitish to purplish / Eurasia, N. Afr.	9

ONONIS - Leguminosae

cenisia - see O. cristata	91
cristata / R / procumbent / fls pink / Alps, Pyrenees	91
fruticosa / Sh / 10-40" / pink fls / Spain, se France	91
minutissima / Sh / to 1' / yellow fls / w Medit. region, Jugoslavia	91
mitissima / A / 1-2' / pink fls / Medit. region, Portugal	91
natrix / Sh / 8-24" / yellow fls / s & w Europe	91
pubescens / A / 1' / yellow fls / Mediterranean region	91
pusilla / R / 10" / yellow fls / s Europe, Czecho-slovakia	91
reclinata / A / procumbent to 6" / fls pink or purple / s & w Eu.	91
rotundifolia / Sh / 14-20" / pink or whitish fls / Spain, Italy	91

(1) - BEAN - Trees & Shrubs Hardy in the British Isles, 7th ed. 1951
(2) - Anon. in Jour. Royal Hort. Soc. Nov. 1965
(3) - Anon. in Jour. Royal Hort. Soc. June 1963

ONOPORDUM - Compositae
  acanthium / B / 3-10' / purplish fls / Europe
  arabicum - see O. nervosum   72
  illyricum / B / 3-9' / fls purple / Morocco, Near East   (1)
  nervosum / B / 9' / rose fls / Spain, Portugal   (1)
                                                                          (1)

ONOSMA - Boraginaceae
  albopilosa / HH Sh / ? / fls white, aging rose / Asia Minor   20
  alborosea / R / 1' / fls white, turning rose / Asia Minor   6
  cinerara - see O. alborosea   6
  decipiens / R / 4" / white fls / Cappadocian alps   33
  echioides / R / to 1' / pale yellow fls / Italy, w Balkans   92
  erecta / R / 6-10" / fls pale yellow / s Greece, Crete   92
  helvetica / P / 8-20" / fls pale yellow / sw Alps   92
  nana - see C. decipiens   92
  sericea / R / 1' / creamy-yellow fls / Caucasus   33
  stellulata / R / 10" / pale yellow fls / w Jugoslavia   35
       "   helvetica - see O. helvetica   92
       "   taurica - see O. taurica   92
  taurica / R / 4-16" / fls pale yellow / se Europe   92
                                                                         92

OPHIOPOGON - Liliaceae
  planiscapus 'Nigrescens' - blackish-leaved Lily-turf, Japan   (2)

OPHRYS - Orchidaceae
  apifera / P / 6-20" / pink & brownish-purple fls / Eurasia, N. Afr.   30
  fusca / R / 9" / purple fls / Mediterranean region   9
  insectifera - see O. muscifera   30
  lutea / R / to 1' / greenish-yellow fls / Eurasia, N. Africa   30
  muscifera / P / to 2' / multi-colored fls / Europe   30
  sphegoides / P / to 2½' / brown to buff fls / w, c & s Europe   30

OPLOPANAX - Araliaceae
  horridus / Sh / 6'+ / greenish-white fls; purple frs / w N. America   46

OPUNTIA - Cactaceae
  compressa / R / prostrate / yellow fls / Atlantic Coast to Okla.   82
  cymochila ≠ horticultural segregate of O. compressa   9
  engelmannii / HH P / 2-5' / fls yellow, fading red / US, Mexico   9
  fragilis / R / prostrate / greenish-yellow fls / Wisc. to Rockies   9
  phaeacantha / HH Sh / 5' / yellow fls / s United States   42
  polyacantha / R / prostrate / yellow fls / wc United States   9
  rafinesquii - see O. compressa   *
  whipplei / HH Sh / 2' / greenish-yellow fls / sw US, Mexico   9

ORCHIS - Orchidaceae
  coriophora / P / 8-16" / brown & wine-purple fls / Medit. region   64
  elodes - see O. ericetorum   30
  ericetorum / P / 8-16" / varii-colored fls; acid soils / Europe   30
  fuchsii / P / 8-16" / varii-colored fls; limy soils / Europe   30
  incarnata / P / 6-24" / varii-colored fls; marshes / Europe   30
  latifolia - may be O. incarnata, O. majalis or O. purpurella   30
  maculata - either O. ericetorum or O. fuchsii, above   30
  mascula / P / 12-22" / violet fls, white patch / Europe, Asia   30
  militaris / P / 8-24" / pink fls, purple spotted / c & w Europe   30
  morio ssp. picta - 6-10", pale red-violet fls - widespread in Eu.   30
  picta - see O. morio ssp. picta   64

(1) - DRESS in Baileya 14:2
(2) - SKINNER in Jour. Royal Hort. Soc. Aug. 1971

ORCHIS, con.
  praetermissa / P / to 30" / lilac to magenta fls / n Europe   30
  provincialis / R / to 1' / yellow fls / Switzerland, s Europe   30
  purpurea / P / 8-16" / varii-colored fls / Medit. region   64
  purpurella / R / 8" / purple or magenta fls / w Europe   30
  romana / R / to 1' / red or yellow fls / Medit. region   30
  simia / P / 8-18" / white & pink fls / c & s Europe, Near East   30
  traunsteineri / P / 8-18" / purple fls / n Europe   30

ORIGANUM - Labiatae
  amanum / HH Sh / 2-4" / deep rose fls / Greece   38
  dictamnus - see AMARACUS dictamnus   32
  majorana / P gr. as A / 1-2' / Sweet Marjoram / Europe   9
  pulchellum - see AMARACUS pulchellus   (1)
  scabrum ssp. pulchrum - HH P, 1½', pink fls, Mt. Evveria, Greece   92

ORNITHOGALUM - Liliaceae
  arabicum / Gh Bb / 2' / white fls / Arabia   36
  arcuatum / Bb / 8-18" / milky white fls / Caucasus   54
  balansae / Bb / 6" / white fls, striped gray-green / Middle East   36
  caudatum / Gh Bb / to 20" / greenish-white fls / n Africa   55
  comosum / Bb / to 6" / greenish-white fls / s Eu., e Medit. region   84
  concinnum / Bb / to 1' / white fls, green banded / c & n Portugal   65
  exscapum / Bb / 6" / green & white fls / s Europe   9
  fimbriatum / Bb / 5" / starry white fls, green banded / A. Minor   36
  flavissimum / Gh Bb / to 1' / orange-yellow fls / S. Africa   70
  montanum / Bb / 18" / green & white fls / se Europe   36
  nanum / Bb / dwarf / green & white fls / Greece, Asia Minor   21,51
  narbonense / Bb / 1½' / green & white fls / Medit. region   84
  nutans / Bb / 1' / soft jade-green fls / s Europe   42
  pyramidale / Bb / 2' / green & white fls / se Europe   36
  pyrenaicum / Bb / 2' / greenish-yellow fls / s Europe   84
       "   v. flavescens - pale yellow fls, Atlas Mts.   55
  reverchonii / Bb / to 16" / pure white fls / s Spain   65
  saundersiae / Gh Bb / 2-3' / white fls / South Africa   9
  schelkovnikovii / Bb / 16-20" / white fls / Caucasus   54
  subcucullatum / Bb / 18" / white fls / sw Europe   36
  tenuifolium / Bb / 3" / green & white fls / Medit. region   9
  thrysoides / Gh Bb / 1½' / white to golden-yellow fls / S. Africa   41
  unifolium concinnum - see O. concinnum   65

OROBANCHE - Orobanchaceae
  elatior / parasitic / 18" / yellow fls / Britain on clover   45
  uniflora / parasitic / 6-24" / white to purple fls / nw US   75

OROBUS - Leguminosae
  aurantiacus - see VICIA crocea   (2)
  aureus - see LATHYRUS aureus   91
  owerinii / R / acaulescent / purple fls / Caucasus   (2)
  vernus albo-roseus - see Lathyrus vernus 'Albo-roseus'   91

ORONTIUM - Araceae
  aquaticum / Aq / 2' / yellow & white fls / e United States   34

OROSTACHYS - Crassulaceae
  spinosa / B / to 12" / fls greenish-yellow / e Russia   90

  (1) - De WOLF in Baileya 2:2
  (2) - SHISHKIN & BOBROV - Flora U.S.S.R. Vol. 13 1972(trans.)

ORTHOCARPUS - Scrophulariaceae
  copelandii / R / 4-14" / rose-purple & white fls / Calif. Ore.   75

ORTHROSANTHUS - Iridaceae
  chimboracensis / HH P / 1½' / dark blue fls / Mexico, Peru   32
  multiflorus / HH P / 1-2' / sky-blue fls / s & w Australia   9

OSMORHIZA - Umbelliferae
  claytonii / P / 1-3' / plant villous-pubescent / Can. to N. Carol.   9
  longistylis / P / 1-3' / nearly glabrous plant / Can. to Virginia   9

OSTRYA - Betulaceae
  virginiana / T / 30' / yellow autumn color / e North America   9

OTANTHUS - Compositae
  maritimus / P / to 16" / yellow fls; white lvs / Medit. region   64

OUILLAJA saponaria - see QUILLAJA saponaria   10

OURISIA - Scrophulariaceae
  alpina / R / neat rosette / carmine-crimson fls / Peru   21
  caespitosa / R / creeper / white fls / New Zealand   85
    "   v. gracilis - smaller and slenderer   85
  coccinea / R / 6-12" / scarlet-red fls / Chilean Andes   32
  elegans - darker fls than O. coccinea, perhaps a var.   21
  fragrans / R / close creeper/ white & blush-pink fls / Argentina   21
  macrocarpa / R / mat / white fls / New Zealand   35
    "   v. calycina - colonial form from creeping rhizomes   78
  macrophylla / R / 8-10" / white fls / New Zealand   38
  microphylla / R / crevice-plant / rosy-lilac fls / Argentina   21
  poeppigii / R / 4-8" / crimson-scarlet fls / S. America   21
  pygmaea / R / ? / single rose fls / Andes Range   21
  racemosa - allied to O. poeppigii   21

OXALIS - Oxalidaceae
  acetosella f. rosea - see O. montana f. rhodantha   34
  adenophylla / R / 4" / lilac-pink fls / Chile   42
  comberi / HH R / creeping / yellow fls, veined red / Argentina   21
  corniculata / R / prostrate / fls yellow / Europe   9
    "   v. atropurpurea - lvs red-purple   9
    "   purpurea - see O. c. var. atropurpurea   9
  depressa / HH Tu / 4" / fls bright rosy-pink / South Africa   36
  enneaphylla 'Rosea' - R, 3", rose fls, Falkland Isls., Patagonia   6
  griffithii / R / 6"+ / white or pale rose-purple fls / Far East   60
  hirta / HH Tu / weak-stemmed / deep rose to lavender fls / S. Africa 36
  magellanica / R / carpeter / white fls, bronzy lvs / Magellan Str.   17
  montana f. rhodantha - creeping American woodland plant; rose fls   34
  obtusa / Gh Tu / ? / orange-red fls / Cape of Good Hope   70
  oregona / R / 2-6" / white or pink fls / California, Oregon   75
  simsii / Gh Tu / 1' / deep red fls / Chile   9
  valdivensis / Gh Tu / 6-10" / yellow fls, red veins / Chile   9

OXYDENDRON - Ericaceae
  arboreum / T / 20' / white fls / se United States   42

OXYPETALUM - Asclepiadaceae
  caeruleum / P / 1-3' / pale blue fls / Argentina   9

OXYRIA - Polygonaceae
  digyna / R / to 1' / pink winged frs / northern hemisphere   35

OXYTROPIS   - Leguminosae
  campestris / R / to 8" / purple fls / se Russia, n Asia   91
      "   ssp. sordida - fls varying to light violet, Finland 63
  deflexa / R / to 1' / fls pale purple / B. C. to Utah   9
  lambertii / R / 4-6" / creamy fls, varii-tinged / wc N. America 68
  megalantha / R / 8" / fls bluish-purple / Hokkaido   60
  montana / R / 10" / fls blue to red-violet / Europe   32
  nigrescens / R / mats / purple or white fls / n Arctic regions 63
  owerinii - see OROBUS owerinii   (1)
  pilosa / P / to 20" / light yellow fls / c & e Europe   91
  pyrenaica / R / to 8" / fls purplish or bluish-violet / s & sc Eu. 91
  uralensis / R / to 1' / blue to purple fls / Ural Mts.   91
  yezoensis / R / dwarf / purple fls; white-woolly lvs / Hokkaido 60

OZOTHAMNUS - Compositae
  thyrsoides / HH Sh / 6' / white fls / Australia, Tasmania   46

PACHYLAENA - Compositae
  atriplicifolia / R / rosetted / carmine-pink daisies / Andes Mts. 21

PACHYSTEGIA - Compositae
  insignis / HH Sh / 9' / white & yellow fls; evergreen lvs / N. Z. 46
    "   'Minor' - rock-garden sized plant   46

PAEDEROTA - Scrophulariaceae
  bonarota / R / to 8" / fls violet-blue / e Alps   92

PAEONIA - Ranunculaceae
  anomala / P / 2-3' / red fls / ne Russia, n Asia   90
  broteri / HH P / 14" / fls carmine or purplish / sw Spain, Portugal 64
  brownii / P / 12-15" / fls deep red & yellow / w North America 35
  cambessedesii / P / 1½' / rose-pink fls / Balearic Isls.   42
  caucasica - see P. mascula   90
  'Chameleon' - yellow to red crepy fls, near P. mlokosewitschii (2)
  coriacea / HH P / 20" / rose-pink fls; leathery lvs / s Spain 64
  daurica / P / 3' / red fls / se Europe   90
  delavayi / Sh / 3' / dark purple or crimson fls / China   9
    "   angustifolia - see P. d. var. angustiloba   *
    "   v. angustiloba - lvs more finely divided   69
  emodi / P / ? / white fls / Kashmir   (3)
  humilis - see P. officinalis ssp. humilis   90
  japonica / P / 16-20" / white fls / Japan, China, Manchuria 60
  lactiflora / P / 20-32" / white to rose-purple fls / Asia   60
  lutea / Sh / 2' / yellow fls / China   9
    " v. ludlowii - larger fls   42
  mascula / P / to 3' / red fls / s Europe   90
    "   ssp. arietina - lvs pubescent beneath, e Europe   90
    "   ssp. russii - with ovate leaflets, islands of w Mediterranean 90
  mlokosewitschii / P / 2' / citron-yellow fls / Caucasus   42
  obovata / P / 16-20" / pale rose fls / Far East   60
    "   'Alba' - white fls   9
    "   v. willmottiae - white fls, lvs densely hairy beneath 32
  officinalis / P / 1½-2' / solitary red fls / France to Albania 42
    "   'Anemonaeflora Rubra' - crimson fls, enlarged stamens 85
    "   ssp. humilis - segmented leaflets, glabrous pods 90
    "   'Lobata' - lvs distinctly lobed   9
  peregrina / P / 2' / fls red / Italy, Roumania, Balkans   26

(1) - SHISHKIN & BOBROV in Flora USSR. Vol. 13 1972(trans.)
(2) - WORTH in corres.
(3) - RAU - Illustrations of West Himalayan Flowering Plants. 1963

PAEONIA, con.
```
  potaninii 'Alba' - 1½", white fls, China                              (1)
  russii - see P. mascula ssp. russii                                    90
  suffruticosa / Sh / 3-4½' / fls in showy colors / nw China, Tibet      60
  tenuifolia / P / 1-1½' / dark crimson fls / se Europe                  90
  veitchii / P / 2' / purplish-crimson fls / w China                      9
     "     v. woodwardii - a dwarfer form                                32
  wittmanniana / P / 2-3' / solitary white or yellowish fls / Caucasia   9
  woodwardii - see P. veitchii v. woodwardii                            32
```

PANAX - Aralaiceae
```
  quinquefolius / P / 12-18" / white fls; red frs / e United States      35
  trifolius / R / to 9" / white fls; frs yellowish / e N. America        34
```

PANCRATIUM - Amaryllidaceae
```
  illyricum / Bb / 1½' / fls white / Mediterranean region                42
  maritimum / Bb / 1' / white fls / Medit. region, coastal               84
```

PANDOREA - Bignoniaceae
```
  pandorana / HH Cl / twining / yellow or pinkish-white fls / Australia  41
```

PAPAVER - Papaveraceae
```
  alaskanum - see P. radicatum                                        21,63
  alboroseum / R / to 8" / white or rose fls / Kamchatka                 63
  alpinum / A or B / 4-8" / varii-colored fls / e Alps, Carpathians      42
     "    'Album' - white fls                                            9
     "    burseri - see P. burseri                                      90
  apokrinomenon / R / 15" / reddish-orange fls / w Turkey            (2),33
  arenarium / A / 8-10" / bright red fls / Caucasus, n Iran             (3)
  atlanticum / P / 1-2' / dull orange fls / Morocco                     90
  bracteatum / P / to 3' / purplish-crimson fls / Iran, Caucasus        26
  burseri / R / 8" / white fls / n Alps, Carpathians                    90
  cambricum - see MECONOPSIS cambrica                                    *
  caucasicum - see P. fugax                                            (2)
  commutatum / A / 2' / red fls, spotted black / Crete, Asia Minor      90
     "       'Ladybird' - A, 18", brilliant scarlet fls marked black   (4)
  corona-sancti-stephani / R / 5" / yellow fls / e & s Carpathians      90
  dubium / A / to 2' / red fls; weedy / Europe                          90
  fauriei / R / 4-8" / greenish-yellow fls / Hokkaido                   60
  fugax / B / 1-2' / vermilion fls / Caucasus                          (2)
  heldreichii - see P. apokrinomenon                                   (2)
  kerneri / R / 8" / yellow fls / se Alps, c Jugoslavia                 90
  lapponicum / R / 6-8" / yellow fls / arctic Norway & Russia           90
  macounii / R / 1'+ / yellow fls / arctic North America & Eurasia      63
  monanthum / R / stemless / orange to pink fls to 1'+ / Caucasus, alps(3)
  myabeanum / R / 8" / lemon-yellow fls / Japan                          6
     "      fauriei - see P. fauriei                                    60
     "      'Takewoki' - miniature with silvery lvs                     (5)
  nudicaule / B / 1' / white or yellow fls / arctic regions              9
     "      ssp. album - white fls                                     (2)
     "      croceum - see P. n. ssp. xanthopetalum                     (2)
     "      radicatum - see P. radicatum                               90
     "      ssp. rubro-aurantiacum - reddish or orange fls             (2)
     "      ssp. xanthopetalum - yellow fls                            (2)
```

```
  (1) - STERN - A Chalk Garden.  1960
  (2) - CULLEN in Baileya  16:3
  (3) - POPOV - Flora U. S. S. R.  Vol. 7  1970(trans.)
  (4) - BURPEE - Catalog. 1974
   (5) - HAYWARD in Bull. Am. Rock Garden Soc.  26:3
```

PAPAVER, con.
  orientale / P / 2-3' / scarlet fls / Armenia   42
      "   'Mrs. Perry' - single pink fls   (1)
  pilosum / P / 2'+ / orange-red fls / Bithynia, Galatia   26
  'Pink Chiffon' - see P. somniferum 'Pink Chiffon'   *
  pyrenaicum - see P. rhaeticum   90
      "   rhaeticum - see P. rhaeticum   90
      "   sendtneri - see P. sendtneri   90
  radicatum / R / to 1' / fls yellow, pink, white / nw Europe   90
  rhaeticum / R / to 8" / golden-yellow fls / s, w & e Alps   90
  rhoeas / A / 1½-2' / scarlet fls / north temperate zone   42
  rupifragum / HH P / to 20" / brick-red fls / s Spain   90
      "   atlanticum - see P. atlanticum   90
  sendtneri / R / 6" / white fls / c & e Alps   90
  sanctae-coronis - see P. corona-sancti-stephani   *
  somniferum / A / 3'+ / white to purple fls / w & c Medit. region   90
      "   'Pink Chiffon' - double pink fls   *
  <u>NOTE</u> - cultivation of P. somniferum forbidden by law in the US
  splendissimum - synonym of P. orientale   (2)
  strictum / R / ? / orange fls; deeply divided lvs / w Turkey   (2)
  syriacum / A / to 1' / deep crimson fls / Cilicia, Syria   26
  tianschanicum / R / tufted / orange fls / c Asia, in alpine meadows (3)

PARADISEA - Liliaceae
  liliastrum / P / 1½-2' / pure white fls / Alps, Pyrenees   84
      "   'Major' - to 3', larger fls   9

PARAHEBE - Scrophulariaceae
  X bidwillii - see P. decora   46
  catarractae / HH Sh / dwarf / white to rose-purple fls / Australasia 46
      "   'Diffusa' - densely matting, fls white, veined rose-pink 46
      "   'Rosea' - selection for pink fls   *
  decora / HH Sh / low / fls white or pink / New Zealand   46
  hookeriana / HH Sh / dwarf / white fls, pink veins / New Zealand   (4)
  lyallii / HH Sh / prostrate / white fls, veined pink / New Zealand   46
  perfoliata / HH Sh / 1-1½' / fls violet-blue / Australia   46
  spathulata / HH Sh / dwarf / white fls; gray lvs / Ruapehu, N. Z.   (4)

PARIS - Liliaceae
  japonica / P / 12-32" / white fls / Honshu, in high mts.   60

PARNASSIA - Parnassiaceae
  alpestris - see P. palustris ssp. alpestris   33
  asarifolia / R / 10-16" / white fls / Virginia & N. Carolina   72
  fimbriata / R / 6" / white fls / nw North America   38
  glauca / R / 3-12" / white fls / New Brunswick to Virginia   35
  grandifolia / R / 1' / white fls / Florida, Texas, Missouri   34
  kotzebuei / R / to 10" / white fls / n N. America, ne Asia   34
  palustris / R / 4-20" / white fls / n Asia & Europe   60
      "   ssp. alpestris - taller, larger fls, Alps   33

PAROCHETUS - Leguminosae
  communis / HH R / 1-2" / vivid blue fls / Himalayas   38

(1) - BLOOM - Perennials in Your Garden. 1971
(2) - CULLEN in Baileya 16:3
(3) - POPOV - Flora USSR. Vol. 7 1970(trans.)
(4) - ADAMS - Mountain Flowers of New Zealand. 1965

PARONYCHIA - Caryophyllaceae
  argentea / R / mats / fls concealed by silvery bracts / s Europe   90
  canadensis / A / to 1' / minute lvs; green fls / n & c US   35
  capitata / R / 6" / conspicuous bracts / s Europe   90
  cephalotes / R / 6" / silvery bracts / e, c & se Europe   90
  kapela / R / to 6" / silvery bracts / s Europe to Austria   90
    " ssp. serpyllifolia - stems procumbent, Alps   90
  serpyllifolia - see P. kapela ssp. serpyllifolia   90

PARROTIA - Hamamelidaceae
  persica / Sh or T / to 30' / crimson stamens / Iran, Caucasus   46

PARRYA menziesii - see PHOENICAULIS cheiranthoides   32

PARSONSIA - Apocynaceae
  capsularis / HH Cl / high / white to yellow to dark red fls / N. Z.   2

PARTHENOCISSUS - Vitaceae
  incerta / Cl / trailer / lvs lustrous / North America   34
  tricuspidata / Cl / high / bloomy dark blue frs / Far East   46
  vitacea - see P. incerta   34

PASSIFLORA - Passifloraceae
  cinnabarina / Gh Cl / high / fls reddish-brown / Australia   16

PATERSONIA - Iridaceae
  longiscapa / Gh / 6-20" / fls blue / Australia   45
  occidentalis / Gh / 1' / fls yellow / w Australia   16
  umbrosa / Gh / 2' / blue fls / w Australia   37

PATRINIA - Valerianaceae
  heterophylla / R / 1' / yellow fls / China   45
  palmata - see P. triloba v. palmata   60
  triloba / P / to 2' / yellow short-spurred fls / Honshu   60
    " v. palmata - long-spurred yellow fls, Japan   60

PAULOWNIA - Scrophulariaceae
  tomentosa / T / 50' / pale lilac-mauve fls / China   42

PEDICULARIS - Scrophulariaceae
  apodochila / R / to 6" / red fls / alps of Japan   60
    "   v. japonica - included in the sp.   *
  attollens / P / 6-16" / purple or lavender fls / Oregon   75
  bracteosa / P / 1-4' / yellow to red fls / California to B. C.   75
  canadensis / R / 1'+ / yellow fls / e North America   34
  carpatica - see P. hacquetii   92
  chamissonis v. japonica - 8-24", reddish fls, n Japan   60
  densiflora / P / 4-20" / bright red to purplish fls / Calif. to Ore.   75
  elegans / R / decumbent / fls pinkish-red / c & s Apennines   92
  foliosa / P / 8-20" / fls pale yellow / s & sc Europe, in mts.   92
  groenlandica / P / 1-2' / fls rose to red / n North America   35
  hacquetii / P / 1-4' / fls pale yellow / Alps, Carpathians   92
  oederi / R / to 6" / yellowish fls / northern hemisphere   60
  palustris / P / 4-32" / rose-purple fls / arctic Europe   63
  recutita / P / to 2' / greenish-yellow fls, tinged crimson / Alps   92
  rostratocapitata / R / to 8" / pink to purplish-red fls / e Alps   92
  rostratospicata / P / 6-18" / fls pink to purplish-red / Alps   92
  sylvatica / R / to 10" / pink or red fls / w & c Eu. to c Sweden   92
  verticillata / R / to 6" / red fls / northern hemisphere   60

PEDIOCACTUS - Cactaceae
  simpsonii / R / 4" / fls yellow-green to purple / Col., Wyo.   9

PELLAEA - Polypodiaceae
  atropurpurea / F / 15" / gray to blue-green fronds / North America   50
  calomelanos - see PITYROGRAMMA calomelanos   (1)
  glabella / F / 9" / smaller plant / Que. to Va. & Colorado   34
  rotundifolia / Gh F / 12" arching fronds / round leaflets / N. Z.   41

PELTIPHYLLUM - Saxifragaceae
  peltatum / P / 2-3' / white to pale pink fls / California   42

PELTOBOYKINIA - Saxifragaceae
  tellimoides   / 1-2' / creamy white fls / Honshu   60

PENNISETUM - Gramineae
  alopecurioides / P Gr / 12-32" / purple or green fls / Far East   60
  japonicum - see P. alopecurioides   60

PENSTEMON - Scrophulariaceae
  acuminatus / P / to 2' / lilac to violet fls / Neb., Minn. s&e-ward   9
  adamsianus - see P. fruticosus   14
  albertinus / R / 6-8" / fls light blue / nw United States   35
  alpinus / R / to 15" / dark blue to purple fls / Wyo., Col.   15
  ambiguus / P / 8-20" / fls whitish to bright pink   / Kan., Col.   76
  angustifolius / P / 8-20" / blue to pinkish-lav. fls / N. Dakota & s 74
      "   'Pygmeus' - of the 8" range?   *
  antirrhinoides ssp. microphyllus - from edge of Col. & Mohave deserts 59
  arizonicus - see P. virgatus ssp. arizonicus   14
  attenuatus / P / 1-2' / blue-purple or yellow fls / Wash., Mont.   76
  azureus / P / to 3' / blue-violet fls / California   9
  barbatus / HH P / 2½-3½' / coral-red fls / Mexico   42
      "   'Nanus' - 15", listed as 'Praecox Nanus'   89
      "   'Rose Elf' - 18", clear shell-pink fls   62
  barrettiae / Sh / 1' / lilac-purple fls / Columbia River Gorge   35
  brachyanthus - see P. procerus ssp. brachyanthus   47
      "   f. albus - see P. procerus ssp. b. 'Albus'   *
  'Blue of Zurich' - see P. heterophyllus 'Blue of Zurich'   (2)
  brevisepalus / P / 1-3' / purple or violet fls / Va. to Tenn.   34
  bridgesii / Sh / 1' / red fls / Colorado, N. Mexico, Arizona   74
  californicus / HH R / 6" / blue or purplish fls / s & S. California   74
  calycosus / P / to 3' / fls white or purplish / c United States   34
  campanulatus / P / to 2' / fls purple, rose, blue / Mexico   9
      "   pulchellus - included in the sp.   14
  canescens / P / 1-3' / purple or violet fls / Pa. to Alabama   34
  cardinalis / P / 16-28" / fls dull red or crimson / New Mexico   9
  cardwellii / Sh / 10" / purplish fls / Oregon, Washington   35
      "   v. albus - white form   (3)
      "   'John Bacher' - strong white form   (4)
  cinicola / P / 2' / purplish fls / n California, se Oregon   75
  comarrhenus / P / 12-24" / pale blue fls / Col., Utah, Arizona   15
  confertus / R / 6-20" / cream to yellow fls / Rocky Mts.   38
      "   'Kittitas' - mats of olive green lvs; sulphury fls   (4)
  cordifolius / HH Sh / to 2' / red fls / California   95

(1) - PROCTOR - A Preliminary Checklist of Jamaican Pteridophytes. 1953
(2) - BENNET in Bull. Am. Penstemon Soc. Vol. 30 1971
(3) - MANTON in Bull. Am. Rock Garden Soc. 20:1
(4) - DAVIDSON in Bull. Am. Rock Garden Soc. 27:4

PENSTEMON, con.
  crandallii ssp. glabrescens - 6-8", bluish fls, New Mexico   (1)
  crantzii - presumably strayed from POTENTILLA   *
  cristatus - see P. eriantherus   14
  cyananthus / P / 12-32" / deep blue fls / e Idaho, Wyo., Utah   76
  dasyphyllus / P / ? / violet-blue fls / New Mexico   74
  davidsonii / R / 6-9" / ruby-red fls / California   38
  "   ssp. menziesii - finely toothed lvs, Wash. & Oregon   (2)
  " " " f. albus 'Martha Raye' - wide-mouthed cv.   (3)
  " " " 'Microphyllus' - 4" miniature   38
  deustus / HH Sh / 8-24" / yellowish-white fls / California   75
  diffusus - see P. serrulatus   14
  " 'Albus' - see P. serrulatus 'Albus'   *
  digitalis / P / to 4½' / fls white or whitish / e North America   34
  " albus - included in the sp.   *
  X edithae - is P. rupicola X P barrettiae   (3)
  eriantherus / P / to 16" / purple fls / Dakotas n & w-ward   35
  'Evelyn' - P. campanulatus cultivar   (3)
  'Flathead Lake' - see P. X johnsoniae   (3)
  frutescens / R / 4-8" / pale purple fls / Far East   60
  fruticosus / Sh / variable / purple fls / nw United States   35
  " cardwellii - see P. cardwellii   *
  " v. crassifolius - included in the sp.   (3)
  " ssp. scouleri - violet-purple fls, Wyoming to Oregon   9
  " " " 'Albus' - good white form   38
  " " " 'Six Hills' - 6-9", purplish-pink fls   38
  " ssp. serratus - best alpine form, wide color range   (3)
  gairdneri / R / bushlet / orchid to rose fls / inland Oregon   (2)
  'Garnet' - 1½-2', deep red fls : P. hartwegii X P. cobaea   85
  glaber / P / 2' / blue to purple fls / Missouri River & w-ward   35
  glabrescens - see P. crandallii ssp. glabrescens   14
  globosus / R / 10-16" / bright blue fls / c Idaho, Wallowa Mts., Ore. 75
  gormanii / R / 10" / fls purple / Alaska   10
  gracilis / P / to 20" / fls pale violet / c North America   71
  grandiflorus / P / 2'+ / fls lilac or blue / Illinois & w-ward   9
  hallii / R / 6-8" / violet fls / Colorado, in mts.   35
  heterophyllus / R / to 1' / blue fls, pink tinged / California   38
  " 'Blue of Zurich' - gentian-blue fls   (3)
  " ssp. purdyi - useful as annual bedder   (4)
  " 'True Blue' - azure-blue fls   38
  hirsutus / P / 2' / purple to flesh-colored fls / e North America   9
  " albus - see P. h. forma albiflorus   14
  " f. albiflorus - white fls   14
  " 'Minimus' - 4-6", like 'Pygmaeus' except stems stiffly erect (5)
  " 'Pygmaeus' - 4", pale violet or purple fls, 50% from seed   (3)
  'Holly' - cv. P. fruticosus ssp. serratus, 8-10", fls lilac-blue   (3)
  humilis / R / to 1' / blue or bluish-purple fls / Calif., Col.   75
  " ssp. brevifolius - 4", azure-blue fls   (6)
  X johnsoniae - P, 16-40", fls in shades of red   14
  'Kobolt' - P, 24-28", coral-red selection of P. barbatus, presumably *
  labrosus / HH P / 12-28" / scarlet fls / s & S. California   74
  laetus / P / 8-32" / blue-lavender & darker fls / Calif., Oregon   75

(1) - BENNETT - Bull. Am. Rock Garden Soc. 21:2
(2) - DAVIDSON in Bull. Am. Rock Garden Soc. 27:4
(3) - BENNETT in Bull. Am. Penstemon Soc. Vol. 30 1971
(4) - BENNETT in Manual for Beginners with Penstemons. 1957
(5) - BENNETT in Bull. Am. Penstemon Soc. Vol. 31 1972
(6) - WORTH in Bull. Am. Rock Garden Soc. 19:1

PENSTEMON, con.
```
  laevigatus / P / 16-40" / fls white & violet / N. J. to Florida      72
     "      digitalis - see P. digitalis                               *
  menziesii - see P. davidsonii ssp. menziesii                        14
     "      davidsonii - see P. davidsonii                             *
     "      'Microphyllus' - see P. d. ssp. menziesii 'Microphyllus'   38
  microphyllus - see P. antirrhinoides ssp. microphyllus              14
  newberryi / R / 9-12" / rosy-purple fls / California                 38
     "      'Albus' - white fls                                        *
     "      f. humilior - 6-9", fls cherry-red                         38
     "      v. rupicola - see P. rupicola                              14
  nemerosus / P / 12-32" / pink-purple fls / California to B. C.       75
  nitidus / R / to 1' / clear blue fls / Sask. to Mexico              35
  ovatus / P / 12-40" / blue fls, glandular hairy lvs / Oregon, B. C.  75
  parryi / P / to 4' / rose-magenta fls / Arizona, Mexico             74
  parvus / R / 2-4" / blue fls / sc Utah, in mts.                     15
  payettensis / P / 6-24" / deep to purplish-blue fls / Ore., c Idaho  15
  peckii / R / ? / pink or bluish fls / s Oregon                      (1)
  pennellianus / P / 18-20" / fls deep blue / Washington, Oregon       15
  pinifolius / R / to 1' / scarlet fls / Arizona, New Mexico          35
  procerus / R / to 1' / purplish-blue fls / Colorado, w- &n-ward     35
     "      ssp. brachyanthus - flowers larger                         47
     "      ssp. tolmiei - alpine form, lighter-colored fls            14
  pruinosis / R / 4-16" / deep blue to lavender fls / c Wash., B. C.  (2)
  pseudospectabilis / HH P / 3'+ / rose-purple fls / s California      74
  pubescens - see P. hirsutus                                         14
  richardsonii / P / 8-32" / lavender fls / Columbia River & e-ward    75
  roezlii - see P. newberryi f. humilior                              38
  'Royal Beauty' - 2', wine-purple fls                                (3)
  rupicola / Sh / 4" / rose-crimson fls / Oregon, California          35
     "      'Alba' - white fls                                         *
  scouleri - see P. fruticosus ssp. scouleri                          14
     "      'Alba' - see P. fruticosus ssp. scouleri 'Albus'           38
  'Seeba Hybrid' - P. grandiflorus X murrayanus, varii-col. fls       (4)
  serrulatus / P / 8-28" / deep blue to dark purple fls / Ore., B. C.  75
  'Six Hills' - see P. fruticosus ssp. scouleri 'Six Hills'           17
  smallii / P / 16-30" / purplish or crimson fls / N. & S. Carolina    72
  speciosus / P / 8-32" / fls in varying blue shades / Wash., Cal.     15
     "      ssp. kennedyi - 2-16", e California, Nevada                15
  strictus / P / 15-48" / deep violet-blue fls / Col., New Mexico      15
  tenuiflorus / P / to 2' / white fls / Alabama, Tennessee, N. Mexico  34
  tenuifolius / HH Sh / to 15" / lavender & pale purplish blue / Mex. (2)
  tenuis / P / 18-24" / violet-purple fls / marshes, Ark., La., se Tex.73
  thurberi / HH Sh / to 30" / blue or bluish-rose fls / California     74
  tolmiei - see P. procerus ssp. tolmiei                              14
     "      brachyanthus - see P. procerus ssp. brachyanthus           47
  uintahensis / R / 4-16", usually low / lav., blue, purple fls / Utah 15
  unilateralis / P / 18-24" / reddish-purple fls / Wyo., Colorado      15
  utahensis / P / 1-2' / fls crimson-red to carmine / Nevada, Utah     76
  venustus / P / to 2' / light purple fls / Idaho, Oregon, Wsh.         9
  virens / R / 4-14" / blue-violet or blue fls / se Wyo., Colorado     76
  virgatus ssp. arizonicus - 18", pale violet fls, se Arizona          15
  watsonii / P / 12-28" / blue or blue-purple fls / Ida., Nev., Col.   76
  wilcoxii / P / tall / bright blue fls / Montana, Idaho              (5)
  wrightii / P / to 2' / fls bright red / w Texas, Arizona             9
```

(1) - DAVIDSON in Bull. Am. Rock Garden Soc. 27:4
(2) - LODEWICK - Penstemon Field Identifier. 1970
(3) - LAMB - Nursery Catalog. nd.
(4) - BENNETT in Bull. Am. Penstemon Soc. Vol. 30 1971
(5) - ROSE in Bull. Am. Rock Garden Soc. 1:5

PENTACHRONDA - Epacridaceae
  pumila / Sh / procumbent / white fls; red frs / New Zealand   38

PEREZIA - Compositae
  linearis / R / to 1' / pure, brilliant blue fls / South America 21
  multiflora / A / erect / reddish pappus / Brazil 32
  pilifera / R / ? / creamy or blue fls / South America 21
  recurvata / R / 2-3" / deep blue fls / Fuego, Falkland Isls. 38

PERILLA - Labiatae
  frutescens / A / to 4' / white or reddish fls / Far East 9
  fruticans - error for P. frutescens *

PERNETTYA - Ericaceae
  furens / HH Sh / 3' / white fls / Chile 45
  macrostigma / HH Sh / to 10" / white to red fleshy frs / N. Zealand 78
  mucronata / HH Sh / 3'+ / white fls / Chile 92
  nana / HH Sh / 4" / white fls; red frs / New Zealand 35
  tasmanica / HH Sh / prostrate / red frs / Tasmania 43
    "   'Fructo-alba' - white-fruited cv. *

PETALOSTEMON - Leguminosae
  foliosum / P / 1-3' / rose or purplish fls / Tenn., Illinois 72
  gattingeri / P / 8-20" / rose or purplish fls / Tenn., Alabama 72
  purpureum / P / 1-3' / roseate to crimson fls / c North America 34
  searlesiae / R / 10" / rose-pink fls / e Arizona, Utah, Calif. 74

PETROCALLIS - Cruciferae
  pyrenaica / R / 2"+ / fls pale lilac or pink / Pyrenees, Alps 90

PETROCOPTIS - Caryophyllaceae
  glaucifolia / R / 3" / fls purplish / n Spain, in mts. 90
  lagascae - see P. glaucifolia 90
  pyrenaica / R / 3" / fls white or pale purple / w Pyrenees 90
    "   'Alba' - the white form *
    "   'Grandiflora' - larger-flowered selection *

PETROPHYTUM - Rosaceae
  caespitosum / Sh / mat / white fls; blue-gray lvs / w United States 35
  hendersonii / Sh / 6" / fls pale greenish-yellow / Olympic Mts. 85

PETRORHAGIA - Caryophyllaceae
  nanteulii / A / to 20" / pink or purplish fls / w Europe 90
  prolifera / A / 20" / fls pink or purplish / c Europe 90
  saxifraga / P / to 1½' / white or pink fls / c & s Europe 90

PETTERIA - Leguminosae
  ramentacea / Sh / to 7' / yellow fls / Albania, Jugoslavia 46

PEUCADENUM graveolens - see ANETHUM graveolens (1)

PEUMUS - Monimiaceae
  boldus / HH T / to 20' / white fls; edible frs / Chile 9

PHACELIA - Hydrophyllaceae
  bipinnatifida / B / 1-2' / fls violet or blue / N. Carolina to Mo. 9
  dubia / A / to 20" / fls white to lilac / N. Y., Ohio, Tenn., Ga. 34
  franklinii / A / 6-18" / blue or bluish-white fls / c Canada 19

(1) - RYDBERG - Flora of the Prairies and Plains... 1932

PHACELIA, con.
```
  hastata leucophylla - see P. leucophylla                              (1)
  heterophylla / P / 8-48" / white or cream fls / Cascades to Rockies   76
  leucophylla / P / ? / fls pink or lilac; lvs whitish / Colorado       (1)
  magellanica / ? / ? / pinkish fls / Peru                              21
  purshii / A or B / 6-22" / bluish to white fls / c United States      34
  sericea / R / 6" / blue-purple fls / w North America                  38
```

PHALARIS - Gramineae
```
  arundinacea 'Picta' - P Gr, 2-4', white-striped lvs, n hemisphere     42
  caerulescens / P Gr / 1-5' / purplish or green panicles / Medit. reg. 85
```

PHARBITIS purpurea - see IPOMOEA purpurea   (2)

PHASEOLUS - Leguminosae
```
  caracalla / HH Cl / 20' / fls light yellow to purplish / tropics       9
```

PHELLODENDRON - Rutaceae
```
  amurense / T / 50' / pinnate lvs; corky bark / Far East               46
```

PHILADELPHUS - Philadelphaceae
```
  californicus / HH Sh / 9' / fls white / California                    69
  delavayi / Sh / to 15' / fragrant white fls / Yunnan                  69
  lewisii / Sh / 6'+ / fls white / Montana, Washington, Oregon          69
      "    californicus - see P. californicus                           69
  'Virginal' - to 10', double white fls                                 69
```

PHILESIA - Liliaceae
```
  buxifolia / Gh Sh / 2' / pink or red waxy fls / Chile                 41
  magellanica - see P. buxifolia                                        32
```

PHYLLYREA - Oleaceae
```
  latifolia / HH T / 30'+ / white fls / Mediterranean region            92
  media - see P. latifolia                                              92
```

PHLEUM - Gramineae
```
  phleoides / P Gr / 4-24" / green or purplish panicles / Eurasia       85
```

PHLOMIS - Labiatae
```
  fruticosa / Sh / 3-4' / fls deep yellow / s Europe                    42
  italica / HH Sh / 1-2' / purple fls / Balearic Isls., Italy           92
  samia / P / 3'+ / purple fls / Greece                                 92
  tuberosa / P / 5' / purple or pink fls / c & sc Europe                92
  viscosa / Sh / 3' / fls yellow / Asia Minor                            9
```

PHLOX - Polemoniaceae
```
  adsurgens / R / 6-8" / pale shell-pink fls / nw North America         42
  alyssifolia / R / to 4" / fls purple to pink / e Rockies, High Pl.    94
  amoena / R / 6-10" / pink to purple fls / se United States            42
  andicola ssp. parvula - 3", fls pale lavender to white, Gt. Plains    94
  bifida / R / 6-8" / white to pale violet-purple fls / c US            42
  buckleyi / P / 6-20" / purple or pink fls / Virginia, West Va.        83
  'Chatahoochee' - see P. divaricata ssp. laphamii 'Chatahoochee'       94
  diffusa / R / clump / pink to white fls / Sierras, w United States    35
  divaricata / R / 9-15" / fls lavender-blue / e North America          42
      "      ssp. laphamii - with petal blades entire, c US             94
      "       "      "    'Chatahoochee' - deep violet fls, n Florida   94
```

(1) - McDOUGALL & BAGGLEY - The Plants of Yellowstone Park. 1956
(2) - GOULD - Texas Plants... 1962

PHLOX, con.
  douglasii diffusa - see P. diffusa 94
  drummondii / A / 4-20" / reddish-purple fls / Texas 94
  glaberrima ssp. triflora - 2'+, light purple to white fls, se US 94
  hirsuta / HH R / to 8" / fls purple to pink / California 94
  ozarkiana - see P. pilosa v. ozarkana 82
  pilosa / P / 8-18" / purple, red, pink, white fls / c N. America 82
     " v. fulgida - fls with hoary pubescence 82
     " v. ozarkana - with gland-tipped pubescence 82
  speciosa / Sh / 8-20" / purple to white fls / Rocky Mts. 94
  stolonifera / R / 6-8" / pink shades to white fls / Pa. & s-ward 35
     "   'Ariane' - white fls .... (1)
     "   'Blue Ridge' - 6-7", fragrant blue fls .... (2)
  triovulata / R / 4-16" / fls lilac, pink, white / New Mexico & s 94

PHOENOCAULIS - Cruciferae
  cheiranthoides / R / 2-8" / fls pink to reddish-purple / Wash., Ida. 47

PHOENIX - Palmaceae
  canariensis / Gh T / 50'+ / graceful palm / Canary Isls. 9

PHORMIUM - Liliaceae
  colensoi / HH P / 5' / yellow fls / New Zealand 58
     "   'Tricolor' - 3-colored leaf .... *
  cookianum - see P. colensoi 32
  tenax / HH P / to 10' / dull red fls / New Zealand 42
     " 'Variegatum' - red & white leaf striping 32

PHOTINIA - Rosaceae
  villosa / Sh / to 15' / fls white; scarlet frs / Japan, China 9

PHUOPSIS - Rubiaceae
  stylosa / R / 6-8" / tiny pink fls / Caucasus 38

PHYGELIUS - Scrophulariaceae
  aequalis / HH Sh / to 3' / salmon-pink fls / South Africa 46
  capensis / HH Sh / 2-3' / fls purple-scarlet / Cape of Good Hope 9
     "   'Coccineus' - fls crimson-scarlet 46

PHYLLITIS - Polypodiaceae
  americana - see P. scolopendrium v. americana 34
  cristata - see P. scolopendrium f. cristatum 50
  scolopendrium / F / to 2' / simple-leaved fern / s, w & c Europe 90
     "   v. americana - rare North American variety 34
     "   f. cristatum - crimped leaf form 50

PHYLLOCLADUS - Taxaceae
  alpinus / Sh or T / 5-30' / evergreen / New Zealand, in alps 40

PHYLLODOCE - Ericaceae
  aleutica / Sh / to 1' / fls light yellowish-green / Alaska & w-ward 60
  breweri / Sh / 6-12" / deep pink fls / Californica 38
  caerulea / Sh / to 10" / purplish fls / northern hemisphere 60
  empetrifolia - error for P. empetriformis? .... *
  empetriformis / Sh / 6-8" / rosy-purple fls / w North America 35
  glandulifera - error for glanduliflora? .... *
  glanduliflora / Sh / 6-8" / pale greenish-yellow fls / w N. America 38

(1) - GORER in Quar. Bull. of the Alpine Garden Soc. 39:4
(2) - TOTTEN in Am. Rock Garden Soc. Bull. 15:3

PHYLLODOCE, con.
  X intermedia - rose-pink fls, empetriformis X glanduliflora, B.C.   43
  nipponica / Sh / to 8" / rose to white fls / Japan   60
      "   v. amabilis - included in the sp.   60
      "   v. oblongo-ovata - larger plant, Hokkaido, Honshu   60
  tsugaefolia - see P. nipponica v. oblongo-ovata   60

PHYMATODES - Polypodaceae
  scandens / HH F / to 1' / terrestrial or epiphytic / New Zealand   2

PHYSALIS - Solanaceae
  alkekengi / P / to 2' / inflated red-orange calyces / Europe   92
      "   'Pygmaea' - 8", recommended pot-plant   89
  franchetii - see P. alkekengi   92
  heterophylla / P / 1-2'+ / yellowish fls / weedy native of N. Am.   68
  'French Pygmy' - see P. alkekengi 'Pygmaea'   *
  pruinosa / A / 20-32" / yellow fls / e & c United States   83

PHYSARIA - Cruciferae
  didymocarpa / R / 2-3" / pinkish inflated pods / Rocky Mts.   38
  geyeri / R / 4" / yellow fls / w United States   35

PHYSOCARPUS - Rosaceae
  capitatus / Sh / to 20' / white fls / Oregon, California   9
  malvaceus / Sh / 6' / white fls / w North America   46
  opulifolius / Sh / to 10' / white fls / e & c North America   9
      "   aureus - see P. opulifolius 'Luteus'   46
      "   'Luteus' - has yellow lvs   46

PHYSOCHLAINIA - Solanaceae
  orientalis / R / 8" / coppery-blue fls / Georgia of USSR   33

PHYSOSTEGIA - Labiatae
  virginica v. alba - P, 4', white fls, e North America   9
      "   'Summer Snow' - 2½-3', white-flowered selection   85

PHYTEUMA - Campanulaceae
  austriacum - see P. orbiculare   32
  balbisii f. alba - 6", white fls, Piedmont, Valley Piseo   33
  betonicifolium / P / to 20" / fls blue / European Alps   9
  canescens / P / 16-32" / violet-blue fls / e Europe   32
  charmelii / R / to 18" / blue fls / Alps   25
  comosum / R / 3-4" / pale lilac-blue fls / Austrian & Italian Alps   42
  halleri / P / to 3' / dark violet fls / Europe, in mts.   87
  hemisphaericum / R / 3" / clear blue fls / granitic Alps   35
  humile / R / 2" / violet-blue fls / Switzerland   38
  limonifolium / P / 20-28" / light blue fls / Asia Minor   9
  nigrum / R / 1'+ / dense, almost black spike / Bohemia   38
  orbiculare / R / 1' / light blue fls / European Alps   35
      "   austriaca - included in the sp.   *
  pauciflorum / R / 3" / fls violet-blue / w Alps, Carpathians   9
  scheuchzeri / R / 1' / light blue fls / s Europe   35
  sibirica / R / 2" / globularia-like fls / Siberia   29
  sieberi / R / 4" / fls dark blue / s Alps & Apennines   25
      "   'Alba' - white fls   *
  spicatum / R / 1'+ / cream, white or blue fls / Europe   38
  vagneri / R / 1'+ / dark violet fls / Hungary   (1)

(1) - Anon. in Quar. Bull. Alpine Garden Soc. 37:4

PHYTOLACCA - Phytolaccaceae
  americana / P / to 12' / fls purplish to whitish / e N. America   9

PICEA - Pinaceae
  glauca / T / to 80' / dense, conical habit / ne North America   46

PIERIS - Ericaceae
  floribunda / Sh / 2-6' / fls white / Virginia to Georgia, in mts.   35
  formosa / HH Sh / 10'+ / evergreen / e Himalayas   46
     "   v. forrestii - to 8', fls creamy-white, w China   42
     "   "   "   'Wakehurst' - shorter, braoder lvs   46
  X 'Forest Flame' - cross of 'Wakehurst' with P. japonica   46
  japonica / Sh / to 15' / fls creamy-white / Japan   42
     "   f. variegata - lvs creamy-white & pink   69
  taiwanensis / HH Sh / to 6' / white fls / Formosa   69

PIMELEA - Thymelaeaceae
  buxifolia / HH Sh / 3' / white to pink fls / New Zealand, in mts.   2
  coarctica - see P. prostrata 'Coarctica'   43
  ferruginea / HH Sh / 1-3' / rose fls / w Australia   9
  prostrata / Sh / wide mat / white fls; white frs / New Zealand   38
     "   'Coarctica' - prostrate dwarf, white, scented fls   43
  traversii / HH Sh / 2' / white to pinkish fls / New Zealand, montane   2

PIMPINELLA - Umbelliferae
  major / P / 3'+ / white to deep pink fls / most of Europe   91

PINELLIA - Araceae
  ternata / Tu / 8-16" / green fls, bulbil-bearing / Far East   60
  tripartita / Tu / 8-20" / green & purplish spathes / Japan   60

PINGUICULA - Lentibulariaceae
  alpina / R / 3" / white fls / c & n Europe   38
  antarctica / R / ? / small pale fls / South America   21
  grandiflora / R / 4" / violet-blue fls / w Europe   38
  vulgaris / R / 6" / purple fls / northern hemisphere   35

PINUS - Pinaceae
  albicaulis / T / 30' / green or gray-green needles / w N. America   46
  aristata / T / 15-40' / slow-growing conifer / Rocky Mts. & w-ward   40
  banksiana / T / 25-60' / serotinous cones / n Canada   40
  bungeana / T / to 80' / white, scaling bark / c China   40
  cembra / T / to 75' / reddish-gray bark / Alps, Carpathians   90
     "   v. sibirica - taller tree, larger cones   69
  contorta / T / 40'+ / twisted, yellowish-green needles / w N. Am.   46
  elliotii / HH T / 30' / cones armed with prickles / se United States   46
  mugo / T / to 30' / broad bushy habit / Europe, in mts.   40
  muricata / HH T / 45'+ / long needles, persistent cones / Calif.   46
  oocarpa / HH T / 30' / sea-green needles / Central America   46
  parviflora / T / 20-50' / white bands on needles / Japan   60
     "   'Glauca' - needles more glaucous   40
  patula / HH T / 30' / bright green needles / Mexico   46
  pinaster / HH T / 45' / dull gray needles / w Medit. region   46
  pumila / Sh / to 6' / of interest for the large rock garden / e Asia   60
  strobus / T / to 100' / pendant cones to 8" / e North America   46

PIPTANTHUS - Leguminosae
  concolor / HH Sh / to 6' / yellow fls / w China   69
  laburnifolius / HH Sh / to 9' / yellow fls / Himalayas   69

PISTACIA - Anacardaceae
　chinensis / Sh / 10' / small frs, blue / wc China　　　　　　　　　46
　lentiscus / HH Sh or T / 3-24' / fls yellow, purple / Medit. region　91

PITTOSPORUM - Pittosporaceae
　heterophyllum / HH Sh / 3-6' / small lvs & fls / Yunnan　　　　　　(1)
　phillyraeoides / HH Sh / to 15' / yellow fls / Australia　　　　　(2)
　tenuifolium / HH Sh / 12' / choclate-purple fls / New Zealand　　46
　tobira / HH Sh / 10' / creamy fls; glossy lvs / China, Japan　　41
　undulatum / HH Sh / 12' / creamy-white fls, fragrant / Australia　46

PITYROGRAMMA - Polypodiaceae
　triangularis / F / 6-12" / gold-backed frond / Oregon　　　　　　50

PLAGIORREGMA diphylla - see JEFFERSONIA diphylla　　　　　　　　　*
　　　　"　　　dubia - see JEFFERSONIA dubia　　　　　　　　　　　*
　　　　"　　　mandschuriensis - see JEFFERSONIA dubia　　　　　　　*

PLANTAGO - Plantaginaceae
　albicans / HH R / ? / silvery spikes & lvs / Spain, s Portugal　65
　alpina / R / 4" / prominent yellow stamens, linear lvs / Alps　67
　camtschatica / R / to 1' / white-pubescent lvs / Japan　　　　　60
　cynops - see P. indica　　　　　　　　　　　　　　　　　　　32,64
　indica / A / 4-14" / glandular-hairy flower heads / Medit. region　64
　major 'Atropurpurea' - leaf color form　　　　　　　　　　　　　*
　　　"　'Purpurea' - leaf color form　　　　　　　　　　　　　　　*
　　　"　'Rosularis Rubrifolia' - purplish lvs; stalked rosette　　38
　　　"　'Rubrifolia' - 4-5", purple stained lvs　　　　　　　　　38
　maxima / P / ? / white feathery spike / Siberia　　　　　　　　9
　nivalis / HH R / rosette / globular green heads / Spain　　　　38
　purpurea - see P. major 'Purpurea'　　　　　　　　　　　　　　　*
　raoulii / HH R / to 6" / pilose lvs / New Zealand　　　　　　　2

PLATANTHERA - Orchidaceae
　bifolia / P / to 22" / yellowish or greenish fls, vanilla sc. / Eu.　30

PLATANUS - Platanaceae
　orientalis / T / to 90' / exfoliating bark / w Asia, se Europe　69

PLATYCODON - Campanulaceae
　apoyama - see P. grandiflorum 'Apoyama'　　　　　　　　　　　　*
　grandiflorum / P / to 3'+ / fls lilac or white / Far East　　　60
　　　　"　　　'Album' - white fls　　　　　　　　　　　　　　　　9
　　　　"　　　'Apoyama' - 8", large violet fls　　　　　　　　　85
　　　　"　　　　"　　Leucantha' - paler fls?　　　　　　　　　　*
　　　　"　　　'Azureum' - pale blue fls　　　　　　　　　　　　　*
　　　　"　　　'Cronamere Rose' - selection for pink fls　　　　　*
　　　　"　　　'Mariesii' - 1', varii-colored fls　　　　　　　　9
　　　　"　　　'Mariesii Album' - white fls　　　　　　　　　　　*
　　　　"　　　'Roseum' - pinkish fls　　　　　　　　　　　　　　*

PLECTRITIS - Valerianaceae
　congesta / P / 4-24" / fls pink or white / s Calif. to B. C.　75

　(1) - Iconographia Cormophytorum Sinicorum. Tomus ii　1972

　(2) - ENART - Ornamental Shrubs of California. 1962

PLEIONE - Orchidaceae
   bulbocodoides / Gh / 2"+ / varii-colored fls / Far East   85
       "   'Alba' - the rarely white form   85
       "   'Limprichtii' - rich red fls   41
   formosana - see P. bulbocodoides   *
     "   alba   see P. bulbocodoides 'Alba'   *
     "   'Polar Sun' - see P. 'Polar Sun'   *
     "   pricei - synonym of P. bulbocodoides   85
   humilis / Gh / 2-3" / white to pale purple fls / India   85
   limprichtii - see P. bulbocodoides 'Limprichtii'   41
   pricei - see P. bulbocodoides   85
   'Polar Sun' - better of two whites in cultivation   (1)
   yunnanensis / Gh / 2" / bright magenta-rose fls / China 85

PLEUROSPERMUM - Umbelliferae
   camtschaticum / P / 8-16" / large white flowers / Far East 60

PLUMBAGO - Plumbaginaceae
   capensis / Gh Cl / light-blue fls / South Africa   41

POA - Gramineae
   alpina / P Gr / 2-12" / Purplish or greenish panicles / n temp. zone 85
   "   v. vivipara - upper spikelet producing new plants 85

PODOCARPUS - Taxaceae
   alpinus / Sh / low mound / for protected rock garden / Austral., Tas. 46
   andina / HH T / 20' / evergreen / Chile   9
   nivalis / HH Sh / to 9' / fleshy red frs / New Zealand   78

PODOLEPIS - Compositae
   acuminata / HH P / 1-2' / yellow daisies / Australia   21
   jaceoides / A / small / yellow fls / Australia, Tasmania   16

PODOPHYLLUM - Berberidaceae
   emodi / R / 1' / pale pink to white fls / Himalayas   42
   " 'Majus' - 2'+, orange-scarlet frs   33
   peltatum / P / 1-1½' / white waxy fls / North America   9

POLEMONIUM - Polemoniaceae
   archebaldiae / P / 3'+ / conical inflorescence / Colorado, in mts. 77
   boreale / R / 8" / pale purple fls / n circumpolar   63
   brandegei / R / 6-12" / golden yellow fls / Colorado   38
   caeruleum / P / to 3' / blue fls / Europe   35
   "   v. album - white fls   9
   "   yezoense - see P. yezoense   60
   carneum / R / 6-8" / flesh-pink fls / w North America   38
   "   f. luteum - soft yellow fls   21
   cashmirianum / R / 1' / blue fls / Kashmir   89
   "   'Album' - white fls   *
   confertum / R / 6-8" / mauve-blue fls / Colorado, Utah   38
   delicatum / R / dwarf / light blue fls / Rocky Mts.   35
   elegans / R / to 6" / blue fls / Washington, British Columbia 75
   flavum / P / 2-3' / fls yellow tinged red / New Mexico, Arizona 74
   foliosissimum / P / 1½-2½' / blue fls / Rocky Mts.   42
   grandiflorum / R / 12" / lilac or yellow fls, large / Orizaba, Mex. 33
   haydenii / R / dwarf / blue fls / w United States   35
   lanatum boreale - see P. boreale   *
   mellitum / R / dwarf / creamy-white fls / Rocky Mts.   35
   occidentale / P / to 3' / blue fls / Rocky Mts.   9

(1) - ADEY in Jour. Royal Horticultural Soc. April 1961

POLEMONIUM, con.
  pauciflorum / P / 1-2' / yellowish & red fls / Mexico   35
  pulcherrimum / P / 6-22" / blue & white fls / Rocky Mts.   9
      "   v. calycinum - 12-20", laxer, more robust, Ida., Mont.   47
  reptans / P / 6-30" / deep blue fls / e & c United States   34
  viscosum / R / 4-5" / clear blue fls / Rocky Mts.   38
  yezoense / P / 1-1½' / blue fls / Hokkaido   60

POLIANTHES - Amaryllidaceae
  geminiflora / Tu / 1-2' / red fls, orange-tinged / Mexico   32

POLYGALA - Polygalaceae
  amarella - see P. calacrea   20
  calcarea / R / 3-5" / pink to blue fls / England, Europe   42
  chamaebuxus v. purpurea - Sh, 6", fls purple-red   43
  pauciflora - error for P. paucifolia   *
  paucifolia / R / 3-6" / rosy purple fls / e North America   9
  senega / R / to 1' / fls white or greenish / New Brunswick & w & s   9
  vulgaris / Sh / 1'+ / blue, pink or white fls / Europe   91

POLYGONATUM - Liliaceae
  biflorum / P / 2-3' / greenish-white fls / e North America   35
  canaliculatum / P / to 8' / numerous white fls / n & s N. America   34
  commutatum - see P. canaliculatum   34
  multiflorum / P / 2-3' / small white fls / Europe   42
  odoratum / P / 1-2' / white fls, toothed green / Europe, Asia   32
  officinale - see P. odoratum   32
  racemosum - see SMILACINA racemosa   *
  roseum / P / to 2' / rose fls; brownish-red frs / c Asia   54
  stewartianum / P / 3' / greenish-white fls; red-dotted frs / Yunnan   (1)
  verticillatum / P / 1-2' / white fls, violet-red frs / Europe   54

POLYGONUM - Polygonaceae
  affine / R / 4-6" / rosy-red fls / Himalayas   85
     "   'Donald Lownes' - selected cultivar   42
     "   'Lownes Var.' - see P. a. 'Donald Lownes'   42
  amplexicaule / P / 3-4' / fls bright crimson / Himalayas   42
  bistorta 'Superbum' - P, to 3', fls light pink   42
  capitatum / A / trailing / pink fls / Himalayas   89
  macrophyllum / R / tuft / brilliant pink fls / Himalayas   33
  millettii / P / 6-18" / deep pink or crimson fls / w China, Himal.   85
  sphaerostachyon - see P. macrophyllum   85
  viviparum / R / 2-16" / flesh-col. fls / circumpolar, s in mts.   (2)

POLYPODIUM - Polypodiaceae
  hesperium / F / to 6" / of moist cliffs / Cascade Mts.   47
  scouleri / F / to 4" / lvs thick & leathery / B. C. to Calif., coast   47
  vulgare / F / 4-10" / creeping on rocks / Europe, United States   9
     "   v. columbianum - from rock ledges   (3)
     "   v. occidentale - from tree trunks, logs & cliffs   (3)

POLYSTICHUM - Polypodiaceae
  acrostichoides / F / 6-8" / evergreen frond / e United States   9
  andersonii / F / 1-3' / of deep woods / w North America   47
  braunii / F / 18-24" / loses fronds in December / e N. America   9
  cytoslegia / F / 2-6" / sori large, domed / New Zealand   50

  (1) - BRICKELL in Lilies and Allied Plants. 1972
  (2) - Mountain Flowers of New England. App. Mt. Club.
  (3) - MUENSCHER - Flora of Whatcom Co., Washington. 1941

POLYSTICHUM, con.
  munitum / F / 4-12" / Western Sword-fern / Utah, n- & w-ward   9
  setiferum 'Acutilobum' - narrow fronds with abundant bulbils   50
      "   'Proliferum' - see P. s. 'Acutilobum'   50

PONCIRUS - Rubiaceae
  trifoliata / Sh or T / to 20' / fragrant white fls / n China   69

PORTULACA - Portulacaceae
  grandiflora / A / 6-12" / varii-colored fls / Brazil   9
      "   'Flore Plena' - doubled fls   *

POTENTILLA - Rosaceae
  alchimilloides / R / to 1' / white fls / Pyrenees   91
  alpestris - see P. crantzii   91
  ambigua / Sh / tufted / fls yellow / Himalayas   9
  andicola - see P. dombeyi   21
  apennina / R / 8" / silvery lvs; fls white / Balkans   91
  argentea / R / 1' / pale yellow fls / n Europe, Alps   91
      "   v. calabria - see P. calabra   91
  argyrophylla / P / 8-16" / amber fls / Himalayas   9
      "   f. leucochroa - yellow fls; silvery lvs   89
  atrosanguinea / P / to 2' / dark purple fls / Himalayas   9
      "   'Gibson's Scarlet' - 1½', brilliant scarlet fls   85
ARGS · aurea / R / mats / yellow fls / s & c Europe in mts.   91
S'80   "   ssp. chrysocraspedia - leaflets always three, Balkans   91
    "   'Plena' - neat tufts, double golden fls, 2"   17
    "   rathbonii (rathboneana) - see P. a. 'Plena'   17
  beesii - see P. fruticosa 'Beesii'   43
  blaschkiana - see P. gracilis v. glabrata   47
  buccoana / P / to 2' / fls yellow / nw Anatolia   26
  calabra / R / 8", procumbent / yellow fls / Italy, in mts., Balkans   91
  caulescens / R / to 1' / white fls / Alps, s Europe, in mts.   91
  chinensis / P / to 3' / fls yellow / China, Japan   (1)
  chrysocraspedia - see P. aurea ssp. chrysocraspedia   91
  cinerea / R / mats / yellow fls / c, e & s Europe   91
  clusiana / R / 2-4" / white fls / Alps, Albania   91
  crantzii / R / 8'+ / fls yellow / n Eu., c & s Europe, in mts.   91
      "   'Pygmaea' - 4-6", yellow fls, circumpolar   (2)
  cuneata / R / 5" / yellow fls / Nepal   29
  delphinensis / P / 12-20" / yellow fls / sw Alps   91
  detommasii / R / to 1' / fls yellow / Balkans, Italy   91
  dombeyi / R / decumbent / yellow fls / Chile   29
  eriocarpa / R / mat / clear yellow fls / Himalayas   38
  flabellifolia / R / 3-12" / yellow fls / nw North America   75
  fragiformis - see P. megalantha   60
  fruticosa / Sh / to 3' / fls yellow / northern hemisphere   91
      "   'Beesii' - 10", golden yellow fls, China   43
  fulgens / P / tall / golden yellow fls / Himalayas   33
  'Gibson's Scarlet' - see P. atrosanguinea 'Gibson's Scarlet'   85
  glandulosa / P / 4-28" / fls deep to pale yellow / Calif. to Canada   75
  gracilis / P / 12-32" / yellow fls / Calif., Alaska, Rocky Mts.   75
      "   v. glabrata - lvs green, sparingly hirsute   47
      "   v. pulcherrima - lvs grayish beneath   47
  grandiflora / R / 4-16" / fls yellow / Alps, Pyrenees   91
  hirta / P / 4-28" / fls yellow / w Mediterranean region   91
    "   pedata - see P. pedata   91
  hyparctica / R / 3-13" / yellow fls / n circumpolar   63

(1) - STEWARD - Vascular Plants of the Lower Yangtze. 1958
(2) - DREW in Am. Rock Garden Soc. Bull. 33:1

POTENTILLA, con.
  matsumurae / R / 4-8" / yellow fls / Hokkaido, Honshu   69
  megalantha / R / 4-12" / fls golden yellow / Kuriles, Hokkaido   60
  miyabei / R / to 4" / yellow fls / Hokkaido   60
  nepalensis / P / 1-2' / purple fls / Himalayas   9
      "   'Miss Willmott' - 1', carmine fls   42
      "   'Roxana' - orange-scarlet fls   42
  nevadensis / R / 6-12" / yellow fls / s Spain   85
  nitida / R / mats / rosy fls / s Europe, in mts.   35
    " 'Alba' - desirable white form   43
    " 'Lissadell' - best pink form   17
    " 'Rubra' - deeper pink and freer flowering tah type   42
  nivea / R / to 8" / fls yellow; lvs white-tomentose / n Europe   91
  nuttallii - see P. gracilis v. pulcherrima   34,47
  palustris / P / to 18" / fls deep purple / Europe   91
  pedata / P / to 2' / yellow fls; pinnatifid lvs / se Europe   91
  pulcherrima - see P. gracilis v. pulcherrima   47
  pyrenaica / R / 4-16" / fls yellow / n & c Spain   91
  recta / P / 4-28" / fls yellow / c, e & s Europe   91
    " macrantha - see P. r 'Warrenii'   42
    " 'Warrenii' - 1½', fls golden   42
  'Roxana' - see P. nepalense 'Roxana'   42
  rupestris / P / to 2' / white fls / w & c Europe, Balkans   91
    "   'Nana' - dainty form   (1)
    "   'Warrenii' - error for P. recta 'Warrenii'   *
  sanguisorba - / R / 6-12" / fls cream-colored / Siberia   29
  thurberi / P / 1'+ / red-purple fls / New Mexico, Ariz., n Mexico 74
  X tormentilla-formosa - R, rosette, apricot & red fls   (2)
  tommasiniana - see P. cinerea   91
  tonguei - see P. X tormentilla-formosa   (2)
  tridentata / Sh / 6-10" / white fls / n North America   35
  valderia / P / 16" / white fls; gray-tomentose lvs / Maritime Alps 91
  verna / R / mat / yellow fls / Great Britain, w & c Europe   38
    " f. nana - in miniature   38
  villosa / R / 4" / golden yellow fls / Siberia   43
    " v. parviflora - of nw North America, lvs thick, leathery 47
  warrensii - see P. rupestris 'Warrenii'   *

POTERIUM sitchense - see SANGUISORBA sitchensis   47
     "   spinosum - see SARCOPOTERIUM spinosum   26

PRATIA - Campanulaceae
  angulata / HH R / carpeter / white fls; purplish frs / N. Zealand 35
    "   'Treadwellii' - larger fls; brighter frs   38
  macrodon / HH R / creeping / yellowish to white fls / N. Zealand 2
  physalodes / HH P / 3' / pale blue fls; purplish frs / N. Zealand 78
  treadwellii - see P. angulata 'Treadwellii'   38

PRENANTHES - Compositae
  purpurea / P / to 4½' / violet fls / Europe   32

PRIMULA - Primulaceae
  acaulis - see P. vulgaris   38
    "   coerulea - presumably P. vulgaris 'Hortensis Caerulea' 89
  algida / R / to 8" / fls violet / Caucasus, Asia Minor   35
  allionii 'Apple Blossom' - Gh, rosette, light mauve-pink fls 43

(1) - DOWBRIDGE in Bull. Am. Rock Garden Soc. 20:1
(2) - KLABER - Rock Garden Plants. 1959

PRIMULA, con.

alpicola / R / 12" / white, lavender, yellow fls / Tibet ... 35
    "   'Alba' - white fls, comes true from seed ... 62
    "   'Luna' - pale yellow fls ... 35
    "   'Violacea' - purple fls, less dependable from seed ... 62
altaica 'Grandiflora' - see P. vulgaris ssp. sibthorpii ... (1)
amoena / R / 5-6" / mauve-pink fls / Caucasus, n Turkey ... 38
  "   'Grandiflora' - selection for larger fls ... *
anisodora / P / 2' / brownish-purple fls / Yunnan ... 62
X 'Arctotis' - P. auricula X hirsuta, 4-5", fls lilac-purple ... 9
'Asthore Hybrid' - candelabra type, mixed colors ... 17
aurantiaca / R / 8-12" / reddish-orange fls / Yunnan ... 38
    "   'Candy Pink' - presumably P. vulgaris 'Candy Pink' ... *
auricula / R / 4-8" / deep yellow fls / Alps ... 42
    "   v. albocincta - lvs densely farinaceous, Monte Baldo ... 9
    "   'Alpina' - indicating the wild sp. ... 17
    "   'Arctotis' - see P. X 'Arctotis' ... 9
    "   v. balbisii - to 3", deep yellow fls, Dolomites ... 38
    "   'Barnhaven Strain - a Polyanthus group of US origin ... (1)
    "   'Bauhinii' - see P. a. var. albocincta ... 33
    "   'Decora' - 6", fls violet-blue ... 5
    "   'Dusty Miller' - class of Auriculas usually by color ... (1)
    "   'Goldlace' - Polyanthus developed as florist's fls ... (1)
    "   'Lynn Hall Strain' - recommended strain of Auriculas ... 44
    "   '(The) Mikado' - large deep maroon fls ... (1)
    "   'Old Irish Blue' - violet to pale lilac frilled fls ... (1)
    "   'Old Red Dusty Miller' - wallflower-red fls ... (1)
    "   v. serratifolia - serrate-lvd form from the Banat ... 33
auriculata / R / 4-14" / rose, violet or lilac fls / Greece to Iran ... 9
'Barnhaven Strain/Hybrids - referrable to Polyanthus or P. Sieboldii ... *
beesiana / P / 1½-2' / fls purple-lilac in whorls / w China ... 42
bellidifolia / R / 4" / red-blue fls / Tibet ... 43
boreana - possibly an error for P. boveana ... *
boveana / Gh / to 10" / yellow fls / Sinai ... 9
bulleyana / P / 1½-2½' / deep yellow fls / Yunnan ... 35
burmanica / P / to 2' / reddish-purple fls / Upper Burma ... 35
'Candelabra Hybrid' - 2', fls in mixed colors ... 89
capitata / R / 6-12" / violet fls / Sikkim, se Tibet, Bhutan ... 38
    "   ssp. mooreana - deeper and more open fls ... 38
    "   ssp. sphaerocephala - purplish fls, sw China ... 9
carniolica / R / 6" / fls pink, white-eyed / Adriatic Sea region ... 35
cashmiriana - see P. denticulata v. cachemiriana ... 33
cawdoriana / R / 5" / pale lavender fls / ? ... 35
chionantha / R / to 1' / fragrant white fls / Yunnan ... 38
chungensis / P / 1½' / fls yellow & orange-red / w China ... 35
clarkei / R / 2" / fls rose-red / Kashmir ... 17
clusiana / R / 4-7" / crimson & white fls / Austrian Alps ... 35
cockburniana / R / 10-14" / orange-scarlet fls / w China ... 35
columnae - see P. veris ssp. columnae ... 92
concholoba - most inferior of all Muscaroid Primulas ... 21
conspersa / R / 9-12" / pale lilac-pink fls / Kansu ... 33
cordifolia / R / 6-8" / large, clear yellow fls / High Caucasus ... (2)
cortusoides / R / 6-12" / fls rose-colored / w Siberia ... 35
cusickiana / P / 2'+ / fls deep violet or white / w United States ... 85
darialica / R / 2"+ / fls rose / Caucasus ... 35
decipiens - see P. hirsuta ... 33

(1) - HECKER - Auriculas & Primroses. 1971
(2) - SCHWARZ in Quar. Bull. Alpine Garden Soc. 43:2

PRIMULA, con.

denticulata / R / 6-12" / fls in mauve shades / Himalayas		42
" 'Alba' - white fls		62
" v. cachemiriana - deep purple fls, later		38
" 'Rubra' - magenta-red fls		62
deorum / R / to 8" / dark violet fls / sw Bulgaria		92
edelbergii / R / ? / ? / Kabul, Afghanistan		(1)
edgeworthii / HH R / 3" / variable mauve fls / w Himalayas		38
elatior / R / to 1' / yellow fls / s, w & c Europe		92
" ssp. intricata - pale yellow fls, s & sc Europe, in mts.		92
" ssp. leucophylla - lvs gray-tomentose beneath, Carpathians		92
" ssp. ruprechtii - fls bright yellow, Caucasian alps		92
ellisae / R / 6" / purple fls / New Mexico		(2)
farinosa / R / 3-6" / fls pale to lilac-pink / European Alps		42
" v. groenlandica - see P. stricta		80
" v. laurentiana - to 14", lilac fls, Gaspe Peninsula		35
fauriei - see P. modesta v. fauriei		60
firmipes / R / to 1' / fls pale yellow, fragrant / Sikkim		21
floribunda / R / 5-8" / fls golden yellow / Himalayas		9
forrestii / R / 8-12" / orange-yellow fls / Yunnan		42
frondosa / R / 5-7" / pink fls / Balkans		38
gambeliana gemmifera - see P. gemmifera		*
gaubeana / P / to 20" / yellow fls / Iran		(3)
gemmifera / R, may be A / 3-12" / varii-colored fls / China		33
geraniifolia / R / 6" / deep rose-red fls / Sikkim		43
glutinosa / R / 3-4" / fragrant royal-purple fls / Austrian Alps		33
goebellii - see P. X pubescens		33
groenlandica - see P. stricta		80
halleri / R / 3-6" / fls clear pink to deep rose / European Alps		38
X heerii - rose-red fls, occurs in Swiss Alps; rubra X integrifolia		17
helodoxa / P / 2-3' / fls bright yellow / Yunnan		42
hirsuta / R / rosettes / rose fls, white centers / Alps		35
ianthina / R / 12"+ / crushed raspberry fls / ?		21
incana / P / 12-16" / lilac to rose fls / Rocky Mts.		(4)
'Inschriach Hybrid' - candelabra type, mixed colors		17
integrifolia / R / 2" / rosy purple fls / Pyrenees, Alps		35
intercedens / R / 4-6" / pink fls, fading white / Great Lakes reg.		(5)
'Inverewe' - candelabra type, brilliant brick-red fls		(6)
involucrata / R / 4-12" / fls yellowish / Himalayas		9
'Itton Court' - candelabra hybrid, Chinese-red, true from seed		(7)
ioessa / R / 9" / lilac or white fls / Tibet		6
" f. subpinnatifida - white to creamy-white fls		(8)
'Jack-in-the-Green' - Polyanthus with calyx a ruff of green lvs		(9)
japonica / P / 1½' / fls purplish-red in whorls / Japan		42
" 'Alba' - white flowered		9
" 'Millers Crimson' - dark crimson-purple fls		62
" 'Postford White' - white fls with pink eye		42
" 'Red Hugh' - selection from Lissadell Hybrids		21
" 'Rosea' - rose-colored fls		9

(1) - CAIN in Quar. Bull. Alpine Garden Soc. 35:2
(2) - CORSAR in Gardeners' Chronicle May 4, 1937
(3) - PARSA - Flore de l'Iran. Vol. iv 1952
(4) - STRONG in Bull. Am. Rock Garden Soc. 27:2
(5) - COLE in Bull. Am. Rock Garden Soc. 35:2
(6) - PEARCE in Bull. Am. Rock Garden Soc. 27:2
(7) - GOPLERUD in Far North Gardens 1973 catalog.
(8) - FLETCHER in Jour. Royal Hort. Soc. Jan. 1953
(9) - HECKER - Auriculas & Primroses. 1971

PRIMULA, con.
```
jesoana / R / 8-16" / fls rose-purple / Hokkaido, Honshu          60
    "    v. pubescens - with more pubescence, Hokkaido           60
juliae / R / 4" / red or purple fls / Caucasus                   62
X kewensis - Gh, 1', yellow fragrant fls in whorls               41
latifolia / R / 2-7" / purple to dark violet fls / Alps, Pyrenees 92
leucophylla - see P. elatior ssp. leucophylla                    92
lichiangensis - see P. polyneura                                 32
'Linda Pope' - see P. marginata 'Linda Pope'                     43
'Lissadell' - hybrids from P. pulverulenta                       21
longiflora - see P. hallii                                       92
luteola / R / 4-6" / fls pale sulphur-yellow / e Caucasus         9
macrophylla - see P. auriculata                                  80
marginata / R / 3-4" / fls blue-lilac / Maritime & Cottian Alps  35
    "     'Linda Pope' - fls rich lavender-blue with white eye   43
X 'Marven' - R, 6-7", fls blue-purple, white eye                 38
melanops / R / 8" / fls rich purple, black eye / sw Szechuan      38
minima / R / clump / delicate pink fls / se Europe               35
mistassinica / R / 2-4" / pale pink fls / North America          38
modesta / R / 3-6" / rose-colored fls / Japan, in mts.           60
    "   'Alba' - white fls                                       60
    "   v. fauriei - smaller, from rocky cliffs near sea         60
    "   v. yuparensis 'Alba' - see P. yuparensis 'Alba'          60
mollis / R / 1' / fls bright rose / Himalayas                     9
muscarioides / R / 8-12" / blue fls / Shensi, c China            32
nivalis / R / to 1' / rose-violet fls / Siberia                  80
nutans / R / to 12" / fls lilac to pink, yellow center / n Russia 92
obconica v. werringtonensis - hardier var. from upland China     21
officinalis - see P. veris                                       92
'Pagoda Hybrid' - 2', candelabra type, mixed colors             (1)
palinuri / HH R / 6-8" / fls deep rich yellow / s Italy          38
parryi / R / 6-12" / deep magenta-pink fls / Colorado            38
pedemontana / R / 6" / fls rose or white / sw Alps               35
poissonii / P / 18" / magenta fls / Yunnan                       38
X polyantha - R, 9-12", fls variously colored                    42
polyneura / P / 12-18" / varii-colored fls / c China             35
prolifera / P / 2' / fls golden yellow / Assam                   85
X pubescens - R, 3-5", fls almost any color                      38
    "     'Faldonside' - deep crimson fls                        43
    "     'Mrs. J. H. Wilson' - 4-5", violet fls                 38
    "     'Rufus' - deep terra-cotta red fls                     42
    "     'The General' - velvety terra-cotta fls                38
pulverulenta / P / 2-3' / claret-red fls / w China               42
    "     'Bartley Strain' - soft pink fls                       42
reidii / R / 3-4" / white fls / nw Himalayas                     42
    "   v. williamsii - pale bluish-lilac fls                    42
    "       "        'Alba' - white fls                           *
reticulata / P / 7-18" / yellow or white fls / Nepal to Tibet    32
rosea / R / 3-4" / glowing rose-pink fls / Himalayas             35
    "   'Grandiflora' - to 10", larger fls                       38
    "   'Micia Visser de Geer' - 6-8", fls larger & deeper color 38
rotundifolia / R / 6" / fls mauve-pink / Nepal                   43
rubra - see P. hirsuta                                           35
ruprechtii - see P. elatior ssp. ruprechtii                      80
rusbyi / R / 4-6" / fls bright rose / New Mexico, Arizona         9
saxatilis / R / 8" / fls rose-violet / e Siberia                 9
scandinavica / R / to 6" / fls dark purple / Norway, Sweden      92
scotica / R / 2" / fls deep purple / n Scotland                  38
secundiflora / R / to 1' / fls dark ruby-purple / sw China       35
```

(1) - GOPLERUD - Far North Gardens catalog. 1973

PRIMULA, con.
  serratifolia / P / ? / pale yellow fls / sw China   9
  sibirica - see P. nutans   92
  sieboldii / R / 6-9" / fls dark pink to white / Japan   42
      "   'Barnhaven' - large-flowered strain   *
  sikkimense / P / 2' / yellow fls / Sikkim   35
      "   v. hopeana - fls white, slender plant   20
      "   v. pudibunda - alpine form, smaller fls   32
  sinoplantaginea / R / 6" / violet-purple fls / Yunnan   43
  sinopurpurea / P / 8-16" / purple fls / w China   9
  sorachiana - small-flowered; possibly a variant of P. yuparensis   60
  stricta / R / 1' / fls violet to lilac / Scandinavia, Iceland   92
  suffrutescens / R / 4" / deep rose fls / California   38
  takedana / R / to 6" / white fls / Hokkaido, in high mts.   60
  X tommasinii - P. veris x P. vulgaris   92
  tschukschorum / R / to 10" / violet fls, lavender eye / n arctic reg.63
  X variabilis - see X tommasinii   92
  X venusta - 3-4", crimson to purple fls   38
  veris / R / 4-8" / fragrant yellow fls / Europe   35
      "   ssp. columnae - white-hairy plant, mts. of s Europe   92
      "   v. macrocalyx - long calyx, orange fls   (1)
      "   suavolens - see P. v. ssp. columnae   92
  verticillata / Gh / ? / tiered yellow fls / Arabia   33
  vialii / P or B / 1-1½' / fls bluish-violet / nw China   42
  villosa / R / 4" / fls rose or lilac / e Alps   35
  viscosa - see P. latifolia   92
  vulgaris / R / 4-5" / fls cream-yellow / Europe   42
      "   ssp. ingwerseniana - white fls, Mt. Olympus, Greece   21
      "   ssp. sibthorpii - fls usually red or purple, Balkans   92
  waltonii / P / to 2'+ / fls purple to red / Tibet, Bhutan   32
  werringtonensis - see P. obconica v. werringtonensis   (2)
  wilsonii / P / to 3' / purple fls / w China   9
  wulfeniana / R / 2" / fls rose-colored / Austrian Alps   35
  yargonensis / R / 9" / pale lilac fls / w China   17
  yuparensis / R / 9" / pale rose-purple fls / Hokkaido   60
      "   'Alba' - white form   *

PROBOSCIDEA - Martyniaceae
  jussieuii - see P. louisianica   32
  louisianica / A / to 12" / whitish to purplish fls / sc US   (3)

PROSARTES oregana - see DISPORUM smithii   9

PRUNELLA - Labiatae
  asiatica albiflora - see P. vulgaris f. albiflora   34
  'Blue Loveliness'- see P. grandiflora 'Blue Loveliness'   *
  grandiflora / R / 4" / purple-violet fls / Europe   38
      "   'Alba' - white fls   35
      "   'Blue Loveliness' - blue fls   *
      "   'Loveliness' - purple fls   (4)
      "   'Pink Loveliness' - pink fls   38
      "   'Rosea' - darker pink fls   *
  laciniata / R / to 1' / fls yellowish-white / s, w & c Europe   92

(1) - HECKER - Auriculas & Primroses. 1971
(2) - EDWARDS & WINSTANLEY - List of Primula Species in Cult. (mss.)
(3) - LAWRENCE in Baileya 5:3
(4) - KLABER in Bull. Am. Rock Garden Soc. 20:4

ARGS
882

PRUNELLA, con.
  vulgaris - naturalized weed of lawns   35
      "   'Alba' - see P. v. var. lanceolatum f. candida   82
      "   f. albiflora - white fls on typical P. vulgaris   34
      "   laciniata - see P. laciniata   29
      "   v. lanceolata f. candida - narrow lvs, white fls   82
      "   v. lanceolata f. rhodantha - narrow lvs, pink fls   34
      "   v. lilacina - blue-purple fls, Japan   60
      "   rosea - see P. v. var. lanceolata f. rhodantha   34
  webbiana - horticultural form with bright purple fls   9

PRUNUS - Rosaceae
  incisa / Sh or T / 15-30' / fls white or pink / Japan   9
  serotina / T / 100' / white fls in racemes / e North America   9
  tenella / Sh / to 4½' / bright pink fls / e & ec Europe   90

PSEUDOMUSCARI - Liliaceae
  azureum / Bb / 4-6" / pale blue fls with darker stripe / Caucasus   56
      "   f. album - 3", white fls, weak grower   4
      "   v. amphibolis - 12", pale blue fls, tall var. from Turkey   4
  chalusicum / Bb / 4" / pale china-blue fls / Iran   56

PTELEA - Rutaceae
  angustifolia - see P. baldwinii   69
  baldwinii / Sh / 10'+ / small lvs; large fls / sw US, Mexico   46
  trifoliata / T / to 24' / winged wafer frs / e North America   69

PTEROCEPHALUS - Dipsacaceae
  parnassi / R / 3-4" / pinkish-mauve fls / Greece   38

PTEROSPORA - Pyrolaceae
  andromeda / P / 3' / red, white fls; parasitic / w N. America   75

PTILOTRICHUM - Cruciferae
  purpureum / R / low tufts / rosy-purple fls / s & se Spain   65
  pyrenaicum / Sh / 20" / white fls / e Pyrenees   90
  reverchonii / Sh / 20" / white fls / se Spain   90
  spinosum / Sh / 2' / white or purplish fls / e & s Spain   90
      "   'Roseum' - rare pink form   43

PULMONARIA - Boraginaceae
  angustifolia / R / 6-12" / bright blue fls / Europe   92
  azurea - see P. angustifolia   92

PULSATILLA - Ranunculaceae
  alba / P / 2' / fls white / c Europe, in mts.   90
  albana / R / 5" / fls pale colors / e Caucasus to India   33
    "   ssp. armena - violet-blue fls, Turkey, Iran   26
    "   'Albicyanea' - white & blue fls   *
    "   'Albicyanea Lutea' - see P. albana 'Lutea'   *
    "   'Armena' - see P. albana ssp. armena   *
    "   'Lutea' - included in the sp.   (1)
    "   'Violacea' - see P. albana ssp. armena   26
  albocyanea - see P. albana 'Albicyanea'   *
    "   lutea - see P. albana 'Lutea'   *
  albo-violacea - see P. albana ssp. armena   21

(1) - YUZEPCHUK in Flora of the USSR. Vol. VII. 1970(trans.)

PULSATILLA, con.
```
    alpina / P / 1-1½' / white fls / European Alps                        42
       "    alpicola - see P. alba                                        90
       "    ssp. apiifolia - fls pale yellow                              90
       "    ssp. austriaca - see P. alba                                  90
       "    ssp. sulphurea - see P. a. ssp. apiifolia                     90
    ambigua / R / to 1' / fls blue-violet, rarely pink / w Siberia       (1)
    apiifolia - see P. alpina ssp. apiifolia                              90
    armena - see P. albana ssp. armena                                    26
    aurea / R / to 14" / golden yellow fls / Caucasus                    (1)
    'Budapest' - see P. vulgaris ssp. grandis                          85,90
    campanella / R / to 10" / fls violet-blue / w Siberia, c Asia        (1)
    caucasica - see P. albana                                            (2)
    cernua / R / 4-16" / red-brown or purple fls / Far East              60
    georgica / R / to 1' / fls pale blue / Caucasus                      (1)
    grandis - see P. vulgaris ssp. grandis                               90
       "    'Alba' - see P. vulgaris ssp. grandis 'Alba'                 (3)
    halleri / R / 6-12" / fls pale mauve-violet / e Alps                 42
       "    'Alba' - white fls                                           33
       "    'Budapest' - see P. vulgaris ssp. grandis                  85,90
       "    grandis - see P vulgaris ssp. grandis                        *
       "    ssp. rhodopea - basal lvs petioled                          90
       "    ssp. slavica - basal lvs divides into 3                     90
       "      "      "     'Alba' - white fls                            *
       "      "      "     'Rubra' - reddish fls                         *
       "    ssp. styriaca - basal lvs divided into 5                    90
    montana / R / 4" / fls bluish to dark violet / w Europe              90
       "    rubra - see P. rubra                                         *
    multifida / R / 5" / bluish-violet fls, much dissected lvs / Siberia(1)
    nigricans - see P. pratensis ssp. nigricans                          90
    nipponica / R / to 1' / pale yellow & white fls / Hokkaido, Honshu   60
    occidentalis / P / to 2' / white fls / w North America               35
    patens / R / 5" / bluish-violet fls / e & ec Europe                  90
    pratensis / R / 4" / fls variously colored / c & e Europe            90
       "    ssp. hungarica - fls muddy yellow, se range                  90
       "    ssp. nigricans - dark purple fls, northern range             90
       "      "      "     lutea - see P. p. ssp. hungarica              90
    ranunculoides - see ANEMONE ranunculoides                            *
    regeliana - see P. ambigua                                          (1)
    rhodopea - see P. halleri ssp. rhodopea                              90
    rubra / R / 4" / dark reddish fls / France, Spain                    90
    slavica - see P. halleri ssp. slavica                               90
       "    rubra - see P. halleri ssp. slavica 'Rubra'                  *
    sulphurea - see P. alpina ssp. apiifolia                             *
    turcrakinovii - error for P. turczaninovii                          *
    turczaninovii / R / 2-14" / blue-violet fls / Manchuria, e Mongolia (1)
    vernalis / R / 4-8" / fls white / Alps                               42
    vulgaris / R / 4-8" / fls violet-purple / Europe                     42
       "    'Alba' - white fls                                           42
       "    'Budapest' - see P. v. ssp. grandis                          85
       "    'Coccinea' - bright red fls                                 (2)
       "    ssp. gotlandica - like ssp. grandis, from Gotland            90
       "    ssp. grandis - lvs appearing after the fls                   90
       "      "      "     'Alba' - white fls                           (3)
       "    'Red Cloak' - dwarf with red fls                            17
       "    'Rubra' - deep red fls                                       38
       "    slavica - see P. halleri ssp. slavica                       90
```
E79

(1) - YUZEPCHUK in Flora of the USSR. Vol. VII. 1970(trans.)
(2) - ELLIOTT in Quar. Bull. Alpine Garden Soc. 35:4
(3) - STAREK in Bull. Am. Rock Garden Soc. 24:1

PUNICA - Punicaceae
  granatum 'Nana' - HH Sh, to 2', fls orange-scarlet   42

PUSCHKINIA - Liliaceae
  libanotica - see P. scilloides   84
        "   'Alba' - see P. scilloides 'Alba'   84
  scilloides / Bb / to 6" / fls pale blue / Near East   42
        "   'Alba' - white form from Lebanon   84

PUTORIA - Rubiaceae
  calabrica / HH Sh / to 1' / rosy-red fls; fetid lvs / Medit. reg.   64

PUYA - Bromeliaceae
  berteroniana / Gh / 10-12" / blue-green fls / c Chile   85
  caerulea / Gh / 3-4' / blue fls / Chile   9

PYCNANTHEMUM - Labiatae
  virginianum / P / 1-3' / whitish to purplish fls / e & c N. America   9

PYCNOSTACHYS - Labiatae
  urticifolia / HH P / 5-7' / bright blue fls / Tropics, S. Africa   9

PYRACANTHA - Rosaceae
  angustifolia / Sh / to 12' / frs orange-yellow / w China   46
  coccinea / Sh / 10'+ / rich red frs / s Europe, Asia Minor   46

PYROLA - Pyrolaceae
  asarifolia / R / to 1' / pink fls / N. America, Asia   35
        "   v. purpurea - despite name separated by leaf characters   34
  chlorantha / R / to 1' / yellowish-green fls / Europe   92
  dentata / R / to 1' / fls cream to greenish-white / Calif.,Montana   47
  minor / R / 8" / fls whitish to lilac-pink / Europe   92
  picta / R / to 1' / purplish fls / Pacific Slope of N. America   35
        "   v. dentata - see P. dentata   47
  promiscua secunda - see P. secunda   *
  rotundifolia / R / to 1' / white fls / Europe, North America   38
  secunda / R / 5" / fls greenish white / boreal n hemisphere   60

QUAMOCLIT - Convolvulaceae
  pennata / A Cl / 6-8' / orange-scarlet fls / Peru, intro. in s US   41

QUERCUS - Fagaceae
  sadleriana / Sh / 3-5' / serrate lvs / n Calif., sw Oregon   46

QUILLAJA - Rosaceae
  saponaria / HH T / 50' / white fls / Chile   9

RAMONDA - Gesneriaceae
  'Mont Serrat' - see R. myconi 'Mont Serrat'   (1)
  myconi / R / 4-6" / fls pale mauve / n Pyrenees   42
        "   'Alba' - should be pure white fls   38
        "   'Mont Serrat' - large rosettes, correspondingly fine fls (1)
        "   'Rosea' - pale, clear pink fls   38
  nathaliae / R / 4-6" / lavender-blue fls / Balkans   35
  serbica / R / 3-4" / mauve fls / Balkans   38

  (1) - WORTH in corres.

RANUNCULUS - Ranunculaceae

aconitifolius / P / to 20" / sepals reddish to purplish / c Europe   90
acris / P / 20-40" / common Buttercup, weedy in US / Eurasia   68
adoneus / R / 4-8" / yellow fls / Col., Mont., Utah in mts.   35
alpestris / R / to 5" / white fls / Europe, in mts.   90
amplexicaulis / R / 6-8" / white fls / Pyrenees   42
anemoneus / R / ? / pure white fls / Australian alps   (1)
asiaticus / Tu / 6-12" / varii-colored fls / Asia Minor   42
brevifolius / R / 8" / yellow fls / Italy, Balkans   90
buchanani / HH R / to 1' / white fls / subalpine, New Zealand   2
bulbosus / P / to 20" / yellow fls / most of Europe   90
calandrinioides / R / to 1' / pink or white fls / N. Africa   35
cardiophyllus / P / 6-18" / yellow fls / Sask. to Colorado   19
cassubicus / P / 20" / yellow fls / c & e Europe   90
constantinopolitanus / P / 18" / yellow fls / se Europe   90
cortusifolius / HH P / 3'+ / yellow fls; coriaceous lvs / Azores   90
crenatus / R / 4" / white fls / e Alps, Iceland   90
enysii / R / to 1' . fls bright to pale yellow / New Zealand   2
ficaria / R / to 1' / fls yellow / Europe   90
flammula / P / to 32" / yellow fls / Europe, mostly n   90
glaberrimus / R / 2-6" / yellow fls, ageing white / n Sierra Nevada   75
glacialis / R / 3-6" / white fls / European Alps, Iceland   42
gouanii / R / 1' / fls yellow / Pyrenees   90
gramineus / R / 4-8" / bright yellow fls / s.Europe   42
gunnianus / R / dwarf / yellow, pink or white fls / Australia   21
haastii / R / 3-6" / golden fls / alps of New Zealand   33
illyricus / P / 20" / pale yellow fls / c & se Europe   90
insignis / HH P / 3' / waxy yellow fls / New Zealand   78
lappaceus / HH P / to 20" / yellow fls / New Zealand, Australia   78
lingua v. grandiflora - aquatic, 3'+, golden fls, England   33
lyallii / HH P / to 4' / fls white / New Zealand   78
macrophyllus / P / 1-2' / yellow fls / w Medit. reg.   90
micranthus / R / 6" / fls pale yellow / e & c United States   34
millefoliatus / R / 6" / yellow fls / s & ec Europe   90
monspeliaceus / P / 20" / yellow fls; lvs whitish / w Medit. region   90
montanus / R / variable / yellow fls / Alps   33
muelleri / R / rosette / yellow fls / Australian alps   21
nemerosus / P / 3'+ / fls golden-yellow / Europe   90
obesus / P / 18" / golden fls / n Armenia   26
paludosus / P / to 20" / yellow fls / w Europe, Medit. region   90
parnassifolius / R / 4'+ / fls white or reddish / European Alps   90
pedatifidus / R / 1' / yellow fls / Spitzbergen   90
pseudomontanus - as P. montanus except achene short-beaked, Balkans   90
pyraneus / R / 2-6" / white fls / Alps, Pyrenees, Corsica   90
rupestris / HH R / to 12" / yellow fls / s Portugal, s Spain, Sicily   90
seguieri / R / to 8" / fls white / Alps, Apennines, Jugoslavia   90
sericophyllus / R / 10" / fls golden yellow / New Zealand, in mts.   2
spruneranus / P / 10-16" / yellow fls / Balkans, Syria   26
thora / R / to 1' / yellow fls / Europe, in mts.   90

RANZANIA - Podophyllaceae

japonica / R / 6-16" / fls pale lavender-violet before lvs / Japan   85

RAOULIA - Compositae

australis / R / carpet / fls pale sulphur-yellow / New Zealand   38
eximia / R / cushion / scarlet fls, rare in cult. / New Zealand   85
glabra / R / carpet / green lvs; white fls / New Zealand   35
grandiflora / R / cushion / silvery lvs / New Zealand   2

(1) - ELLIOTT in Quar. Bull. Alpine Garden Soc. 38:4

RAOULIA, con.
  hookeri / R / mat / yellow fls / New Zealand   78
      "   v. albo-sericea - compact habit, snow-white lvs   2
      "   v. apice-nigra - inner phyllodes black-tipped   2
  lutescens / R / mat / bright yellow fls / New Zealand   42
  petriensis / R / tuft / silvery lvs; showy frs / New Zealand   21
  rubra / R / 6" cushion / crimson to purplish fls / New Zealand   2
  subsericea / R / compact / silvery lvs; white fls / New Zealand   21
  tenuicaulis / R / carpet / silvery lvs; yellow fls / New Zealand   35
  youngii / R / carpet / silvery lvs; white daisies / New Zealand   21

RAPHIOLEPIS - Rosaceae
  umbellata / HH Sh / to 6' / white fls; frs bronzy-black / Far East   46

RATIBIDA - Compositae
  columnaris - see R. columnifera   (1)
  columnifera / B / 1-4' / bright yellow fls / North America   (1)
  pinnata / P / to 4' / yellow fls / e & c North America   82

RECHSTEINERIA - Gesneriaceae
  leucotricha / Gh / 6-10" / coral-red fls; silvery lvs / Brazil   41

RESEDA - Resedaceae
  alba / A or B / 1-3' / fls white / Mediterranean region   64

RESTIO - Restionaceae
  tetraphyllus / HH P / 3' / apetalous fls, related to rushes / Austrl.   45

RHAMNUS - Rhamnaceae
  cathartica / Sh or T / 15'+ / frs shiny black / Europe   46
  frangula / Sh / 18' / frs red changing to black / Europe   46
  purshiana / T / 30' / large lvs / w North America   46
  saxatilis / Sh / 2-3' / spiny branches; black frs / c & s Europe   69

RAPHITHAMNUS - Verbenaceae
  cyanocarpus / HH T / 20' / lilac fls; blue frs / Chile   9

RHAPONTICUM - Compositae
  scariosum / P / to 3'+ / fls rosy-purple / Alps   96

RHEUM - Polygonaceae
  alexandrae / P / 3-4' / straw-colored bracts / China, Tibet   62
  emodi / HH P / 6-10' / purple plumey fls / Himalayas   62
  palmatum / P / 5-6' / lvs deeply lobed / ne Asia   9
      "   'Bowles Red' - crimson lvs with blood-red veins   (2)

RHEXIA - Melastomaceae
  lutea / HH R / 1' / fls yellow / N. Carolina to Florida   9
  mariana / P / to 2' / pale purple fls / N. Jersey, Florida, Kentucky   35
  virginica / P / 12-18" / rosy-purple fls / Maine to Florida & Mo.   35

RHINANTHUS - Scrophulariaceae
  alectorolophus / P / 8-32" / yellow fls / Alps, Pyrenees, Apennines   96
  alpinus / P / to 20" / pale yellow fls / se & ec Europe, in mts.   92
  aristatus / P / to 20" / yellow fls / se Europe   92
  cristi-galli / A / to 3' / yellow fls / Eurasia, North America   34
  minor / P / to 20" / yellow fls / most of Europe   92

(1) - DRESS in Baileya 9:2
(2) - HILL in Jour. of the Royal Hort. Soc. May 1968

RHINOPETALUM - Liliaceae
bucharicum / Bb / to 1' / fls white, green or lt. violet / c Asia   54
karelinii / Bb / 4-8" / fls rosy-violet / c Asia   54
stenantherum / Bb / 6" / light rosy-violet fls / c Asia   54

RHODEA japonica - error for ROHDEA japonica   *

RHODIOLA - Crassulaceae
dumulosa / R / to 8" / white fls / China   21
himalaiense - see Sedum quadrifidum in 21,33.   Genus ref. (1)
    "   v. stephanii - dwarfer, longer fls, narrower lvs   33
rosea / R / to 1' / dull yellow fls / n Europe, s Europe, in mts.   90

RHODODENDRON - Ericaceae
aberconwayi / Sh / 3-5' / fls white, tinged pink / Yunnan   46
albrechtii / Sh / 5' / deep rose-pink fls / Japan   42
arborescens / Sh / 9' / white or pinkish fls / Pa. to Alabama   69
arboreum / HH Sh / to 20' / white to blood-red fls / Himalayas   46
atlanticum / Sh / 3'+ / white fls, occ. pinkish / e United States   46
aureum - see R. xanthostephanum   (2)
austrinum / HH Sh / 6'+ / yellow fls / Florida   69
barbatum / HH Sh / 18' / crimson-scarlet fls / Nepal, Sikkim   46
'Blue Peter' - vigorous hybrid, fls cobalt-blue   46
brachyanthum v. hypolepidatum - 3', yellow fls, China, Tibet   43
'Buzzard' - straw-yellow Knap Hill azalea   46
calendulaceum / Sh / 12' / fls yellow to scarlet / e United States   46
californicum / Sh / 8'+ / fls rosy-purple / California & n-wards   9
calostrotum / Sh / 1' / fls in rose shades / Burma   38
    "   'Gigha' - fls deep claret-red, gray-green lvs   46
campylocarpum / Sh / 5'+ / clear yellow fls / Nepal   46
campylogynum / Sh / 12-18" / brownish-red fls / China   38
    "   v. charopoeum - more spreading, larger fls   (2)
    "   v. myrtilloides - fls plum-purple, Tibet   46
camtschaticum / Sh / to 1' / red fls / Japan, Alaska   60
canadense / Sh / 3'+ / fls rose-purple / ne North America   46
canescens / Sh / 10' / fls white flushed pink / se United States   46
'Caracticus' - 10'+, dark purple fls   (3)
X 'Carmen' - glistening dark crimson fls   46
chameunum / Sh / dwarf / rosy-purple fls / w & sw China   46
chapmanii / Sh / to 6' / pink fls / w Florida   46
charitopes / HH Sh / 1½-3' / pink fls / Burma   38
chrysanthum / Sh / prostrate / yellow fls / n Asia   43
ciliatum / Sh / to 5' / white to pink fls / Himalayas   42
X cilpinense - 3', fls white, flushed pink   46
'Conewago' - lavender-pink fls   (4)
dalhousiae / Gh Sh / straggling / tubular white fls / ?   (2)
'Day Dream' - Exbury Hybrid azalea, crimson buds, pink fls   46
degronianum - see R. metternichii v. pentamerum   60
falconeri / HH Sh / 15' / creamy-yellow fls / Nepal, Bhutan   46
fargesii / Sh / 10'+ / fls rosy-lilac / w China   46
fastigiatum / Sh / to 3' / light purple fls / Yunnan   38
ferrugineum / Sh / 3½' / rosy-crimson fls / European Alps   42
fimbriatum / Sh / 1-3' / fls purplish / Szechwan   46

(1) - Iconographia Cormophytorum Sinicorum. Tomus II 1972
(2) - COX & COX - Modern Rhododendrons. 1956
(3) - STREET - Hardy Rhododendrons. 1954
(4) - CLARKE - Rhododendrons for Your Garden. 1961

RHODODENDRON, con.
```
  flavidum 'Album' - 3', lax habit, large white fls                         46
  glaucophyllum / Sh / 3' / lilac-rose fls / Sikkim                         46
          "      v. luteiflorum - lemon-yellow fls, Burma                   46
          "      v. tubiforme - Ludlow & Sheriff coll.                      (1)
  glomerulatum / Sh / to 3' / fls purple-mauve / Yunnan                     46
  grande / HH Sh / 15' / ivory-white fls / Nepal, Sikkim                    46
  griersonianum / Sh / to 6' / strong red fls / Yunnan                      42
  hanceanum 'Nanum' - 1', fls yellowish                                     46
  hippophaeoides / Sh / 3'+ / lavender-rose fls / Yunnan                    46
  hirsutum / Sh / 1-2' / rosy fls / c Europe                                38
  impeditum / Sh / 6-18" / fls in shades of blue / China                    38
  imperator / Sh / 6" / pinkish-purple fls / Burma                          38
  X intermedium - to 5', rose-pink fls, European Alps                       (2)
  japonicum / Sh / to 6' / vermilion to yellow fls / Japan                  60
  kaempferi / Sh / 3-9' / fls in red shades / Japan                         46
  keiskei / Sh / to 3' / pale greenish-yellow fls / Japan                   60
  keleticum / Sh / 6-12" / clear pink fls / Tibet                           38
  kiusianum / Sh / to 3' / lilac-purple fls / Kyushu                        46
          "    'Album' - white fls                                          *
  kotschyi - see R. myrtifolium                                             92
  lapponicum / Sh / to 20" / purple fls / n Europe, n North America         92
  lepidotum / Sh / to 3' / pink to purple fls / Szechwan                    46
  leucapsis / Sh / 1-2' / solid white fls / Tibet                           38
  lowndesii / Sh / 6" / pale yellow fls / Nepal                             43
  macrophyllum - see R. californicum                                        93
  maddenii / Gh Sh / white fls, faint rose flush / Himalayas                (2)
  maximum / Sh / 10'+ / fls purple-rose to white / e United States          46
  metternichii / Sh / to 12' / rose-colored fls / Japan                     60
  micranthum / Sh / to 6' / white bell fls / China                          46
  molle - see R. japonicum                                                  46
  moupinense / HH Sh / 3' / white fls, spotted / w China                    69
  mucronulatum / Sh / 3-6' / fls rose-purple / Far East                     60
  myrtifolium / Sh / 20" / fls clear pink / Carpathians                     92
  myrtilloides / Sh / 6-12" / fls purpleis / ne Burma                       38
  neriifolium / Sh / 6'+ / fls rose to crimson / Yunnan                     46
  nipponicum / Sh / 3-6' / white fls / Honshu, in mts.                      60
  nitens / Sh / to 3' / deep purple fls / Burma                             46
  nudiflorum / Sh / 6'+ / pale pink fls / e North America                   46
  occidentale / Sh / 6'+ / white to pink fls / w North America              46
  pemakoense / Sh / 6-12" / pale purple fls / se Tibet                      42
  'Pioneer' - 4', lavender-rose fls                                         (3)
  'P. J. M.' - 4', lavender-pink fls                                        (4)
  'Puck' - 3', pink fls                                                     (4)
  ponticum / Sh / 10'+ / mauve to lilac-pink fls / Asia Minor               46
  pumilum / Sh / prostrate / fls pink or rose / Sikkim                      46
  quinquefolium / Sh / to 6' / fls white / Japan                            42
  racemosum / Sh / 5-6' / fls white or pink / China                         42
          "    'Forrests Dwarf' - bright pink fls                           46
  X 'Racil' - shell pink fls                                                85
  radicans / Sh / 3-4" / solitary purple fls / Tibet                        38
  reticulatum / Sh / to 24' / fls rose-purple to magenta / Japan            69
  roseum / Sh / 9' / fls pale to deep pink / e North America                46
  X 'Rosy Bell' - to 6', bell-shaped rose-pink fls                          46
  rupicola / Sh / 1-2' / fls deep plum-crimson / China                      (2)
```

(1) - GIBSON in Jour. Royal Horticultural Soc. August 1967
(2) - COX & COX - Modern Rhododendrons. 1956
(3) - CLARKE - Rhododendrons for Your Garden. 1961
(4) - Greer Gardens catalog. 1973

RHODODENDRON, con.
  russatum / Sh / 2-4' / fls blue-purple / China   38
  saluense / Sh / 12"+ / deep purple fls / Yunnan   43
  sanguineum / Sh / 3'+ / bright crimson fls / Yunnan, se Tibet   46
  sargentianum / Sh / 1' / fls white or yellow / Szechwan   42
  schlippenbachii / Sh / 9'+ / fls rose pink / Korea   46
  scintillans / Sh / 1-3' / fls lavender-blue / Yunnan   46
  'Scintillation' - Dexter Hybrid, deep pink fls   (1)
  searsiae / Sh / 5-8' / white, rose, mauve fls / Szechwan   46
  sperabile / Sh / to 6' / bell-shaped fleshy fls, red / ne U. Berma   46
  X spinulosum - bell-shaped, deep pink fls   46
  tephropeplum / Sh / 4' / fls pink, carmine-rose / Tibet   46
  trichostomum / Sh / 3-5' / fls white, pink, rose / Yunnan   46
      "   v. radinum - densely scaly corolla   43
  tsangpoense / Sh / 3' / fls crimson to violet / Burma   46
  uniflorum / Sh / compact / pink fls / China, Tibet   (2)
  vaseyi / Sh / 9' / rose-pink to white fls / North Carolina   46
  virgatum / Sh / 4' / lilac-purple fls / Bhutan   46
  viridescens / Sh / to 3' / fls greenish-yellow / Tibet   46
  viscosum / Sh / 5' / fragrant white fls / e North America   46
  wardii / Sh / 8' / clear yellow fls / Szechwan   42
  williamsianum / Sh / 4' / shell-pink fls / Szechwan   42
  'Windbeam' - apricot fls fading white   (2)
  'Winsome' - wavy-edged deep pink fls   46
  'Wyanoki' - white fls   (2)
  yakusimanum / Sh / 3' / white fls / Island of Yakushima   42
  yedoense / Sh / 3-5' / rosy-purple fls / from cult., Japan & Korea   46

RHODOHYPOXIS - Amaryllidaceae
  baurii / HH Bb / 1-3" / rose-red fls / South Africa   38
    " v. platypetala - white fls   32
    " v. rubella - see R. rubella   21
  platypetala - see R. baurii v. platypetala   32
  rubella / HH Bb / to 3" / fls bright pink / Drakensberg Mts., S. Afr.56

RHODOPHIALA - Amaryllidaceae
  andicola / HH Bb / to 10" / light carmine-pink fls / Chile, Argent. (3)
  bifida / HH Bb / 12" / dark red fls / Argentina   (4)
  elwesii - suggested to be a ssp. of R. mendocina, Argentina   (3)

RHODOTHAMNUS - Ericaceae
  chamaecistus / Sh / 1' / pure pink fls / European Alps   35

RHODOTYPOS - Rosaceae
  scandens / Sh / 6' / fls white; shiny black frs / Far East   91

RHUS - Anacardiaceae
  aromatica / Sh / 3-5' / fls yellowish / e & s North America   46
  cotinus atropurpurea - see COTINUS coggyria f. purpureus   46
  glabra / Sh / to 10' / scarlet frs / e North America   46
  sylvestris / HH T / to 30' / frs brownish-yellow / Far East   69
  typhina / Sh or T / to 30' / crimson frs / e North America   42
    "   'Laciniata' - cut-leaved form, tenderer & smaller   9

(1) - Greer Gardens catalog. 1973
(2) - CLARKE - Rhododendrons for Your Garden. 1961
(3) - RAVENNA in Herbertia 1970
(4) - TRAUB in Herbertia 1953

RIBES - Grossulariaceae
  bracteosum / Sh / to 9' / greenish or purplish fls / Alaska, Cal.   69
  lacustre / Sh / 3'+ / pale yellow to white fls / w North America   46
  lobbii / HH Sh / to 6' / fls purple-red; purple frs / B.C. to Cal.   69
  sanguineum / HH Sh / to 10' / red fls; black frs / B. C. to Calif.   9

RICHEA - Epacridaceae
  continensis / Sh / alpine / lvs in rosettes, creamy fls / N.S. Wales(1)

RICINUS - Euphorbiaceae
  communis / A / 3-15' / great variety in leaf / tropical Africa   9

RIGIDELLA - Iridaceae
  flammea / HH Bb / 3' / deep scarlet-red fls / Michoccan, Mexico   (2)

RIVINA - Phytolaccaceae
  humilis / Gh / 6-24" / fls white; frs crimson / Florida, S. America   41

RODGERSIA - Saxifragaceae
  aesculifolia / P / 2½-6' / white fls, compound lvs / China   9
  pinnata 'Superba' - to 4', fls delicate rose; frs dark red   9
  tabularis / P / 3-4' / creamy-white fls / China   42

ROHDEA - Liliaceae
  japonica / HH R / 4-8" / pale yellow fls; red frs / s Japan, China   60

ROMANZOFFIA - Hydrophyllaceae
  californica / R / to 6" / creamy-white fls / nw North America   38
  sitchensis - see R. californica   38
  suksdorfii / R / to 1' / white fls / c Calif. to Washington   75
  traceyi / R / 4" / white fls / n California to Washington   75
  unalaschkensis / R / 3-5" / fls purplish to white / Unalaska   9

ROMNEYA - Papaveraceae
  coulteri / Sh / to 8' / satiny white fls / California   42

ROMULEA - Iridaceae
  atroviolacea / C / small / deep violet fls / Corsica   37
  bulbocodium / C / 6" / bright violet fls / s Europe   84
      "   'Album' - a white form   84
      "   v. leitchliniana - fls white, creamy, violet mkgs, Greece(3)
  citrina / HH C / 5" / bright yellow starry fls / Namaqualand   84
  clusiana / C / 6" / violet-mauve fls / Spain   84
  columnae / C / 6" / whitish or pale mauve fls / c Portugal   65
  crocea / C / 6" / bright golden-yellow fls / Asia Minor   84
  cruciata v. parviflora - HH C, pale violet fls streaked, S. Africa   37
  duthiae / HH C / 6" / fls white flushed lavender / Stellenbosch   37
  gaditana / C / 6" / violet to violet-purple fls / sw Spain   65
  grandiscapa / C / ? / purple & orange fls / n Africa   21
  linaresii / C / 6" / violet & purple fls / France to Turkey   64
  longifolia - see R. rosea   56
  longituba / HH C / 7-14" / yellow fls / South Africa   37
      "   v. alticola - 8", yellow fls, Basutoland   (4)
  lutea nigra - see R. longituba v. alticola   (4)
  macowanii / HH C / ? / golden yellow fls / mts. of e Cape Province   84

(1) - VALDER in Jour. Royal Horticultural Soc. Sept. 1964
(2) - CRUDEN in Brittonia 23:2
(3) - HUXLEY in Jour. Royal Horticultural Soc. ____ 1963
(4) - MURRAY-LYON in Bull. Am. Rock Garden Soc. 27:2

ROMULEA, con.
```
  nivalis / HH C / 6" / yellow, white, lilac fls / Lebanon              56
  parviflora - see R. cruciata v. parviflora                           37
  rabularis - error for R. tabularis                                    *
  ramiflora / C / ? / purple-pink fls / Mt. Elgon, Africa              21
  requienii / C / 5" / deep purple-violet fls / Corsica                84
  rosea / HH C / 5" / deep pink fls / Cape Districts, South Africa      84
    "   'Tabularis - to 1', rose-violet fls , Cape Peninsula           37
  sabulosa / HH C / 3" / bright cherry-red fls / Natal                 36
  speciosa / HH C / 5" / deep carmine-pink fls / Cape of Good Hope     84
  tabularis - see R. rosea 'Tabularis'                                 37
  tempskyana / C / ? / fls purple / Cyprus                            (1)
  thodei / HH C / 6" / deep violet fls / Drakensberg Mts., Africa       56
  zahnii / C / ? / white & gold & violet fls / Greece                  21
```

ROSA - Rosaceae
```
  arvensis / Sh / dense mounds or drapes / scentless white fls / Eu.    46
  carolina / Sh / 3-5' / fragrant rose-pink fls / e North America       46
  centifolia 'Cristata' - Sh, 3', pink fls, crested petals             (2)
  chinensis / HH Sh / 5'+ / crimson or pink fls / c China               46
  cristata - probably R. centifolia 'Cristata'                          *
  eglanteria - see R. rubignosa                                         46
  farreri / Sh / 6' / pale pink or white fls / s Kansu, China           46
    "   f. persetosa - to 6', soft pink fls, s Kansu                    46
  gallica / Sh / 5' / deep pink fls / c & s Europe                      69
  gymnocarpa / Sh / to 10' / pale pink fls / B.C., Calif., Mont.         9
  hugonis / Sh / 6' / fls yellow / w China                              9
  moyesii / Sh / 10' / blood-crimson fls / w China                      46
    "   'Geranium' - 8', lighter green lvs, orange hips                42
    "   f. rosea - fls light pink                                       69
  nutkana / Sh / 8' / bright pink fls / w North America                 46
  palustris / Sh / 6' / pink fls / e North America                      69
  pendulina / Sh / 4' / magenta-pink fls / c & s Europe, in mts.        46
  persetosa farreri - see R. farreri f. persetosa                       46
  pimpinellifolia / Sh / 4' / white or pale pink fls / Eu., n Asia      46
    "        v. altaica - 6', creamy-white fls, Altai Mts.             46
  pisocarpa / Sh / 6' / pink fls / B. C. to Idaho                       69
  rubrifolia / Sh / to 6' / fls clear pink / c & n Europe               46
  rubignosa / Sh / 10' / clear pink fls; aromatic lvs / Europe          46
  rugosa / Sh / to 6' / purplish-rose fls / ne Asia                     46
    "   'Alba' - white fls                                              46
    "   'Frau Dagmar Hastrop' - 5', fls pale rose-pink                  46
    "   'Hansa' - 5', double, deep-crimson-purple fls                  (3)
  setigera / Sh / 6' / fls deep rose / c North America                   9
  spinosissima - see R. pimpinellifolia                                 46
    "        altaica - see R. pimpinellifolia v. altaica               46
  ultramontana / Sh / 9-10' / fls small, rose-colored / e Ore., e Wash. 47
  villosa / Sh / 4½' / pink fls / c & s Europe                         91
  virginiana / Sh / 4' / bright pink fls / e North America              46
  wichuriana / Sh / trailing / white fls, small red frs / Japan         46
  woodsii ultromontana - see R. ultramontana                          (4)
```

ROSCOEA - Zingiberaceae
```
  alpina / R / 4-8" / pinkish-purple fls / Himalayas                    38
  cauteloides / R / to 1' / pale lemon-yellow fls / w China             42
    "        'Grandiflora' - larger yellow fls                        (5)
```

(1) - Anon. in Jour. Royal Horticultural Soc. Sept. 1963
(2) - THOMAS - The Old Shrub Roses. 1971
(3) - THOMAS - Shrub Roses of Today. 1962
(4) - HAYES & GARRISON - Key to Imp. Woody Plants..Ore. & Wash. 1960
(5) - FINNIS in Jour. Royal Horticultural Soc. April 1964

ROSCOEA, con.
  humeana / R / 4-8" / pinkish-purple fls / Himalayas   42
  procera - see R. purpurea v. procera   43
  purpurea / R / 12"+ / purple fls / Kuamon, Sikkim   38
      "   v. procera - 8", deep purple-blue fls, Sikkim   43

ROSMARINUS - Labiatae
  lavendulaceus / HH Sh / low / blue fls / s Europe   46
  officinalis / HH Sh / 4½' / lilac fls / circum-Medit. region   64

ROSULARIA - Crassulaceae
  aizoon / R / rosettes / fls pale yellow / Armenia, Iran   26
  sempervivoides - see SEDUM sempervivoides   26

RUBUS - Rosaceae
  lasiocarpus - see R. niveus   69
  leucodermis / Sh / to 6' / fls white; purple-black frs / nw US   69
  niveus / HH Sh / to 6' / fls rosy-purple / India, w China   69
  odoratus / Sh / 7' / fls purple-rose / e North America   46
  parviflorus / Sh / 3½-7½' / white fls / w North America   46
  parvus / HH Sh / 2' / white fls / New Zealand   46
  pedatus / R / mat / unarmed; white fls / Alaska, Oregon, Montana   47
  phenicolasus / Sh / to 9' / clustered pale pink fls / Far East   46
  spectabilis / Sh / 3-4' / bright magenta-rose fls / w N. America   46
  X tridel - Sh, to 9', glistening white fls   46
  ursinus / Sh / trailing or clambering / fls white, pale pink / nw N.A 47

RUDBECKIA - Compositae
  fulgida v. speciosa 'Goldsturm' - P, 2', orange-yellow fls   85
      "   'Gloriosa Daisy' - see R. hirta 'Gloriosa Daisy'   85
      "   'Goldflame' - see R. hirta 'Golden Flame'   85
      "   'Goldstrum' - see R. f. var. speciosa 'Goldsturm'   85
  hirta / A or B / 1-3' / golden yellow fls / North America   9
      " 'Gloriosa Daisy' - A, 3-3½', gold & bronze shades   85
      " 'Golden Flame' - A, 2', golden yellow fls, dark centers   89
  laciniata / P / 1½-9' / yellow fls / e & c North America   34
  sullivantii 'Goldsturm' - see R. fulgida v. speciosa 'Goldsturm'   *

RUELLIA - Acanthaceae
  carolinensis / P / to 3' / fls lavender to lilac-blue / se US   34
  ciliosa - see R. carolinensis   34
  humilis / P / to 2½' / fls lavender to bluish / c & e US   34
  pedunculata / P / to 30" / fls violet or purple / c United States   34
  strepens / P / 3' / blue fls / sc United States   33

RUMEX - Polygonaceae
  scutatus / P / 10-20" / helmet-shaped lvs / c & s Europe, in mts.   96

RUPICAPNOS - Papaveraceae
  africana / R / decumbent / white fls / sw Spain   90

RUSCUS - Liliaceae
  aculeatus / HH Sh / to 3' / green flattened stems, red frs / s Eu.   46

RUTA - Rutaceae
  bracteosa - see R. chalepensis   91
  chalepensis / HH P / 8-24" / fringed yellow fls / s Europe   91
  graveolens / P / 18" / yellow fls / Balkan Peninsula   91
      "   'Jackmans Blue' - vivid glaucous blue lvs   46
  montana / P / 6-28" / leaf-segments linear / sw Europe   91
  patavina - see HAPLOPHYLLUM patavina   91

SABATIA - Gentianaceae
   angularis / A or B / 1½-2' / fls light rose to white / e N. Am.   9

SABINEA chinensis v. procumbens - see JUNIPERUS procumbens   *

SAGINA - Caryophyllaceae
   subulata / R / mat / white fls / w & c Europe   90

SALIX - Salicaceae
   arctica / Sh / procumbent / catkins 5 X 1 cm. / arctic Asia   90
   lanata / Sh / 1½-3' / yellow-gray woolly catkins / n Eurasia   46
   mackenzieana / T / 15-30' / branches pale yellow-green / w N. Am.   46
   myrtilloides / Sh / to 20" / rounded lvs / n & c Europe   90
   repens / Sh / creeping / small, gray-green lvs / Europe, Asia   46
   reticulata / Sh / dwarf / lvs with conspicuous veins / n Europe   90
   retusa / Sh / procumbent / stalked yellow catkins / c & e Europe   43

SALPIGLOSSIS - Solanaceae
   sinuata / A / 1-3' / varii-colored fls / Chile   42
      "   'Golden Queen' - selection for yellow fls   *

SALVIA - Labiatae
   aethiopis / B or P / 1-3' / white fls / s & se Europe   92
   argentea / B or P / to 3' / white fls / e Medit. region   85
   blepharophylla / HH Sh / 1-1½' / fls crimson-red / Mexico   85
   bulleyana / P / to 3' / yellow to purple fls / China   85
   caespitosa / Sh / 3-6" / fls violet or blue / Anatolia   85
   canariensis / Gh Sh / to 6' / white lvs; fls purplish / Canary Isls.   9
   coccinea / P gr. as A / 2' / fls deep scarlet / Brazil   85
   compacta / R / to 1' / pinkish-lavender fls / Turkey   (1)
   farinacea / P / 2-3' / fls purple or violet / Texas   9
   forskhalii / P / to 3' / fls blue or violet / Bulgaria   85
   glutinosa / P / 3' / yellow fls / Europe to sw Asia   85
   grahamii / HH Sh / 3-4½' / ruby-red fls / Mexico   95
   haematodes / P gr. as A / 4½' / violet-blue fls / Greece   95
   hians / P / 2' / blue fls / Kashmir   9
   indica / HH P / 4' / bluish fls / Syria, Iraq, Lebanon   85
   lavandulifolia / P / 20" / blue, violet-blue fls / c, s & e Spain   92
   jurisicii / P / 12-16" / fls violet-blue to pink / Serbia   85
      "   'Alba' - a white form   *
   nutans / P / 5'+ / violet fls / c Hungary, sc Russia   92
   officinalis / Sh / 2' / violet, pink, blue or white fls / s & se Eu.   92
   patens / HH P / 30" / fls bright deep blue / Mexico   85
   pratensis / P / to 3' / blue fls / Europe, incl. Britain   85
      "   'Rosea' - rosy-purple fls   9
   roemeriana / HH P / 1-2' / deep scarlet fls / Texas, Mexico   9
   sclarea / B or P / to 4' / fls pinkish / Europe   85
      "   v. turkestanica - white fls tinged pink   42
   verticillata / P / to 3' / fls lilac or violet-blue / Europe   85
      "   'Alba' - white form   *
   virgata / P / to 40" / fls violet-blue / Italy, s & e Balkans   92

SAMBUCUS - Caprifoliaceae
   caerulea / Sh or T / to 50' / fls yellowish-white / B.C. to Mont.   9
   callicarpa / Sh / 10'+ / scarlet frs / Alaska to California   9
   canadensis 'Acutiloba' - 10', lvs much dissected   69
      "   'Laciniata' - see S. c. 'Acutiloba'   69
   racemosa / Sh / 10' / bright scarlet frs / Europe, w Asia   46
      "   v. arborescens - see S. callicarpa   *

(1) - WORTH in corres.

SANDERSONIA - Liliaceae
  aurantiaca / HH Tu / 2' / fls pale orange / Natal   84

SANGUINARIA - Papaveraceae
  canadensis / R / 6-9" / fls white / e North America   35

SANGUISORBA - Rosaceae
  canadensis / P / 4-5' / whitish fls / North America   42
  minor / P / to 2½' / sepals green, pink margins / Europe   91
  officinalis / P / 2' / brownish-red fls / Europe   (1)
  sitchensis / P / 1-3' / sepals greenish-white / nw North America 75

SANICULA - Umbelliferae
  arctopoides / R / flat leaf-rosette / yellow fls / Calif. to Wash. 75
  marilandica / P / 1½-4' / fls greenish-white / n North America   9

SANTOLINA - Compositae
  chamaecyparissus 'Nana' - under 1', dense Sh, white lvs   38
  incana 'Nana' - see S. chamaecyparissus 'Nana'   38
  neapolitana / Sh / dwarf / fls bright lemon-yellow / Italy   46
  virens / Sh / dwarf / lvs thread-like; fls yellow / ?   46

SAPINDUS - Sapindaceae
  saponaria / HH T / to 30' / orange-brown frs / s Fla., W. Indes 9

SANVITALIA - Compositae
  procumbens / A / 6" / yellow fls / Mexico   42

SAPONARIA - Caryophyllaceae
  bellidifolia / R / 8-16" / yellow fls / Balkans   90
  'Bressingham Hybrid' - R, 3-4", clear pink fls   38
  calabrica / A / 6-12" / fls lively rose-red / Italy, Greece   32
     "   'Compacta' - a dwarf form   32
  caespitosa / R / dense / fls purplish / Pyrenees   90
  lutea / R / to 4" / fls yellow / s, w & c Alps   90
  officinalis / P / 1-3' / fls flesh-pink / Europe   90
  ocymoides / R / procumbent / fls pale purplish / s Europe   90
     "   compacta - see S. o. 'Rubra Compacta'   *
     "   'Rubra Compacta' - dwarf, deep pink fls   42
  X olivana - R, mat, bright pink fls   38
  pulvinaris - see S. pumilio   90
  pumila - see S. pumilio   95
  pumilio / R / caespitose / fls pale purplish / Alps   90

SARCOCOCCA - Buxaceae
  confusa / Sh / 3' / fragrant fls; black frs / China?   46
  hookerana humilis - see S. humilis   46
  humilis / Sh / 1½' / black frs / w China   46
  ruscifolia / Sh / 3' / dark red frs / c China   46

SARCOCAPNOS - Papaveraceae
  enneaphylla / R / to 1' / fls white to yellow / Spain   90

SARCOPOTERIUM - Rosaceae
  spinosa / Sh / 2½' / green sepals, white-rimmed / e Medit. region 26

  (1) - SMITH - Easy Plants for Difficult Places. 1967

SARRACENIA - Sarraceniaceae
```
flava / P / 10-34" / yellow fls / Virginia to Florida          9
jonesii / HH P / 1-2½' / petals dark red / N. Carolina to Florida  (1)
minor / HH P / 8-24" / pale yellow fls / N. carolina to Florida  9
purpurea / P / 12" / red-purple fls / e North America          35
rubra / HH P / 6-20" / crimson fragrant fls / N. Carolina to Fla.  9
```

SATUREJA - Labiatae
```
alpina - see ACINOS alpina                                     (2)
douglasii / R / trailing / fls white or purplish / w N. America  75
montana / Sh / 6-12" / fls purplish / Europe, N. Africa         9
thymifolia - see MICROMERIA thymifolia                         92
```

SAUSSUREA - Compositae
```
alpina / R / 1'+ / violet-blue fls / Alps                      67
discolor / R / 4" / purplish-blue fls / w Alps                 96
gossipiphora / R / 9" / white shaggy lvs; fls hidden / Himalayas  (3)
stella / R / 2" rosette / blue-purple fls / Tibet              38
yanigisawae / R / to 1' / purplish cobwebby fls / Hokkaido     60
```

SAXIFRAGA - Saxifragaceae
(Sections - as in Winton Harding's _Saxifrages_ - Alpine Garden Soc. 1970)

```
(1)  - Micranthes.  Northern. Small horticultural importance.
(2)  - Hirculus.  Bog plants.  Limited horticultural importance.
(3)  - Robertsoniana.  The "London Pride" group.
(4)  - Miscopetalum.  Small-flowered.  Negligible horticultural value.
(5)  - Cymbalaria.  Annuals.  Limited horticultural usage.
(6)  - Tridactylites.  Annuals, mostly.  Little horticultural value.
(7)  - Nephrophyllum.  Meadow Saxifrage group.  Of limited interest.
(8)  - Dactyloides.  Mossy Saxifrage group. Of considerable interest.
(9)  - Trachyphyllum.  Mat-forming.  Of no great importance.
(10) - Xanthizoon.  One northern species of negligible interest.
(11) - Euaizoon.  "Encrusted" group.  Of major interest.
(12) - Kabschia.  Includes "Englerias".  Of considerable interest.
(13) - Porphyrion.  Mat-forming.  Of definite importance.
(14) - Tetrameridium.  Asian spp.  Mostly of unknown value.
(15) - Diptera.  From Japan or China.  Doubtful hardiness.
```

```
(6) adscendens / B / to 10" / white fls / Europe, in mts.      90
(10) aizoides / R / to 10" / yellow, orange, red fls / Europe  90
         "    v. atrorubens - blood-red fls                    43
      aizoon - see S. paniculata                               90
        "  'Alba' - see S. paniculata 'Alba'                    *
        "  balcana - see S. paniculata v. balcana              33
        "  baldensis - see S. paniculata 'Minutifolia'         39
        "  brevifolia - see S. paniculata v. brevifolia        33
        "  correvoneana - see S. paniculata 'Correvoneana'     33
        "  lutea - see S. paniculata v. lutea                  38
        "  minor - see S. paniculata v. minor                  43
        "  'Minutifolia' - see S. paniculata 'Minutifolia'     39
        "  notata - see S. paniculata 'Notata'                 33
        "  paradoxa - see S. X paradoxa                        33
        "  portae - see S. paniculata 'Portae'                  *
        "  'Rex' - see S. paniculata 'Rex'                     38
        "  rosea - see S. paniculata v. rosea                  43
```

(1) SMALL - Manual of the Southeastern Flora. 1933
(2) DeWOLF in Baileya. 2:2
(3) KITAMURA in KIHARA - Fauna & Flora of Nepal Himalaya. 1955

SAXIFRAGA, con.

      (1) - HORNY, SOJAK, WEBR in Bull. Am. Rock Garden Soc. 33:4
      (2) - CALDER & SAVILE in Brittonia. 11:4
      (3) - GORER in Quar. Bull. Alpine Garden Soc. 43:4

SAXIFRAGA, con.
```
 (8)    cebennensis / R / 4" / fls white or cream / s France              90
 (7)    cernua / R / to 10" / white fls / n North America, n Europe       34
 (8)    cespitosa / R / 3" / fls dull white / arctic Europe & N. Am.      90
          "      v. uniflora - 2½", greenish-white fls, Jura Mts.,Norway96
        X chrystalie - see S. X biasolettii 'Chrystalie'                  39
(11)    X churchillii - 9", fls white, e Alps                             43
(11)    cochlearis / R / to 8" / fls white, red spotted / Maritime Alps   90
          "        'Major' - larger plant                                 43
          "        'Minor' - smaller plant                                43
          "        probinii - see S. C. 'Minor'                          43
 (8)    conifera / R / 4" / white fls / n Spain                           90
 (8)    corbariensis / HH R / 5-10" / pure white fls / e Pyrenees         39
        coriifolia - see S. rotundifolia v. coriifolia                    26
        corymbosa - see S. luteoviridis                                   90
(11)    cotyledon / R / to 20" / white fls / Alps, Pyrenees, Iceland      90
          "      v. caterhamensis - fls heavily spotted red, Norway       43
          "      v. icelandica - blue-gray rosette, pure white fls        43
          "      'Montafoniensis' - stocky, red-stemmed plant             33
          "      v. norvegica - 18", red stems, Norway                    43
          "      'Pyramidalis' - broadly conical inflorescence            39
          "      'Southside Seedling' - 18", white fls spotted red         5
(12)    'Cranbourne' - 1½", large rose fls                                38
(11)    crustata / R / 1' / fls white / e Alps, Jugoslavia                90
 (8)    cuneata / R / 6" / fls white / w Pyrenees, n Spain                90
 (3)    cuneifolia / R / 6" / fls white / s & sc Europe, in mts.          90
          "      v. bucklandii - larger plant                             33
          "      v. capillipes - smaller plant, fls speckled purple       39
          "      'Multicaulis' - spatulate lvs                            20
 (5)    cymbalaria / A / decumbent / fls yellow / sw Asia, n Africa       90
          "      ssp. huetiana - smaller fls                              90
        daimatica - see Farrer's reference to S. dalmatica                33
 (1)    davurica / R / 7" / small white fls / Siberia, North America      39
        decipiens - see S. rosacea                                        90
          "      alba - see S. rosacea                                    90
          "      'James Brenner' - see S. X 'James Brenner'               39
          "      sternbergii - see S. rosacea 'Sternbergii'              33
 (8)    demnatensis / R / 6" / white fls / Atlas Mts.                     26
(12)    diapensoides / R / deep, rigid cushion / white fls / sw Alps      90
          "      f. lutea - 2", yellow fls                                35
          "      primulina - see S. d. forma lutea                        43
 (2)    diversifolia / R / 10" / golden-yellow fls / Burma, China         39
        'Dulcimer' - see S. X petraschii 'Dulcimer'                      (1)
(12)    X elisabethae 'Jason' - pale yellow fls                          (1)
(11)    X engleri / R / 12" / white fls / Carinthian & Venetian Alps      43
 (8)    erioblasta / R / compact cushion / white fls / se Spain, in mts.  90
(11)    'Esther' - 6", light yellow fls                                   43
 (8)    exarata / R / 4" / fls white to pale cream / Alps, Balkans        90
 (8)    'Fairy' - compact, late-flowering, low                           39
(12)    'Faldonside' - gray hummocks, yellow fls                         39
(12)    ferdinandi-coburgii/ R / 2-3" / fls bright yellow / Bulgaria      42
          "                v. radoslavovii - fls somewhat darker          32
 (2)    flagellaris / R / 3-6" / yellow fls / New Mexico to Alaska, Eu.   74
(15)    fortunei / R / 9" / cream-white fls / Far East                    17
(11)    'Francis Cade' - 9", pure white fls on reddish stems             39
        gemmifera - see S. hypnoides 'Kingii'                              9
 (8)    geranioides / R / 8" / white, scented fls / e Pyrenees            90
          "      corbariensis - see S. corbariensis                       *
```

        (1) - HORNY, SOJAK, WEBR in Bull. Am. Rock Garden Soc. 33:4

SAXIFRAGA, con.
```
(3)   X geum - R, procumbent, white fls, Pyrenees                       90
      " dentata - see S. hirsuta                                          9
      " hirsuta - see S. hirsuta                                         90
(8)   globulifera / HH R / to 5" / small white fls / s Spain            39
(7)   granulata / R / to 20" / white fls / n, c & w Europe              90
      "     'Flore Plena' - fls doubled                                   *
(12)  grisebachii / R / 9" / pinkish fls / Greece, Albania              90
      "      'Alba' - albino form                                         *
      "      'Wisley Var.' - larger rosettes, stem lvs red               6
      groenlandica - see S. cespitosa v. uniflora                       96
(12)  X gusmussii - R, 4", reddish-orange fls                           43
(12)  X haagii - R, 2-3", golden-yellow fls                             39
(8)   hartii / R / to 2" / pure white fls; sepals reddish / nw Eire     39
(1)   hieracifolia / R / 4-16" / greenish-purple fls / arctic Eu.       90
      'Hindhead Seedling' - see S. X boydii 'Hinhead'                   (1)
(2)   hirculus / R / 8"+ / bright yellow fls / n, c & e Europe          90
(11)  hirsuta / R / caespitose / fls white / Pyrenees                   90
(11)  hostii / R / to 1' / white fls, may be spotted red / s Alps       39
      huetiana - see S. cymbalaria ssp. huetiana                        90
(8)   hypnoides / R / to 1' / fls white / sw & nw Europe                32
      "     'Densa' - 4-5", creamy flo                                  33
(7)   irrigua / R / to 1' / fls white / Crimea, in mts.                 90
(12)  X irvingii - 1½", pale pink fls                                   38
      'Jason' - see S, X elisabethae 'Jason'                           (1)
(12)  X jaeggeana - 2-3", white fls                                     33
(8)   X 'James Bremner' - 8-10", hugh white fls                        39
(12)  X jenkinsae - 2", lilac-pink fls                                  39
(12)  juniperifolia / R / caespitose / yellow fls / Caucasus            26
(8)   X kingii - prostrate habit, white fls                            39
(11)  kolenatiana / R / 6-9" / rose-pink fls / Caucasus                 38
(12)  X kyrillii - 4-5", fls clear citron-yellow                       33
(12)  laevis / R / short shoots / yellow fls / Caucasus                 33
(7)   latepetiolata / B / 1' / white fls / e Spain                      39
(12)  lilacina / R / flat mat / lilac fls / Himalayas                   39
      lingulata - see S. callosa                                        90
      "     alberti - see S. calloas 'Albertii'                          5
      "     albida - see S. callosa 'Albertii'                          33
      '     lantoscana - included in S. callosa                         90
      "     superba - see S. callosa 'Superba'                           5
(8)   'Lloyd Edwards' - mossy hybrid, fine foliage                      81
(11)  longifolia / R / 18" / starry white fls / Pyrenees                42
(12)  luteoviridis / R / 4" / fls pale greenish-yellow / Bulgaria       90
(11)  X macnabiana - 9", white fls, heavily spotted                      5
(12)  marginata / R / 3½" / fls white or pale pink / Italy, Balkans     90
      "     v. coriophylla - columnar shoot of lvs                      90
      "     v. karadzicensis - 1", shiny white fls                      43
      "     v. rocheliana - flat rosettes                               90
(12)  media / R / to 6" / fls purplish-pink / Pyrenees                  90
(1)   mertensiana / R / ½-2" / white fls / Calif., Alaska, Rocky Mts.   75
(1)   michauxii / R / to 20" / white fls / Virginia, Georgia, Tenn.     34
      minima - see S. paniculata v. minima                              33
      minutifolia - see S. paniculata 'Minutifolia'                      *
      montavoniensis - see S. cotyledon 'Montafoniensis'                33
      montenegrina - see S. grisebachii                               9,90
      "     alba - see S. grisebachii 'Alba'                             *
```

(1) - HORNY, SOJAK, WEBR in Bull. Am. Rock Garden Soc. 33:4

SAXIFRAGA, con.
```
(8)    moschata / R / to 4" / varii-colored fls / s & c Europe        90
       "      f. acaulis - densely tufted                             20
       "      'Alba' - selection for white fls                         *
       "      f. intermedia - dense-growing                           20
       "      f. pygmaea - selection for compactness                  39
       "      'Rhei' - 6", large rose-colored fls                      9
       "      'Rosea' - selection for pink fls                          *
       muscodes rhei - see S. moschata 'Rhei'                          9
(11)   mutata / R / to 20" / orange fls / Alps                        90
       neogana - see S. paniculata 'Neugana'                          81
(8)    nevadensis / HH R / 3" / white fls, occ. red-veined / s Spain  39
(1)    nivalis / R / to 8" / fls white or pink / arctic Europe        90
(12)   X ochroleuca - pale yellow fls                                 21
(13)   oppositifolia / R / mat / fls pink to purple / Eu., N. Am.     90
       "        v. alba - small starry white fls                      43
       "        ssp. apennina - red fls, compact, c Italy             39
       "        ssp. arcto-alpina - tight mat                         67
       "        ssp. glandulifera - purple, starry fls                39
       "        ssp. latina - rosy-purple fls, Italy                   9
       "        ssp. pyrenaica - large crimson fls                     9
       "        ssp. rudolphiana - rose-purple fls, compact, Alps     39
       "        'Ruth Draper' - large-flowered                       (1)
       "        'Splendens' - intense rose-purple fls                  9
       "        'Wetterhorn' - rich crimson fls, Bernese Oberl.       43
(11)   paniculata / R / to 1' / fls white to pale cream / c & s Eu.   90
       "        'Balcana' - 5", fls heavily dotted crimson            33
       "        'Baldensis' - see S. p. "Minutifolia'                 39
       "        ssp. cartilaginea - acuminate lvs, Caucasus, n Iran   26
       "        'Lutea' - 6-8", lemon-yellow fls                      38
       "        'Minor' - 3", creamy-white fls                        43
       "        'Minutifolia' - 2", creamy-white fls, Mt. Baldo       39
       "        'Neugana' - fls rose-colored                          81
       "        portae - see S. X portae                              43
       "        'Rex' - silvery lvs; red stems; creamy-white fls      38
       "        'Venetia' - flat mat, pure white fls, 2" stems        39
(9)    paradoxa / R / decumbent / pale green fls / se Alps            90
(2)    paradanthina / R / to 1' / deep orange fls / sw China          39
(8)    'Pearly King' - mossy hybrid, white fls                        35
(11)   X pectinata - 6", creamy fls, natural hybrid in Carniola       39
(8)    pedemontana / R / to 6" / white fls / sw Alps                  32
       "        ssp. prostii - rosette lvs not incurved, s France     90
(1)    pensylvanica / P / 2' / yellowish-white fls / Maine to Minn.   34
       perdurans - see S. wahlenbergii                                90
(8)    'Peter Pan' - mossy hybrid, 2-4", deep pink fls                42
(12)   X petraschi 'Dulcimer' - white fls                            (2)
(1)    petrophila / R / 3" / by inference, yellow-flowered, Himalayas 21
(8)    'Pixie' - mossy hybrid, red fls                                35
(12)   porophylla / R / 3" / purplish-pink fls / c & s Iyaly          90
       "        v. thessalica - see S. sempervivum                     6
(11)   X portae - 6", creamy fls                                      43
(12)   pravislava / R / 2" / deep yellow fls / Macedonia              43
(10)   X primulaize - 3", red, salmon or carmine fls                  38
(12)   X prosenii - 2-3", fls reddish-orange                          38
       prostii - see S. pedemontana ssp. prostii                      90
       pulchella - see S. hypnoides                                   21
(1)    punctata / P / 20" / white fls, lvs in rosette / Asia, N, Am.  39


       (1) - GORER in Quar. Bull. Alpine Garden Soc.  40:4
       (2) - HORNY, SOJAK, WEBR in Bull. Am. Rock Garden Soc.  33:4
```

SAXIFRAGA, con.
```
     (12)  X pungens - 2", yellow fls                                        33
           pyrenaica - see S. oppositifolia v. pyrenaica                      9
           radoslowowii - see S. ferdinandi-coburgii v. radislavovii         32
     (1)   reflexa / R / 3-18" / spotted white fls / nw North America        63
     (13)  retusa / R / mat / purplish-red fls / Pyrenees to Bulgaria        90
     (7)   rivularis / R / 6" / white or pinkish fls / arctic Eu., N. Am.   (1)
           rocheliana - see S. marginata v. rocheliana                       90
 AR@3(8)   rosacea  / R / to 10" / pure white fls / nw & c Europe            90
 6/82?           "  'Sternbergii' - solid massed plant, cream-white fls      33
           'Rosaleen' - see S. X salmonica 'Rosaleen'                       (2)
     (4)   rotundifolia / R / to 16" / fls white, spotted / c & s Europe     90
                "      v. coriifolia - leathery lvs                          26
     (1)   sachalinensis / R / 4-16" / white fls / Hokkaido, Kuriles         60
     (12)  X salmonica 'Rosaleen' - white fls                               (2)
     (8)   X 'Sanguinea Superba' - 9", deep crimson fls                       6
     (12)  sancta / R / 1½" / yellow fls / Greece, Turkey                    26
     (12)  scardica 'Erythrantha' - 5-6", red fls                           33
                "    v. obtusa - 3-4½", pure white fls                       39
     (8)   sedoides / R / mat / greenish-yellow fls / e Alps, Balkans        39
     (12)  sempervivum / R / to 5½" / fls purplish-pink / Balkans            90
     (5)   sibthorpii / A / trailing / fls yellow / Greece                   26
           'Southside Seedling' - see S. cotyledon 'Southside Seedling'       5
     (3)   spathularis / R / caespitose / fls white, red spots / Portugal    90
     (12)  spruneri / R / 3" / fls white / Balkan Peninsula                  90
     (12)  squarrosa / R / to 4" / white fls / se Alps                       90
     (1)   stellaris / R / 8" / white fls, yellow spots / Europe, in mts.    90
     (15)  stolonifera / HH R / 9-24" / fls white / China, Japan             41
     (12)  stribrnyi / R / caespitose / fls purplish-pink / Bulgaria         90
                "    v. zollikoferi - fls more prominent                     43
     (2)   strigosa / HH R / 8" / white fls / Himalayas                      33
     (12)  X suendermannii - 2", large white fls                            38
                "        'Major' - 2½", pale blush-pink fls                  39
           symons-jeunii - see S. X calabrica 'Tumbling Waters'             (3)
     (4)   taygetea / R / 6" / fls white / Albania, Greece                   90
     (8)   tenella / R / to 6" / fls creamy-white / se Alps                  90
           thessalica - see S. sempervivum                                   39
     (1)   tolmiei / R / mat / white fls / California to Alaska              75
     (9)   tricuspidata / R / 2-9" / fls white or cream, spotted / N. Am.   (4)
     (8)   trifurcata / R / 4-12" / white fls / n Spain                      90
           'Tumbling Waters' - see S. X calabrica 'Tumbling Waters'         (3)
     (3)   umbrosa / R / caespitose / white fls, red spots / Pyrenees        90
                "    'Melvillei' - see S. X urbium 'Melvillei'               33
                "    'Primuloides' - see S. X urbium 'Primuloides'           39
     (3)   X urbium - 6-12", white fls with red spots                        90
                "    'London Pride' - the common name                         *
                "    'Melvillei' - lvs nearly round                          33
                "    'Ogilvieana' - starry pink fls, darker dots             33
                "    'Primuloides' - 8", deep pink fls                       42
                "        "    Elliots Form' - 4-6", deep rose fls            38
                "        "    Ingwersens Form' - see below                   39
                "        "    Walter Ingwersen' - smaller pl., rose-pink     39
     (11)  valdensis / R / to 5" / white fls / sw Alps                       90
                "    'Pygmaea' - smaller plant                                *
     (8)   vayredana / R / to 4" / fls white / ne Spain                      90
```

```
     (1) - Mountain Flowers of New England.  App. Mt. Club.  1964
     (2) - HORNY, SOJAK, WEBR in Bull. Am. Rock Garden Soc.  33:4
     (3) - GORER in Quar. Bull. Alpine Garden Soc.  40:4
     (4) - CALDER & SAVILE in Brittonia.  11:4
```

SAXIFRAGA, con.
```
          venetia - see S. paniculata 'Venetia'                             39
   (9)    vespertina / R / 4" / fls white, yellow spots / Wash. Ore.       (1)
   (1)    virginiensis / R / 3-12" / fls white / e North America           35
   (8)    wahlenbergia / R / to 3" / white fls / w Carpathians             90
  (11)    'White Hills' - 5-6", blue-gray lvs, white fls                   39
   (8)    'White Pixie' - 2", white fls                                    39
          whitlavei compacta - see S. hypnoides 'Whitlavei'                39
  (12)    X 'Winifred' - 2", large, deep rose fls                          38
   (8)    X 'Winston S. Churchill' - 4", clear pink fls                    17
  (11)    X zimmeteri - 4", starry white fls, Austria                      43
```

SCABIOSA - Dipsacaceae
```
   alpina - see CEPHALARIA alpina                                           9
   argentea / B or P / 6-24" / fls white or cream / s. Eu., s Russia       26
   atropurpurea / A / 3' / fls in various colors / s Europe                89
        "     'Nana' - dwarf strain of Sweet Scabious                       9
   caucasica / P / 18" / lavender-blue fls / Russia, Iran                  26
        "    'Clive Greaves' - large mauve fls                             53
        "    'Miss Willmott' - cream fls                                   62
   columbaria / P or R / 2"-2' / blue-purple fls / Europe                  38
        "     ssp. ochroleuca - fls yellow or cream                       26
   graminifolia / R / 6-8" / pinkish-lavender fls / s Europe               38
   hladnickiana / P / 1-2' / fls purplish / Jugoslavia, in mts.            29
   japonica / P / 12-32" / fls blue / Japan, in mts.                       60
        "   v. alpina - dwarfed, larger fls, Honshu, Shikoku               60
   lucida / R / 8-12" / rose-lilac fls / Europe, in mts.                   35
   maritima - see S. atropurpurea                                           9
   ochroleuca - see S. columbaria ssp. ochroleuca                         26
   olgae / P / 10-18" / grayish-blue fls / Caucasus                       (2)
   parnassaefolia - see PTEROCEPHALUS parnassi                            (3)
   parnassi - see PTEROCEPHALUS parnassi                                  (3)
   pterocephalus - see PTEROCEPHALUS parnassi                             38
   pyrenaica / R / 8-16" / fls clear blue-lilac / Pyrenees, sw Alps       96
   rumelica / P / 2' / claret-purple fls / ?                              (4)
   silenifolia / R / 7" / rosy-violet fls / Italy, in mts.                (3)
   succisa - see SUCCISA pratensis                                        85
   sylvatica - see KNAUTIA sylvatica                                      10
   ucranica - see S. argentea                                             26
   variifolia / HH Sh / 3' / fls pinkish / Rhodes, Anatolia               26
```

SCHINUS - Anacardiaceae
```
   latifolius / HH T / ? / fls white / Chile                              10
   molle / HH T / 15'+ / evergreen lvs; rosy-red frs / S. America         46
```

SCHIVERECKIA - Cruciferae
```
   bornmulleri - see S. doerfleri                                         26
   doerfleri / R / to 6" / white fls / Jugoslavia, Asia Minor             90
   podolica / R / to 10" / fls white / Ukraine, Roumania                  90
```

SCHIZANTHUS - Solanaceae
```
   grahamii / A / 2' / lilac or rose fls, orange tipped / Chile            9
   hookeri / A / 2' / fls pale rose / Chile                               29
```

```
   (1) - CALDER & SAVILE in Brittonia  11:4
   (2) - SHISHKIN & BOBROV - Flora of the USSR.  Vol. 24 (1972 trans.)
   (3) - SENIOR in Bull. Am. Rock Garden Soc.  25:4
   (4) - BRICKELL in Jour. Royal Horticultural Soc.  July 1964
```

SCHIZOCODON - Diapensiaceae
    soldanelloides / R / 4-5" / pinkish fls / Japan   38
           "   v. illicifolius - holly-leaved   35

SCHIZOSTYLIS - Iridaceae
    coccinea / Tu / 2½' / scarlet to pink fls / South Africa   42
         "   'Mrs. Hegarty' - rose-red fls   36
    'Mrs Hegarty' - see S. coccinea 'Mrs. Hegarty'   36

SCILLA - Liliaceae
    amethystina - see S. pratensis v. amethystina   84
    amoena / Bb / 6" / starry fls, deep indigo-mauve / c Europe   84
    autumnalis / Bb / 8" / fls blue-lilac to purple / Europe   84
    bifolia / Bb / 3-6" / varii-colored fls / s Europe   42
       "   v. rosea - fls pale purplish-pink   84
    campanulata - see ENDYMION hispanica   84
         "   rosea - see ENDYMION hispanica 'Rosea'   *
    chinensis - see S. scilloides   56
    festalis - see ENDYMION non-scripta   9
    hispanica - see ENDYMION hispanica   85
    hohenhackeri / Bb / 4-6" / pale to mid-lilac-blue fls / Iran   56
    hyacinthoides / Bb / 18" / pale lilac-blue fls / Medit. region   84
    italica / Bb / to 8" / fragrant pale blue fls / Italy, s France   84
    lilio-hyacinthus / Bb / 1½' / fls pale lilac-blue / Medit. region   84
    messeniaca / Bb / 6-8" / mid-blue fls / s Greece   56
    monophylla / Bb / 8" / starry blue fls / Spain, Portugal   84
    non-scripta - see ENDYMION non-scripta   85
    persica / Bb / 1' / pale blue fls / w Iran   (1)
    peruviana / HH Bb / lilac-blue fls / Spain, c Medit. region   42
         "   'Alba' - white form   84
    pratensis / Bb / 1' / bluish-mauve fls / Jugoslavia   42
         "   v. amethystina - brighter blue fls   84
    ramburei / HH Bb / 4-12" / bright mid-blue fls / s Spain, s Portugal   56
    rosenii / Bb / 1' / fls pale azure to whitish / Asia Minor   54
    scilloides / Bb / 6" / pink fls in autumn / China, Korea   56
    sibirica / Bb / to 8" / gentian-blue fls / Caucasus   42
         "   'Alba' - white form   84
         "   v. atrocoerulea - earlier and stronger   84
         "   v. taurica - paler form, dark-tipped fls   84
         "   'Spring Beauty' - see S. sibirica v. atrocoerulea   84
    tubergeniana / Bb / 6" / fls pale blue, nearly white / nw Iran   42
    verna / Bb / 6" / fls pale blue-mauve / n Europe   84
    violacea - see LEDEBOURIA socialis   56

SCLERANTHUS - Caryophyllaceae
    biflora / R / mat to 6" / white fls / Australia, Tasmania   16
    brockiei / R / mat / green lvs / New Zealand   2
    perennis / R / to 8" / may be procumbent / most of Europe   90
    uniflorus / B or P / moss-mats / yellowish fls / New Zealand   78

SCLEROCACTUS - Cactaceae
    whipplei / R / 6" / fls purplish to lavender / Colorado, Arizona   10

SCOLIOPUS - Liliaceae
    bigelovii / Bb / 8" / green & purple fls / California   75

SCOPIOLA - Solanaceae
    carniolica / P / 8-24" / brownish-violet fls / c & se Europe   92

    (1) - FURSE in The World of Rock Plants. 1971 Conf. Rept.

SCROPHULARIA - Scrophulariaceae
    canina ssp. hoppii - P, 8-24", fls dark purplish-red, Jura, s Alps   92
    hopii - see S. canina ssp. hoppii   92
    nodosa / P / 12-32" / fls green & brownish / Europe   92
    peregrina / P / to 3' / dark red to purplish fls / Medit. region   92
    vernalis / B or P / 3'+ / yellow fls / Europe, mostly s   92

SCUTELLARIA - Labiatae
    alpina / R / 10" / purple & white fls / Europe   35
      "   'Rosea' - pink fls   9
    baicalensis / R / 1' / blue fls / e Asia   9
    hastifolia / P / 6-20" / fls violet-blue / Europe   92
    incana / P / to 3' / blue fls / New York, Alabama, Kansas   34
    indica v. japonica - 5-6", blue-purple fls, Japan   38
    integrifolia / P / to 2' / fls blue-purple & white / United States   34
    laeteviolacea / R / 6" / purplish fls / Japan   60
    laterifolia / P / 1-2' / fls blue to whitish / United States   9
    orientalis / R / 3" / yellow fls / Altai Mts.   35
    ovata / P / 2'+ / blue & white fls / s United States   34
      " v. rugosa - sprawling, W. Virginia to Arkansas   34
    scordifolia / R / 6" / pure deep blue fls / Korea   38
    serrata / P / 2' / blue fls / se New York to Tennessee   34

SEDUM - Crassulaceae
    acre / R / 1-3" / bright yellow fls / Europe, Asia Minor   42
    aizoon / R / 1' / fls yellow / Japan, Siberia   42
    album / R / to 7" / fls white / Europe   90
    altissimum - see S. sediforme   90
    anacampseros / R / to 10" / fls lilac & dull red / Pyrenees   90
    brevifolium / R / 4" / white or pink fls / France, Medit. region   9
    caeruleum / A / 4-8" / fls blue or white / Medit. region   97
    camtschaticum - see S. kamtschaticum   *
    caucasicum / P / 1'+ / shell lvs with ears / Caucasus   26
    cauticolum / R / 3" / rose-purple fls / Japan   42
    crassipes stephani - see S. stephani   33
    dasyphyllum / R / to 3" / fls white & pink / s Europe   90
    douglasii - see S. stenopetalum   97
    dumulosum - see RHODIOLA dumulosa   (1)
    ewersii / R / 4-8" / pink or mauve fls / c Asia, Himalayas   90
      "   v. homophyllum - very dwarf, glaucous lvs   21
    glaucophyllum / R / 4" / white fls / West Virginia & Virginia   34
    globosum / R / 4" / whitish fls / ?   (2)
    hybridum / R / 6-8" / golden-yellow fls / n Asia   90
    kamtschaticum / R / 4" / yellow fls / n Asia   38
      "   ssp. middendorffianum - R, 10", golden fls, e Asia   97
      "   "   "   'Diffusum' - 4", golden-yellow fls 17
      "   'Variegatum' - white-margined lvs   38
    leibergii / R / 3-5" / short, thick lvs; yellow fls / Idaho, Wash.   76
    lidakense / R / 3" / purplish lvs; carmine-red fls / ?   17
    linearifolium / R / 4-5" / large white fls / India   33
    lydakense - see S. lidakense   &
    maximum - see S. telephium ssp. maximum   90
      "   'Atropurpureum' - see S. t. ssp. m. 'Atropurpureum'   *
    middendorffianum - see S. kamtschaticum ssp. middendorffianum   97
      "   'Diffusum' - see S. k. ssp. m. 'Diffusum'   *
    monregalense / R / 6" / white fls / sw Alps   90
    nevii / R / 4" / white fls / se United States   35

    (1) - Iconographia Cormophytorum Sinicorum. Tomus II. 1972
    (2) - ALLEN in Bull. Am. Rock Garden Soc. 19:3

SEDUM, con.
```
  oreganum / R / 2-3" / yellow fls / w North America               38
  oregonense / R / 2-11" / yellow to whitish fls / n Calif., s Ore.  75
  palmeri / HH R / 6" / deep orange fls / Mexico                     9
  pilosum / R / 2-3" / rose-pink fls / Asia Minor                   38
  populifolium / Sh / 18" / fls pale pink or white / Siberia        35
  pulchellum / R / 6" / rosy-purple fls / Virginia, Missouri, Texas  9
  quadrifidum himalense - see RHODIOLA himalense                     *
  reflexum / R / 6-12" / bright yellow fls / c Europe               90
  roseum - see RHODIOLA rosea                                       90
     "  atropurpureum - see RHODIOLA rosea 'Atropurpurea'            *
  rubens / A / 2-5" / white or pink fls; lvs reddish / s & w Europe  90
  rupestre - see S. forsterianum                                    90
  'Schorbusser Blut' - see S. spurium 'S. B.'                       42
  sediforme / P / to 2' / fls straw-colored / Medit. region         90
  selskianum / P / 1-1½' / yellow fls / Manchuria                    9
  semenowii / P / 20" / white & pink fls / Turkestan                32
  sempervivoides / B / 4-8" / bright scarlet fls / Asia Minor       38
  silskianum - error for S. selskianum                              *
  spathulifolium / R / 4"+ / yellow fls / w North America           35
         "         'Capa Blanca' - silvery gray lvs                 42
         "         v. purpureum - young lvs purplish                38
  spinosum - see OROSTACHYS spinosa                                 90
  spurium 'Dragons Blood' - see S. s. 'Schorbusser Blut'           (1)
      "     'Schorbusser Blut' - fls deep carmine-crimson, procumbent  42
  stenopetalum / R / 12" / yellow fls / nw North America            97
  stephanii - see RHODIOLA rosea v. stephanii                       *
  telephioides / P / 6-32" / pale pink fls / New York to Illinois   34
  telephium / P / 12-18" / fls pink or white / Europe               90
      "     ssp. maximum - to 32", fls whitish                      90
      "       "       "    'Atropurpureum' - vivid purple lvs       62
  ternatum / R / prostrate / white fls / e United States            35
  treleasei / HH R / to 12" / bright yellow fls / Mexico            41
  tsugarense / P / to 20" / fls pale green / Honshu                 60
  villosum / R / 6" / lilac or pale pink fls / w & c Europe         90
  viviparum / R / 8" / fls white to greenish / Manchuria           (2)
  watsonii - see S. oregonense                                     97
```

SELINUM - Umbelliferae
```
  tenuifolium / P / to 8' / whitish fls / India                     9
```

SELLIERA - Goodeniaceae
```
  radicans / HH R / creeping / white fls / Australia, N. Z., Chile  9
```

SEMIAQUILEGIA - Ranunculaceae
```
  adoxoides / R / 4-16" / fls white or pale rose / Far East         60
  ecalcarata - see S. simulatrix                                    6
  simulatrix / R / to 12" / fls dark reddish-violet / s China       6
```

SEMPERVIVUM - Crassulaceae
```
  'Ambergreen' - glaucous green lvs, shaded rose-violet            (1)
  arachnoideum / R / 2-6" / pink to crimson fls / Europe, in mts.   42
         "      'Album' - white fls                                 *
         "      v. doellianum - glabrescent                        32
         "      v. glabrescens - rosettes ovoid, web rather lax    85
         "      'Standfieldii' - red fls                            5
```

(1) - SCHENK - The Wild Garden. n.d.
(2) - JACOBSEN - A Handbook of Succulent Plants. 1960(trans.)

SEMPERVIVUM, con.
```
  arachnoideum v. tomentosum - dense web                              85
       "      'Webbianum' - see S. a. var. tomentosum                 32
  arboreum - see AEONIUM arboreum                                     90
  arvernense - see S. tectorum                                        90
  calcareum / R / 1'+ / pale pink fls / French Alps                   90
       "     'Mrs. Giuseppi' - 2" rosette, light green                 5
  cantabricum / R / open rosettes / fls pink & green / Spain          43
  ciliosum / R / 3-5" / pale yellow fls / Balkans                     85
  'Commander Hay' - 15", pink fls, somewhat tender                    42
  doellianum - see S. arachnoideum v. doellianum                      32
  dolomiticum / R / 1½" rosette / deep rose fls / e Alps              85
  erythraeum / R / 6-8" / fls deep reddish-purple / Bulgaria          90
  X fauconettii - S. arachnoideum x tectorum, less cobwebby        21,33
  X fimbriatum - see reference for two hybrids given this name        85
  X funckii - 8", purple-rose fls                                     85
  glaucum - see S. tectorum                                           90
  grandiflorum / R / 4-8"/fls lemon-yellow / Susa to Simplon, Alps    90
  hueffeli - see JOVIBARBA heuffelii                                  85
  hirtum - see JOVIBARBA hirta                                        85
  'Jubilee' - 3", bronze lvs                                           5
  kindingeri / R / 8-10" / yellow & red fls / Balkans                 43
  kopaonikense - see JOVIBARBA kopaonikense                           32
  marmoratum - see S. marmoreum                                       85
       "     'Rubrifolium Ornatum' - see S. marmoreum 'R. O.'         85
  marmoreum / R / 8" / fls red, white margins / Balkans               90
       "     'Rubrifolium Ornatum' - reddish lvs                      85
  mettenianum / R / 1½" rosette / rose fls / c Europe                  9
  montanum / R / 8-12" / pinkish-purple fls / Europe, in mts.         43
       "    ssp. burnatii - pale green rosettes, sw Alps              90
  pittonii / R / to 6" / pale yellow fls / e Alps                     90
  X pomelii - R, 6-9", rose-red fls, France                           9
  powellii - possibly an error for S. X pomelii                        *
  pyrenaicum - Pyrenees form of S. tectorum with light pink fls       33
  'Queen Amalie' - see S. regina-amaliae                               *
  'Rauhreif' - see SENECIO  cineraria 'Rauhreif'                       *
  reginae-amaliae / R / 3½-5" / fls dark crimson / Greece             85
  X roseum - S. arachnoideum hybrid                                   33
  rubrifolium - see S. marmoreum 'Rubrifolium Ornatum'                85
  sabanum / R / 1-2" rosettes / light green lvs / ?                  (1)
  X schottii - purple fls, S montanum x tectorum                      85
  'Silverine' - silvery-green lvs                                    (1)
  simonkianum - see JOVIBARBA simonkiana                              21
  soboliferum - see JOVIBARBA sobolifera                              85
  stansfieldii - see S. arachnoideum 'Stansfieldii'                    5
  tectorum / R / 1'+ / dull rose fls / Europe, in mts.                85
       "     'Atropurpureum' - darker lvs                             33
       "     ssp. calcareum - see S. calcareum                        90
       "     "         "    'Mrs. Giuseppi' - see S. calcareum 'M. G.'  *
       "     giuseppiae - see S. calcareum 'Mrs. Giuseppi'             *
       "     'Nigrum' - lvs tipped reddish-brown                      38
       "     'Violaceum' - leaf-color form                            33
  X thompsonii - S. arachnoideum x marmoreum                          85
  violaceum - see S. tectorum 'Violaceum'                              9
  wulfenii / R / 6-8" / yellow fls; glabrous lvs / Alps               85

  (1) - SCHENK - The Wild Garden. n.d.
```

SENECIO - Compositae
  abrotanifolius / R / 10-12" / orange-yellow fls / c Europe   38
        "   v. tirolensis - smaller, orange-red fls   35
  adonidifolius / R / 6" / golden yellow fls / Pyrenees   32
  alpinus / P / 3' / orange-gold fls / Alps   32
  antennarifolius / R / 12" / yellow fls / Virginia, West Virginia   (1)
  argyreus / HH Sh / 12"+ / yellow fls / Chile   21
  aurantiacus / R / 12"+ / orange or yellow fls / Europe   (2)
  aureus / P / 1-2' / yellow fls / e & c North America   9
  bolanderi v. harfordii - P, to 2', yellow fls, lvs thin, Oregon   47
  campestris - see S. integrifolius   63
  capitatus / R / 6-12" / golden to orange-red fls / Alps   96
  carniolicus - see S. incanus v. carniolicus   38
  carthamoides / R / to 1' / yellow fls; plant leafy / Col., Wyo.   (77)
  cineraria / HH P / 2½' / white-woolly lvs / Medit. region   9
        "   'Rauhreif' - selection for whiteness of leaf   32
  congestus / R / 3-8" / yellow fls, woolly infloresence / circumpolar   63
  doronicum / P / 2-3' / large bright yellow fls / c Europe   62
  fendleri / P / 4-24" / yellow fls / Wyoming to Utah   76
  fremontii / R / 4" / yellow fls / California to Canada   75
  fuchsii - see S. nemorensis   60
  greyi / HH Sh / 6' / yellow fls / New Zealand   78
  heritieri / Gh Sh / 3'+ / fls white & crimson & purple / Canary Isl.   46
  incanus / R / 2-4" / golden buttons; silvery lvs / Alps   38
        " v. carniolicus - larger flower-heads   38
  kawakamii / R / 12", decumbent / yellow fls / alps of Japan   60
  lautus / A / small / yellow fls / Australia   16
  laxifolius / HH Sh / to 5' / yellow fls / New Zealand   42
  leucostachys - similar to S. cineraria, whiter lvs, Argentina   32
  longilobus / Sh / to 5' / yellow fls / New Zealand   42
  lyallii / P / to 20" / light yellow fls / New Zealand   78
  macrophyllus / P / 3-4' / yellow fls / Europe   9
  monroi / HH Sh / 3-5' / yellow fls / New Zealand   46
  nemoensis / P / 3'+ / fls yellow / Far East, Siberia, Europe   60
        "   fuchsii - included in the sp.   60
  palustris - see S. congestus   63
  przewalskii - see LIGULARIA przewalskii   85
  repens / Gh / to 1' / fls white / South Africa   32
  revolutus / HH Sh / to 20" / yellow fls / New Zealand   2
  robbinsii / P / to 3' / yellow fls / ne North America   34
  rodriguezii / HH Sh / dwarf / purple fls, tinged yellow / Minorca   65
  subalpinus / P / 1-2' / rich yellow fls / Carpathians, Balkans   67
  tomentosus / P / 8-30" / bright yellow fls / N. J., Fla., Ark.   72
  tyrolensis - see S. abrotanifolius v. tirolensis   35

SERIOCARPUS - Compositae
  asteroides / P / 6-24" / white fls / Maine, Michigan, Florida   71

SESELI - Umbelliferae
  caespitosum - see OLYMPOSCIADUM caespitosum   26
  libanotis / B or P / to 4' / fls white or pink / Europe   91

SETARIA - Gramineae
  italica / A Gr / to 5' / mature inflorescence varii-col. / Asia   85

SEVERINA - Rutaceae
  buxifolia / Gh Sh / 3' / fls white; frs black / s China   9

  (1) - HUMPHREY in Bull. Am. Rock Garden Soc. 28:2
  (2) - RUFFIER-LANCHE in Bull. Am. Rock Garden Soc. 21:2

SHORTIA - Diapensiaceae
  galacifolia / R / 6-8" / white fls / s Appalachian Mts.   35
  uniflora / R / 3-6" / shell-pink or white fls / Japan   42

SIBARA - Cruciferae
  virginica / A / 4-16" / fls white or pink-tinged / e & c US   34

SIDERITIS - Labiatae
  hyssopifolia / P / 16" / yellow fls / sw Europe   92
  scordioides / R / to 1' / yellow fls / s France, c & e Spain   92
  syriaca / P / 4-20" / yellow fls / s Europe   92
  taurica - see S. syriaca   92

SIEVERSIA ciliata - see GEUM triflorum   76

SILENE - Caryophyllaceae
  acaulis / R / 1-4" / deep pink fls / arctic & alpine n hemisphere   90
    "   ssp. exscapa - flowering stems short   90
    "   ssp. longiscapa - flowering stems extended   90
    "   'Pedunculata' - strong-growing, large-flowered   79
    "   saxatilis - see S. saxatilis?   *
  alba / A or P / to 32" / fls usually white / most of Europe   90
  alpestris / R / to 1' / fls usually white / Alps & n Balkans   90
  armeria / A or B / 16" / fls usually pink / c & s Europe   90
    " 'Lady Pink' - garden selection   (1)
  boryi / R / mat / fls pink above, red below / Spain   90
  californica / R / flopping / brilliant scarlet fls / w US   35
  caroliniana / R / tuft / deep pink to white fls / e US   35
    "   v. wherryi - rich pink fls   35
  coeli-rosea / P / 8-20" / pink fls / se Europe   90
  compacta / A or B / 15" / pink fls / se Europe   90
    "   pendula - see S. pendula 'Compacta'   9
  cucubalus - see S. vulgaris   90
  delavayi / R / 3-8" / fls deep purple / Yunnan   20
  dioica / P / 30" / red fls / Europe   90
    " 'Rose Queen' - garden selection   *
  douglasii /16"+ / fls white or pink / California to B. C.   76
    "   v. monantha - dwarfer, scarcely hairy   47
  elisabetha / R / 5" / fls dark red to reddish-purple / Alps   90
  flavescens / R / to 1' / fls yellow / Balkans, in mts.   90
  fortunei / P / 1½-3' / fls rose or white / China   9
  frivaldszkyana / P / 1'+ / fls whitish / Balkan Peninsula   90
  gallica / A / to 1½' / fls white or pink / s & c Europe   90
    "   v. quinquevulnaria - fls crimson-spotted   90
  heuffellii / B / to 32" / white fls / n Balkans   90
  hookeri / R / 6" / fls salmon-pink to white / sc Ore., n Calif.   35
  ingramii / R / 6" / glowing cherry-red fls / Oregon   (2)
    " 'Alba' - white fls   *
  integripetala / R / 4-16" / pink fls / s Greece   90
  keiskei / R / 6-8" / fls in shades of pink / Japan   35
    " 'Minor' - 3", bronzy-green lvs; bright pink fls   38
  laciniata / HH P / 18" / pink fls, green nerved / Mexico   9
  'Lady Pink' - see S. armeria 'L. P.'   (1)
  lerchenfeldiana / R / 10" / fls reddish / Carpathians   90
  maritima - see S. vulgaris ssp. maritima   90
    "   rosea - see S. vulgaris ssp. maritima 'Rosea'   38
    " 'White Bells' - see S. vulgaris ssp. maritima 'W. B.'   *
  nutans / P / to 2' / fls variable in color / Europe   90

(1) - INNIS in corres.
(2) - CROCKER in Bull. Am. Rock Garden Soc. 23:3

SILENE, con.
```
odontopetala / R / to 1' / fls whitish to pinkish / Near East          26
paradoxa / P / 2'+ / fls cream or yellow / Europe                      90
pendula / A / 6-16" / pink fls / s Mediterranean region                90
   "    'Compacta' - dwarf bedding strain                               9
pusilla / R / 6" / fls white, rarely pink or lilac / s & c Eu.         90
pygmaea / R / 8" / fls rose-purple / Caucasus                         (1)
regia / P / 3-4½' / fls deep scarlet / Ohio, Alabama, Missouri          9
regis-ferdinandii / R / 4" / solitary white fls / Bulgaria          21,90
'Rose Queen' - see S. dioica 'Rose Queen'                               *
rubella / A / 4-20" / pink fls / w Medit. region                       90
rupestris / R / 10" / fls white or pink / w & c Europe                 90
ruprechtii - see S. saxatilis                                          26
sachalinense / R / low mats / white fls / Far East                    (1)
saxatilis / P / 8-20" / fls whitish or yellowish / n Iran              26
saxifraga / R / 8" / fls whitish or greenish / s Europe                90
schafta / R / 3-6" / fls rose or purple / Caucasus                      9
secundiflora / A / 4-20" / fls pink or white / s & e Spain             90
stellata / P / to 3' / fringy white fls / Mass. to Texas               72
vallesia / R / 6" / fls pale pink above, red below / w Alps            90
virginica / P / 2' / fls crimson to scarlet / e United States          35
vulgaris / P / 2' / fls whitish / throughout Europe                    90
   " ssp. maritima - 10", fls whitish, coasts of Europe                90
   "    "      "      'Rosea' - pink fls                                38
   "    "      "      'White Bells' - selection for white fls           *
waldsteinii / R / 6" / white fls / mts. of Balkan Peninsula            90
wherryi - see S. caroliniana v. wherryi                                35
zawadskyii / R / to 1' / fls white / e Carpathians                     90
```

SILYBUM - Compositae
```
marianum / A or B / 1-2' / fls rosy-purple / s Europe, n Africa        42
```

SISYRINCHIUM - Iridaceae
```
anceps - see S. angustifolium                                           9
angustifolium / R / 8-10" / pale to deep blue fls / e & c N. Am. (2)   34
         "        'Album' - selection for white fls                     *
arizonicum / HH R / 8" / orange fls / New Mexico, Arizona              74
bellum - see S. angustifolium                                          47
   " 'Album' - presumably S. angustifolium 'Album'                      *
birameum - see S. angustifolium                                        47
borealis - see S. californicum                                         47
brachypus - see S. californicum                                        47
californicum / R / 6-16" / bright yellow fls / California              76
campestre / P / to 20" / fls blue, violet, white / c United States     76
convolutum / HH P / 1' / yellow fls / tropical America                  9
cuspidatum / R / tuft / cream fls / South America                      21
douglasii / R / 8-10" / satiny purple fls / w North America            35
      "    'Album' - white fls                                          9
filifolium / R / 6-8" / white fls veined red / Falklands               38
graminifolium / HH R / 6-8" / fls yellow / Chile                       32
         "       v. maculatum - 9", yellow fls, red-spotted, Valparaiso 37
grandiflorum 'Album' - see S. douglasii 'Album'                        35
idahoense / P / to 16" / fls blue / California, Wash., Idaho            76
inflatum / R / 10"+ / fls magenta-pink / w North America               21
iridifolium / HH R / ? / fls yellow / South America                    21
```

(1) - SHISHKIN - Flora of the USSR. Vol. VI 1970(trans.)
(2) - WARD in Taxon. 17:3

SISYRINCHIUM, con.
```
  junceum / HH R / 10" / clear pink fls / Chile                          21
  macounii - see S. angustifolium                                        47
     "      'Album' - see S. angustifolium 'Album'                        *
  montanum / P / 1½' / blue-violet fls / c United States                74
  mucronatum / R / 1' / blue fls / Massachusetts, Virginia, Michigan    32
     "        'Album' - pure white fls                                  (1)
  pachyrhizum / HH P / 2' / fls yellow / Brazil                         10
  sarmentosum - see S. angustifolium                                    47
  striatum / HH P / 2' / creamy-white fls / Chile                       42
  tenuifolium / HH R / tufted / greenish-yellow fls / Mexico            21
```

SKIMMIA - Rutaceae
```
  japonica / HH Sh / 3' / white fls; red frs; evergreen lvs / Japan     46
```

SMILACINA - Liliaceae
```
  amplexicaulis / P / 3' / plumey white fls / w North America           35
  racemosa / P / 2-3' / creamy-white fls / North America                42
  sessilifolia / P / 2' / white fls; purple frs / Pacific States        35
  stellata / P / 18" / starry white fls / United States                 35
```

SMILAX - Liliaceae
```
  aspera / Gh Cl / ? / pale green fls; red frs / s Europe               41
  herbacea / Cl / 4-10' / bluish-black frs / ne United States            9
  rotundifolia / woody Cl / rampant / blue-black frs / e US & Canada      9
```

SMYRNIUM - Umbelliferae
```
  perfoliatum / HH B / 2'+ / yellow fls / around the Mediterranean      64
```

SOLANUM - Solaneaceae
```
  aculeatissimum / P or Sh / 1-2' / frs orange, yellow / tropics         9
  ciliatum - see S. aculeatissimum                                       9
  eleagnifolium / P / 2' / silvery lvs; purplish fls / c US             76
  incanum / HH Sh / 3' / gray-woolly lvs; violet fls / tropics          64
  seaforthianum / Gh / trailing / pink or lilac fls / S. America        41
```

SOLDANELLA - Primulaceae
```
  alpina / R / 2-3" / fls pale to deep mauve / Alps                     42
  austriaca / R / 4" / pale violet fls, / Austrian Alps                 92
  carpatica / R / to 6" / violet fls / w Carpathians                    92
  hungarica / R / ? / violet fls / ec Europe, in mts.                   92
  montana / R / 3-6" / fls pale or deep mauve / Pyrenees                42
  pindicola - similar to S. carpatica, by mt. springs, nw Greece        92
  pusilla / R / 2-3" / pale lavender fls / European Alps                38
  villosa / R / 4-5" / blue-amethyst fls / Pyrenees                     38
```

SOLENOMELUS - Iridaceae
```
  chilensis - see S. pedunculatus                                       32
  pedunculatus / Gh / 1' / golden fls / Chile                           32
  sisyrinchium / Gh / ? / blue fls / Chile                              32
```

SOLIDAGO - Compositae
```
  alpestris - see S. virgaurea v. alpestris                            (2)
  brachystachys - see S. cutleri                                        79
  caesia / P / 2-3' / yellow fls / e North America                      62
  cutleri / R / to 1' / yellow fls / Maine to New York, in mts.         35
  glomerata / P / 1-4' / yellow fls / N. Carolina, Tennessee            72
  minutissima - see S. virgaurea v. minutissima                        60
```

```
  (1) - DOWBRIDGE in Bull. Am. Rock Garden Soc.  20:1
  (2) - FAVARGER & ROBERT. Alpenflora.  1959
```

SOLIDAGO, con.
  mollis / P / 6-20" / bright yellow fls / c United States ... 34
  nemoralis / P / to 4' / fls pale yellow / e & c North America ... 34
      "   v. decemflora - larger flower head ... 82
      "   v. longipetiolata - see S. n. var. decemflora ... 82
  puberula / P / to 3' / fls orange-yellow / e North America ... 34
  roanensis / P / 16-32" / deep yellow fls / W. Va., Tenn., Georgia ... 34
  spathulata f. nana - yellow fls, 6-12", Rocky Mts. ... 75
      "   f. neomexicana - 18", yellow fls , s Rocky Mts. ... 75
  virgaurea v. alpestris - 4-8", deep golden fls, Europe ... 38
      "   v. asiatica - 6-28", yellow fls, Japan ... 60
      "   v. minuta - error for S. v. var. minutissima? ... *
      "   v. minutissima - 2", Kyushu, Yakushima Is., in mts. ... 60

SOLLYA - Pittosporaceae
  fusiformis / Gh Cl / to 6' / fls bright blue / Australia ... 41
  heterophylla - see S. fusiformis ... 41

SOPHORA - Leguminosae
  macrocarpa / HH Sh / 5-8' / yellow fls / Chile ... 46
  microphylla / HH T / to 30' / yellow fls / New Zealand ... 78
  tetraptera / HH T / 40' / bright yellow fls / New Zealand ... 42
      "   'Grandiflora' - slightly larger fls ... 46
  viciifolia / HH Sh / 3-7' / bluish-white fls / China ... 46

SORBUS - Rosaceae
  alnifolia / T / to 60' / small, bright red frs / Far East ... 46
      "   v. submollis - lvs broader, pubescent beneath ... 46
  aria 'Decaisneana' - T, 35', large crimson frs ... 46
      " 'Majestica' - see S. aria 'Decaisneana' ... 46
  aucuparia / T / 20-40' / frs bright red / Europe to w Asia ... 46
  cashmeriana / T / 15' / large white frs / Himalayas ... 42
  chamaemespilus / Sh / 4½' / pink fls; scarlet frs / c & s Europe ... 91
  hupehensis / T / 15'+ / lvs bluish-green; frs white / w China ... 46
      "   v. obtusa - pink frs, w China ... 46
  'Joseph Rock' - T, 25'+, yellow frs, origin a question ... 46
  lancastriensis / T / small / crimson frs / Britain ... 91
  matsumurana / T / small / white fls; red frs / Japan, in mts. ... 60
  occidentalis / Sh / to 9' / frs red, bloomy / B. C. to Oregon ... 69
  pohuashanensis / T / 30'+ / heavy frs, orange-red / n China ... 46
  poteriifolia / T / 15'+ / deep rose-pink frs / China ... 46
  prattii / Sh / 10' / pearly-white frs / China ... 46
      "   v. subarachnoidea - white frs; cobwebby lvs ... 46
  reducta / Sh / 6-18" / frs pink-crimson / n Burma, w China ... 38,42
  rufo-ferruginea / T / 15' / reddish frs / Japan ... 46
  sargentiana / T / 25' / small scarlet frs / China ... 46
  scalaris / T / 30' / orange-scarlet frs / China ... 42
  serotina / T / 15' / small, bright orange-red frs / w China ... 46
  sitchensis v. grayii - Sh, to 4', lvs nearly entire, B.C. to Calif. ... 47
  vilmorinii / T / 15' / cherry-red to pink frs / China ... 42

SORGHASTRUM - Gramineae
  nutans / P Gr / 2-7' / ornamental yellowish fls / e & c US ... 85

SPARAXIS - Iridaceae
  bulbifera / HH C / 9" / violet fls / Cape of Good Hope ... 45
  tricolor / HH C / 15" / orange-red fls / Natal ... 36

SPARTIUM - Leguminosae
  junceum / Sh / to 10' / deep yellow fls / s Europe ... 42

SPECULARIA speculum - see LEGOUSIA speculum-veneris   95
    "   speculum-veneris grandiflorum - see LEGOUSIA s-v. 'G.'   89

SPERGULARIA - Caryophyllaceae
    media / R / 2-16" / fls white or pink / coasts of Europe   90
    rubra / A or P / 10" / pink fls / Europe   90
    rupicola / R / 2-14" / uniform pink fls / Atlantic coasts of Eu.   90

SPHAERALCEA - Malvaceae
    ambigua / P / to 40" / fls orange-red / Utah to Mexico   95
    munroana / P / 1-2' / scarlet or rose fls / B.C. to Idaho & s-wards   9

SPIGELIA - Loganiaceae
    marilandica / P / 1-2' / red tubular fls / New Jersey to Wisc.   9

SPIRAEA - Rosaceae
    betulifolia v. lucida - Sh, 1-2', white fls, B.C. to Oregon   47
    X bullata - Sh, 12", deep rose fls   38
    densiflora / Sh / low / bright pink fls / B.C., Oregon, Montana   9
        "   lucida - see S. betulifolia v. lucida   47
    douglasii / Sh / 3'+ / fls purplish-rose / w North America   35
    japonica bullata - see S. X bullata   38

SPIRANTHES - Orchidaceae
    cernua / P / 6-25" / fls white or yellowish / e North America   35
    gracilis / P / 8-18" / fragrant white fls / e North America   9

SPRAGUEA multiceps - see CALYPTRIDIUM umbellatum   (1)
    "   umbellata - see CALYPTRIDIUM umbellatum   (1)

SPREKELIA - Amaryllidaceae
    formosissima / HH Bb / 1' / deep scarlet fls / Mexico   42

STACHYS - Labiatae
    betonica - see S. officinalis   92
    byzantina / P / 6-32" / fls small, purple / Turkey   92
    candida / R / 4-8" / fls white with purple spots / s Greece   92
    coccinea / P / 1-2' / fls scarlet-red / w Texas, Arizona   9
    densiflora - see S. monieri   92
    grandiflora 'Superba - see S. macrantha 'Superba'   44
    lavendulaeflora / R / 6-8" / red-purple fls / Caucasus to Iran   32
    macrantha / P / 1-2' / fls purple-violet / Caucasus   42
        "   'Superba' - 1', fls intense mauve   9,44
    monieri / R / 4-16" / fls pink / Alps, Pyrenees   92
    officinalis / P / to 3' / fls bright reddish-purple / most of Eu.   92
    saxicola / HH R / prostrate / white woolly lvs; creamy fls / Morocco   21
    sylvatica / P / 1-4' / fls dull reddish-purple & white / most of Eu.   92

STAPHYLEA - Staphyleaceae
    pinnata / Sh / to 15' / inflated fruit capsules / Eurasia   9
    trifolia / Sh / 6-15' / white fls / e & c North America   9

STATICE bellidifolia - see LIMONIUM bellidifolium   92

STELLARIA - Caryophyllaceae
    graminea / R / 6" / white fls / Europe   9
    pubera / R / to 1' / fls white / New Jersey - Illinois & s-ward   34,83

    (1) - HINTON in Brittonia. 27:3

STENANTHIUM - Liliaceae
  gramineum v. robustum - P, 2½', whitish, greenish, purplish fls, e US34
  occidentale / Bb / 10-20" / fls brown-purple / nw North America   9
  robustum - see S. gramineum v. robustum   34

STERNBERGIA - Amaryllidaceae
  clusiana / Bb / 1' / fls bright golden-yellow / Asia Minor, w Iran 84
  colchiciflora / HH Bb / 3" / pale yellow fls / se Europe 36

STEWARTIA - Theaceae
  koreana / T / 10'+ / white fls / Korea 46
  malacodendron / Sh / 10' / purple-eyed white fls / se United States 46
  pseudocamellia / T / 30'+ / fls white / Japan 46
  pteropetiolata / HH Sh / 10'+ / white fls / Yunnan 46

STILBOCARPA - Araliaceae
  polaris / HH P / to 4' / yellowish fls / New Zealand 10

STIPA - Gramineae
  calamagrostis / P Gr / 3' / violet awns / s Europe 42
  capillata / P Gr / 2-3' / non-plumose awns / Europe 9
  joannis / P Gr / 20-30" / Feather Grass / Altai, w Siberia (1)
  pennata / P Gr / 2½' / bearded awns / Europe, Siberia 42
  pulcherrima / P Gr / 3'+ / pinnate Feather Grass / se Europe 32
  sibirica - Siberian Needle-grass, hardy at North Dakota (2)
  spartea / P Gr / 2-3' / Porcupine Grass / prairies, Pa. to N. Mex. (3)

STOKESIA - Compositae
  'Blue Moon' - see S. laevis 'Blue Moon' 44
  laevis / P / 1-1½' / fls lavender-blue / North America 42
    " 'Alba' - white fls 62
    " 'Blue Moon' - large silvery blue to lilac fls 44
    " 'Caerulea' - light blue fls 10

STRANGWEIA - Liliaceae
  spicata / Bb / 2½" / blue fls / Greece 56

STREPTOCARPUS - Gesneriaceae
  X multiflorus - Gh, to 1', large bluish-purple fls 9

STREPTOPUS - Liliaceae
  amplexifolius / P / 3' / greenish-white fls / Eurasia 35
  roseus / P / 1-2' / fls purple or rose / e United States 35
  streptopoides / R / to 1' / fls in light shades / w N. Am., Far East 60

STRUTHIOPTERIS spicant - see BLECHNUM spicant 9

STYLIDIUM - Stylidiaceae
  graminifolium / HH R / 6-12" / pink fls / Tasmania 38

STYLOPHORUM - Papaveraceae
  diphyllum / R / 1' / golden-yellow fls / North America 42

STYRAX - Styracaceae
  hemsleyana / HH T / 15'+ / white fls / c & w China 46
  japonica / Sh / 15'+ / white fls / Japan, Korea 9

(1) - SUSLOV - Physical Geography of Asiatic Russia. 1961(trans.)
(2) - WEINTRAUB - Grasses Introduced into the United States. 1953
(3) - BRAUN - Vascular Flora of Ohio, Vol. I   1967

STYRAX, con.
  officinalis v. fulvescens - large shrub, white fls, s California   93
  obassia / Sh / 18' / fragrant white fls / Japan   46
  wilsonii / HH Sh / 6-10' / white fls / w China   46

SUCCISA - Dipsaceae
  pratensis / P / 6-32" / fls lilac to dark violet / Caucasus   26

SULLIVANTIA - Saxifragaceae
  oregana / R / 5" / white fls / Gorge of the Columbia River   75
  sullivantii / R / to 1' / white fls / Ohio, Kentucky, Indiana   34

SWERTIA - Gentianaceae
  alpestris / P / 6-24" / dark violet fls / Europe   92
  carolinensis / B / 3-4' / greenish-yellow fls, purple dots / e N. Am 34
  kilimandscharica / HH P / to 3' / white fls / Mt. Kilimandschara   (1)
  perennis / R / 6-12" / dull purple fls / northern hemisphere   38
       "   v. alpestris - see S. alpestris   92
  radiata / P / 3-7' / fls greenish-white, purple dots / Calif.   76

SYMPHORICARPOS - Caprifoliaceae
  albus / Sh / 4' / white frs / e North America   46
     " v. laevigatus - larger frs, 6', Alaska, Calif. to Colorado   47

SYMPHYANDRA - Campanulaceae
  armena / R / 1' / blue-violet fls / Caucasus   35
  cretica / P / 2' / fls dark blue / s Apennines, s Alps   25
  hoffmannii / R / to 12" / fls white / Bosnia   38
  langezura - see S. zanzegura   *
  pendula / R / 1' / creamy-yellow fls / Caucasus   35
  wanneri / R / 6" / tyrian-purple fls / Roumania   38
  zanzeguri / R / to 1' / large violet-blue fls / Caucasus   (2)

SYMPHYTUM - Boraginaceae
  hoffmannii - referable to SYMPHYANDRA hoffmannii   *
  orientale / P / 3' / white fls / Turkey   45

SYMPLOCUS - Styracaceae
  paniculata / Sh or T / to 40' / white fls; blue frs / Far East   9

SYNNOTIA - Iridaceae
  bicolor / HH C / 1½' / fls yellow, tinged violet / South Africa   10
  metelerkampiae - see S. variegata v. metelerkampiae   56
  variegata v. metelerkampiae - 6-8", purple fls spotted orange, S. Af 56

SYNTHYRIS - Scrophulariaceae
  missurica / R / 12" / large purple fls / Columbia R. Gorge & e-ward (3)
       "   stellata - see S. stellata   *
  pinnatifida v. lanuginosa - white tomentose lvs   (3)
  reniformis / R / to 1' / blue or purple fls / Oregon, Washington   35
       "   'Alba' - white fls   *
  rotundifolia - see S. reniformis   (3)
  schizantha / R / 4-12" / purplish fls / Oregon, Washington   76
  stellata / R / to 1' / blue-purple fls / Columbia River Gorge   35
       "   f. alba - fine white form   (3)

  (1) - MABBERLEY in Quar. Bull. Alpine Garden Soc. 39:3
  (2) - SHISHKIN & BOBROV in Flora USSR. Vol. 24 1972(trans.)
  (3) - DAVIDSON in Bull. Am. Rock Garden Soc. 30:1

SYRINGA - Oleaceae
  amurensis / Sh / to 18' / white fls / Manchuria, Korea   46
      "   japonica - see S. reticulata   46
  emodi / Sh / to 10' / pale lilac fls / Himalayas   46
  X henryi - Sh, tall, variable fls, S. josikea x villosa   46
  josikea / Sh / to 10' / deep violet-mauve fls / c & e Europe   46
     " 'Pallida' - fls blue-violet fading white   32
  microphylla / Sh / to 6' / fls rosy-lilac / n & w China   46
  oblata v. giraldii - 10', purplish-violet fls, n China   46
  pekinensis / Sh / to 15' / fls yellowish-white / n China   69
  reticulata / Sh / 10'+ / creamy-white fls, fragrant / Japan   46
  sweginxowii 'Albida' - possible S. sweginzowii x tomentella   (1)
  velutina / Sh / 5-6' / fls pale to pinkish lilac / Korea   46
  vulgaris 'Nana' - dwarf or slow-growing clone   (1)
  wolfii / Sh / 8' / pale violet-purple fls / Korea   46
  yunnanensis / Sh / to 10' / pinkish fls / Yunnan   46

SYRINGODEA luteo-nigra - see ROMULEA longituba v. alticola   56

TALINUM - Portulacaceae
  calycinum / R / 8" / cherry-red fls / Arkansas, Missouri   35
  okanoganense / R / 1½" / white fls / nw North America   35
  parviflorum / R / 10" / rose or lavender fls / Texas to Minnesota   74
  rugospermum / R / to 8" / roseate fls / Indiana, Minnesota   34
  spinescens / R / to 1' / fls magenta-purple / Washington   85
  teretifolium / R / to 1' / rose-purple fls / Georgia to Pennsylvania 72

TAMARIX - Tamaricaceae
  africana / HH Sh / 15' / white or pink fls / Mediterranean coast   65

TANACETUM - Compositae
  boreale - see CHRYSANTHEMUM vulgare   60
  densum / HH R / 9" / yellow fls / Syria, Anatolia   85
     " amanum - see T. haradjanii   *
  haradjanii / R / 9-15" / fls yellow; lvs light gray / Anatolia   85
  pallidum ssp. spathulifolium - high mts. of Spain, fls white or yel. 65
  vulgare / P / 2-3' / yellow fls / Europe, adventive in US   9

TANAKAEA - Saxifragaceae
  radicans / R / 4-12" / fls white / wet shaded rocks, Honshu   60

TARAXACUM - Compositae
  albidum / R / 1' / white fls / Honshu, Shikoku, Kyushu   60
  officinale album - see T. albidum   60

TAXUS - Taxaceae
  baccata / T / to 60' / scarlet fleshy frs / Eu., N. Africa, w Asia   69
     " 'Adpressa' - spreading habit, short lvs   40
     " 'Standishii' - fastigiate, golden yellow lvs   28

TECOMARIA - Bignoniaceae
  capensis / Gh Sh / 6-8' / vermilion fls / South Africa   41

TECOPHILAEA - Amaryllidaceae
  cyanocrocus / HH C / 4" / deep blue fls , white eye / Chile   56

TEESDALIOPSIS - Cruciferae
  conferta / R / to 6" / fls white / nw Spain, n Portugal, in mts.   90

  (1) - WISTER - Lilacs for America. 1943

TELEKIA - Compositae
  speciosa / P / to 6' / yellow fls / Europe & w Asia   9,32

TELEPHIUM - Leguminosae
  imperati / Sh / 6-20" / white fls / s Europe   90

TELINE - Leguminosae
  monspessulanus / HH Sh / 3-5' / yellow fls / Mediterranean region   91

TELLIMA - Saxifragaceae
  grandiflora / P / 18" / greenish fls aging red / Calif. - Alaska   35
      "   'Purpurea' - 1', lvs red, fls yellow   20

TELOPEA - Proteaceae
  speciosissima / Gh Sh / 5-6' / coral fls, red bracts / Australia   41

TEPHROSIA - Leguminosae
  virginiana / P / 1-2' / yellowish-white fls / New Hampshire & s-ward 9

TETRAGONOLOBUS - Leguminosae
  maritimus / P / 4-20" / pale yellow fls / c & s Europe   91
  purpureus / A / 4-16" / crimson fls / s Europe, Ukraine   91

TETRANEMA - Scrophulariaceae
  mexicanum / Gh P / 6-8" / purplish-violet fls / Mexico   41

TEUCRIDIUM - Verbenaceae
  parviflorum / HH Sh / 4'+ / fls blue or white / New Zealand   78

TEUCRIUM - Labiatae
  ackermannii / Sh / 4-6" / soft rose-crimson fls / Asia Minor   38
  ackermerum - error for T. ackermannii?   *
  aroanium / R / procumbent / fls blue or lilac / s Greece, in mts.   92
  hircanicum / P / 1-2' / fls purple or red / Caucasus, Iran   9
  lucidum / Sh / to 2' / fls pale to deep purple / sw Alps   92
  montanum / Sh / 4-10" / cream fls / s & c Europe   92
  polium / Sh / 5-6" / yellow or white fls / Europe, w Asia   38
  pyrenaicum / R / 4-6" / fls mauve & white / s Europe   42
  scordonia / Sh / to 20" / pale greenish-yellow fls / s, w & c Eu.   92
  subspinosum / R / to 8" / bright pink fls / Asia Minor   38

THALICTRUM - Ranunculaceae
  acteaefolium / P / 12-28" / white fls / Japan   60
  alpinum / R / 2-8" / fls purplish-green / arctic Europe   90
  amurense - see T. flavum   (1)
  aquilegifolium / P / 2-3' / fls purplish-pink / Europe, N. America   42
  baicalense / P / 20-32" / creamy-white fls / Far East   60
  chelidonii / R / 12"+ / mauve to violet fls / Himalayas   38
  contortum - see T. aquilegifolium   60
  coreanum / R / 6" / rose-pink fls / Korea   38
  delavayi / P / 2-3' / rosy-violet fls / w China   62
  diffusiflorum / R / 12"+ / mauve to violet fls / se Tibet   38
  dioicum / P / 8-30" / purplish fls / e & c North America   34
  dipterocarpum / P / 2-5' / rosy-mauve fls / w China   62
      "   'Album' - white fls   44
  filamentosum / P / 8-28" / white fls / Amur reg., Manchuria, Korea   60
  flavum / P / 2-5' / whitish fls; yellow stamens / Eurasia   (1)
      " ssp. glaucum - P, to 4', yellow fls, Spain, Portugal   90

(1) - NEVSKII in Flora of the USSR. Vol. VII 1970(trans.)

THALICTRUM, con.
```
  kiusianum / R / 4" / mauve-pink fls / s Japan                        38
  minus / P / to 5' / yellowish fls / Europe                          90
    "   adiantifolium - synonym of the sp.                            62
  occidentale / P / 16-40" / fls whitish or purplish / nw N. America  75
  polycarpum / P / 3' / aromatic lvs / California                      9
  polygamum / P / 3-8' / fls whitish / e North America                 9
  rochebrunianum / P / 2-3' / fls pale purple / Honshu                60
  simplex / P / 8-48" / yellowish fls / most of Europe                90
  speciosissimum - see T. flavum ssp. glaucum                         90
  strictum - see T. simplex                                           90
  tuberosum / P / 8-16" / fls yellowish-white / Pyrenees              90
```

THELYMITRA - Orchidaceae
```
  grandiflora / Gh / 9" / fls in blue shades / Australia              20
  longifolia / P / to 16" / fls white to violet / New Zealand         78
  pauciflora - see T. longifolia                                       9
```

THELYPTERIS - Polypodiaceae
```
  hexagonoptera / F / to 20" / Broad Beech Fern / e North America     50
  phegopteris / F / 1½' / Long Beech Fern / n North America          (1)
  palustris v. pubescens - F, 20", Marsh Fern, e & c North America   (1)
```

THERMOPSIS - Leguminosae
```
  caroliniana / P / 5' / bright yellow fls / North Carolina           35
  chinensis / P / 2' / fls yellow / China                            (2)
  montana / P / 3' / yellow fls / w United States                     35
  villosa / P / 3' / yellow fls / Tennessee, Alabama                  72
```

THERORHODIAN camtschaticum - see RHODODENDRON camtschaticum   69

THLASPI - Cruciferae
```
  alpinum / R / 4-6" / fls white / Alps                               90
  bellidifolium / R / densely caespitose / fls dark purple / Albania  90
  bulbosum / R / 4" / fls dark lilac to violet / Greece               90
  dacicum / R / to 10" / white fls / e & s Carpathians                90
  jankae / R / 4-8" / white fls / Czechoslovakia, Hungary             90
  limosellifolium - see T. rotundifolium                              90
  montanum / R / 4-12" / fls white / c Europe                         90
  rotundifolium / R / 2-4" / fls pale slaty-purple / Alps             42
  stylosum / R / 1" / purplish fls / c & s Apennines                  90
  violascens / A / 8" / fls violet / Turkey                           26
```

THRYPTOMENE - Myrtaceae
```
  paynei - see T. 'Paynes Hybrid'                                     16
  'Paynes Hybrid' - HH Sh, to 4', pink fls, s Australia               16
```

THUJA - Pinaceae
```
  occidentalis / T / 60' / lvs yellowish or bluish-green / e & c N. Am. 9
  plicata / T / to 200' / bright green lvs / Alaska to Montana          9
```

THYMOPHYLLA tenuifolia - see DYSSODIA tenuifolia   (3)

THYMUS - Labiatae
```
  cilicicus / R / 4-6" / pale pink fls / Asia Minor                   38
  doerfleri / R / 1-2½" / pale rose-purple fls / Albania              85
```

(1) - MOHLENBROOK - The Illustrated Flora of Illinois - Ferns. 1967
(2) - STEWARD - Vascular Plants of the Lower Yangtze. 1958
(3) - GOULD - Texas Plants. 1962

THYMUS, con.
　hackeliana - see T. serpyllum v. lanuginosum　　　　　　　　　(1)
　herba-barona / R / to 4" / pale purple fls / Corsica　　　　92
　marschallianus - see T. pannonicus　　　　　　　　　　　　　92
　membranaceus / HH R / dwarf / white fls / Spain　　　　　　35
　pannonicus / R / 4-8" / pale pink to reddish fls / ec & e Europe　92
　quinquecostatus / Sh / prostrate / rose purple fls / Far East　60
　serpyllum / R / creeping / fls in wide range of colors / Eurasia　35
　　　"　　'Albus' - light green lvs; white fls　　　　　　　38
　　　"　　'Coccineus' - bright crimson fls　　　　　　　　42
　　　"　　'Lanuginosus' - gray-green lvs　　　　　　　　　9
　vulgaris / R / 4-12" / fls whitish to pale purple / w Medit. reg.　92

THYSANOTUS - Liliaceae
　multiflorus / Gh / 9" / purple fls / w Australia　　　　　　16

TIARELLA - Saxifragaceae
　cordifolia / R / 10" / white starry fls / e North America　38
　polyphylla / P / 18" / white fls / Asia　　　　　　　　　35
　trifoliata / R / 10" / white fls / w North America　　　35
　　　"　　v. unifoliata - mostly simple lvs　　　　　　47
　triviolata - error for T. trifoliata　　　　　　　　　　*
　unifoliata - see T. trifoliata v. unifoliata　　　　　　47
　wherryi / R / 10" / clumpy plant / e North America　　　35

TIGRIDIA - Iridaceae
　chiapensis / HH C / 12" / fls white & yellow, purple spots / s Mex. 56
　pavonia / HH C / 1-1½' / varii-colored fls / Mexico　　　42

TILIA - Tiliaceae
　oliveri / T / to 60' / small fls; lvs whitish beneath / c China　69

TODEA - Osmundaceae
　superba / F / tall / Tree Fern; fronds to 4' / New Zealand　9

TOFIELDIA - Liliaceae
　alpina - see T. palustris　　　　　　　　　　　　　　　42
　calyculata / R / 6" / yellowish fls / Europe　　　　　　　32
　coccinea / R / to 4" / purplish fls / Siberia to e Greenland　63
　glutinosa / R / 3-20" / fls whitish / e & nc North America　34
　palustris / R / 2-4" / whitish fls / arctic Europe　　　　32

TOLMIEA - Saxifragaceae
　menziesii / P / 1½-2' / green & chocolate fls / nw North America　62

TOONA sinensis - see CEDRELA sinensis　　　　　　　　　　　69

TOWNSENDIA - Compositae
　exscapa / R / low mound / fls white or purplish / Rocky Mts.　35
　　　"　　wilcoxiana - synonym of the sp.　　　　　　　　(2)
　formosa / R / 3" / lilac fls / New Mexico　　　　　　　　38
　grandiflora / B / 10" / white fls / South Dakota to New Mexico　(2)
　hookeri / R / dense cushion / white fls / Colorado & n-ward　(2)
　parryi / R / 8" / purple fls / Wyoming, Idaho & n-ward　　35
　rothrockii / R / cushion / violet-blue fls / w Colorado　(2)
　wilcoxiana - see T. exscapa　　　　　　　　　　　　　(2)

　(1) - REHDER - Bibliography of Cultivated Trees and Shrubs 1949
　(2) - DRESS in Baileya 6:3

TRACHELIUM - Campanulaceae
  caeruleum / HH Sh / 2' / fls in shades of blue / Medit. region   25
  rumelianum / R / 8-10" / lilac-blue fls / Bulgaria, Macedonia   32

TRADESCANTIA - Commelinaceae
  hirsuta / Gh / 1½' / fls bright purple / South America   10
  rosea / P / 8-16" / fls pink or roseate / Florida to N. Carolina   34
  virginiana / P / 1½-2' / fls violet-blue / North America   42

TRAGOPOGON - Compositae
  porrifolius / B / 4' / fls purple, edible root / s Eu., weedy in US   9
  pratensis / B or P / 3' / fls yellow / Europe, weedy in US   9

TRICHOMANES cristata - see ASPLENIUM trichomanes 'Cristata'   (1)

TRICHOSTEMA - Labiatae
  dichotomum / A / 4-32" / blue or pink fls / Mass. to Texas   9

TRICUSPIDARIA hookerianum - see CRINODENDRON hookerianum   46
     "   lanceolata - see CRINODENDRON hookerianum   46

TRICYRTIS - Liliaceae
  bakeri / P / 2-3' / fls yellow, spotted red / Japan   20
  formosana / R / 1' / fls whitish-purple / Formosa   20
· hirta / P / 1-2' / white fls, spotted dark purple / Japan   60
    "   'Alba' - unspotted white fls   (2)
  latifolia / P / 16-32" / yellow fls, purple spots / Japan   60
  macrantha / P / 16-32" / yellow fls / Shikoku   60
  macropoda / P / 1½-2½' / greenish-yellow fls / China, Japan   62
  ohsumiensis 'Takokuma Hototugisu' - 6", yellow fls   33
  stolonifera formosana - see T. formosana   20

TRIENTALIS - Primulaceae
  americana - see T. borealis   34
  borealis / R / 6" / starry white fls / e North America   35

TRIFOLIUM - Leguminosae
  agrarium / A / to 22" / yellow fls, Hop Clover / Eu., weedy in US   34
  alpinum / P / 8-20" / fls pink, purple, cream / Alps   91
  arvense / A or B / 1½-16" / whitish or pink fls / Europe   91
  badium / R / 4-10" / golden yellow fls / c & s Europe   91
     " ssp. rhytidoseminum - 1'+, creamy-white fls, Iran, Turkey   (3)
  incarnatum / A / 8-20" / red, pink, cream, white fls / s & w Eu.   91
  macrocephalum / R / 2-3" / deep rose-pink fls / nw N. America   38
  microcephalum / A / weak-stemmed / fls white to pinkish / nw N. Am.   47
  repens 'Purpurascens' - ground cover with purplish lvs, invasive   17
  rytidoseminum - see T. badium ssp. rytidoseminum   (3)
  stellatum / A / 8" / mostly pink fls / Medit. region   91
  thompsonii / P / 8-20" / fls reddish-lavender to deep orchid / c Wash 76
  virginicum / R / 4" / white fls / Md., W. Va., Va., Pa., in mts.   34

TRILLIUM - Liliaceae
  camtschaticum - see T. kamtschaticum   60
  catesbaei / Tu / 8-20" / pink fls / N. Car., Tenn., Ala., Ga.   72
  cernuum / Tu / 1½ / white or pinkish fls / e North America   84

(1) - WORTH in corres.
(2) - DOWBRIDGE in Bull. Am. Rock Garden Soc. 19:2
(3) - HOSSAIN in Notes from the Roy. Bot. Garden, Edinburgh. 23:3

TRILLIUM, con.
```
  chloropetalum / Tu / 1-1½' / greenish-white fls / nw N. Am.          42
        "      v. giganteum - red fls                                  (1)
        "      rubrum - see T. c. var. giganteum                        *
  erectum / Tu / 1' / varii-colored fls / e North America              84
     "     'Album' - white fls                                          62
     "     v. blandum - creamy fls, not ill-scented, Tenn.             34
  flexipes / Tu / to 2' / white fls / e & c US                         34
  govanianum / Tu / ? / greenish fls / Himalayas                       21
  grandiflorum / Tu / 1-1½' / white fls / e North America              42
        "      'Roseum' - pink fls                                      62
  hibbersonii / Tu / 2-3' / pink fls / Vancouver Island                (2)
  kamtschaticum / Tu / tiny / green & white fls / Far East             21
  luteum / Tu / 6" / greenish-yellow fls / e United States             38
  nivale / Tu / 6" / white fls / Pennsylvania, Minnesota, Missouri      35
  ovatum / Tu / 1' / white fls / California to B. Columbia              9
     "   hibbersonii - see T. hibbersonii                              (2)
  ozarkianum - see T. pusillum v. ozarkianum                           82
  pusillum v. ozarkianum - 4-12", white to pink fls, Ark., Missouri    82
  recurvatum / Tu / 1' / fls brownish-purple / Ga. to Ark. & Minn.     9
  rivale / Tu / 5" / white fls with purple base / Oregon               84
  sessile / Tu / 1½' / white or greenish-yellow fls / N. America       42
     "    'Album' - selection for white fls                             *
     "    v. californicum f. rubrum - fls deep purple-red              9
     "    v. rubrum - see T. s. var. californicum f. rubrum            9
  simile - see T. erectum v. blandum                                   72
  smallii / Tu / 8-16" / petals, if present, purplish / Japan          60
  stylosum - see T. catesbaei                                          (3)
  undulatum / Tu / 1' / white fls blotched crimson / e North America   84
  vaseyi / Tu / 10-20" / fls dark purple / Tennessee, Georgia          34
  viride / Tu / 15" / greenish fls, purple base / Illinois to Ark.     82
```

TRIMEZIA - Iridaceae
```
  martinicensis / HH C / 16" / yellow fls with brown base / W. Indies  56
```

TRIOSTEUM - Caprifoliaceae
```
  aurantiacum / P / 2-4' / red-purple fls; red frs / c N. America      72
```

TRIPETALEIA - Ericaceae
```
  bracteata / Sh / 4'+ / greenish-white-pink fls / Japan               46
```

TRIPTEROSPERMUM - Gentianaceae
```
  japonicum / P / 16-32" / fls light blue-purple / Far East            60
```

TRISTAGMA - Liliaceae
```
  nivalis / Bb / little / fragrant green or purplish fls / Chile       21
```

TRITELEIA - Liliaceae
```
  bridgesii / C / 18" / deep blue-purple fls / n Calif., s Ore.        56
  crocea / C / to 1' / bright yellow fls / nw Calif., sw Ore.          84
  hyacinthina / C / 1-2' / fls blue or white / B. C. to Calif.         56
     "      'Alba' - selection for white fls                            *
  ixioides / C / 8-30" / fls cream to golden yellow / Calif., Ore.     56
     "    'Splendens' - 9", fls yellow, Oregon                         43
  laxa / C / 2-3' / deep blue fls / n Calif., s Ore.                   56
  X tubergenii - 9"+. rich blue-lilac fls                              56
```

(1) - BAGGETT in Bull. Am. Rock Garden Soc. 27:3
(2) - GUPPY in Bull. Am. Rock Garden Soc. 26:4
(3) - SMALL - Manual of the Southeastern Flora. 1933

TRITONIA - Iridaceae
  hyalina / HH C / 15" / fls salmon-pink / Natal   36
  'Roseline' - 2-3', deep pink fls   36
  'Salmon Queen' - salmon-orange fls   36

TROLLIUS - Ranunculaceae
  acaulis / R / 6" / lemon-yellow fls / n India   35
  albiflorus - see T. laxus v. albiflorus   47
  altaicus / P / 1-2' / yellow or pale orange fls / Siberia   62
  asiaticus / P / to 2' / orange fls / ne Russia   90
  chinensis / R / 1' / golden fls / n China   62
  europeus / P / 4-28" / lemon-yellow fls / Europe   90
     "   'Lemon Queen' - 2', very pale yellow fls   62
  'Goldquelle' - 2½', rich yellow-orange fls   85
  hybridus - listed as T. X cultorum   85
  laxus / P / to 2' / fls pale greenish-yellow / e United States 35
    " v. albiflorus - 8-32", fls greenish white or white, w N. Am. 47
  ledebourii / P / 2-3' / deep orange fls / Siberia, China   62
  pumilus / R / to 12" / golden fls / n India, w China   38
     "   yunnanensis - see T. yunnanensis   21
  ranunculinus - see T. ranunculoides   *
  ranunculoides - resembling T. pumilus, China   21
  riederianus / R / to1' / yellow fls / Kuriles, Kamchatka   60
     "   v. japonicus - lvs more deeply cut, Hokkaido, Honshu 60
  yumnanensis / P / 2' / flat buttercup fls / China   62

TROPAEOLEUM - Tropaeolaceae
  pentaphyllum / HH Cl / slender / scarlet fls / South America 32
  peregrinum / A Cl / to 12' / canary-yellow fls / Peru   32
  speciosum / HH P Cl / 12' / scarlet fls / Chile   42
  tricolorum / Gh Cl / 3' / lemon-yellow fls / Chile, Bolivia   41
  tuberosum / HH Tu / to 9' / orange-red fls / Peru   42

TSUGA - Pinaceae
  canadensis / T / 60-100' / small cones / e North America   40

TSUSIOPHYLLUM - Ericaceae
  tanakae / Sh / 10" / white fls / Japan   38

TUBERARIA - Cistaceae
  lignosa / P / to 16" / fls yellow / Mediterranean region   91

TULBAGHIA - Liliaceae
  cepaceae / Gh Bb / 9" / brownish fls / Cape of Good Hope   45
  fragrans - may be the same as T. pulchella   20
  pulchella / Gh / 1½' / violet fls / Transvaal   20

TULIPA - Liliaceae
  acuminata / Bb / 18" / fls light yellow & red / Pyrenees   36
  aucheriana / Bb / 3" / pink fls / n Iran   36
  australis / Bb / to 15" / yellow fls marked red / Europe, c Asia 84
  batalinii / Bb / 6-10" / creamy-yellow fls / Turkestan   84
  biebersteiniana / Bb / 6-12" / yellow fls, violet tinged / c Asia 54
  biflora / Bb / 5-12" / mostly white fls / Caucasus   84
     "   turkestanica - see T. turkestanica   84
  celsiana / Bb / 18" / yellow fls / n Africa   84
  chrysantha - see T. clusiana v. chrysantha   56

TULIPA, con.
  clusiana / Bb / 12-16" / white & pinkish-crimson fls / Iran   42
      "   v. chrysantha - fls all yellow inside, stained red outside   56
      "   v. stellata - white fls, yellow centered   56
  cretica / Bb / small / white fls flushed red / Crete   84
  dasystemon - see T. tarda   42
  eichleri / Bb / 12-18" / brilliant scarlet fls / Turkestan   42
  florenskyi / Bb / 4-8" / red or yellow fls / Caucasus   54
  fosteriana / Bb / 12-18" / vermilion-scarlet fls / c Asia   84
  greigii / Bb / to 2' / crimson-scarlet fls / Turkestan   84
  humilis / Bb / 3" / fls in pink-magenta shades / Iran   84
  iliensis / Bb / 4-12" / yellow fls, tinged violet / c Asia   54
  kaufmanniana / Bb / 6-15" / yellow or white fls / c Asia   84
  kopalkowskiana / Bb / 1' / yellow or pink fls / e Turkestan   42
  linifolia / Bb / 6-12" / scarlet fls / Turkestan   42
  maximowiczii / Bb / to 1' / scarlet fls / Bokhara   84
  montana / Bb / 9-12" / cherry-red fls / n Iran   84
  oculis-solis / Bb / 12-16" / scarlet, green & brown fls / s Europe   32
  orphanidea v. pontica - Bulgarian form of a variable tulip   (1)
  ostrowskiana / Bb / 1' / scarlet fls / e Turkestan   84
  persica - see T. celsiana   32
  polychroma / Gh Bb / 6" / starry white fls / Near East   36
  praestans / Bb / 12" / pillar-box red fls / c Asia   42
  primulina / Bb / 12" / fragrant primrose-yellow fls / e Algeria   36
  pulchella / Bb / 4" / pinkish-crimson fls / Asia Minor   84
      "   humilis - see T. humilis   56
  saxatilis / Bb / to 1' / pinkish lilac-magenta fls / Crete   84
  sharonensis / HH Bb / 3" / crimson fls / Iran to Syria   10
  sprengeri / Bb / 14-18" / bright scarlet fls, bronzy outer / Turkey   56
  stellata - see T. clusiana v. atellata   56
      "   chrysantha - see T. clusiana v. chrysantha   56
  sylvestris / Bb / to 1' / yellow fls, green tinted outer / Europe   56
      "   'Tabriz' - free-flowering form from n Iran   56
  tarda / Bb / 6-8" / creamy star-like fls / Turkestan   42
  thracica - see T. orphanidea v. pontica   (2)
  turkestanica / Bb / to 1' / fls creamy-white / Turkestan   42
  urumiensis / Bb / 9" / starry fls, butter-yellow / nw Iran   84
  violacea / Bb / 4-8" / cerise-violet fls / Iran, Kurdistan   42

TUNICA - Caryophyllaceae
  nanteuilii - see PETRORHAGIA nanteuilii   90
  proligera - see PETRORHAGIA prolifera   90
  saxifraga - see PETRORHAGIA saxifraga   90

TUSSILAGO - Compositae
  farfara / P / low / yellow fls in early spring / Eu., escape in US   34

TWEEDIA caerulea - see OXYPETALUM caerulea   32

ULEX - Leguminosae
  minor / Sh / dwarf / golden-yellow fls / sw Europe   46

UMBELLULARIA - Myrtaceae
  californica / HH T / 20-30' / dark purple frs / Oregon   46

  (1) - STOYANOFF & STEFANOFF - Flora of Bulgaria. 1943
  (2) - HALL - The Genus Tulipa. 1940

UMBILICUS - Crassulaceae
  aizoon - see ROSULARIA aizoon   26
  rupestris / P / 8-20" / straw-colored fls / s & w Europe   90

UNGERNIA - Liliaceae
  ferganica / Bb / 4-8" / pale ochreous fls, purple tipped / c Asia   54

URGINEA - Liliaceae
  maritima / Gh Bb / 1-3' / white fls / circum-Mediterranean   64

UROSPERMUM - Compositae
  dalechampii / P / 12-20" / yellow fls / Medit. region   32

URSINIA - Compositae
  chrysanthemoides geyeri - see U. geyeri   85
  geyeri / Gh / dwarf / bright red & purple fls / Cape Province   85

UVULARIA - Liliaceae
  grandiflora / P / 18" / pale yellow fls / e North America   38
  perfoliata / P / 15" / paler yellow fls / e North America   35
  sessilifolia / R / 10" / pale greenish-yellow fls / e North America 35
        "   'Variegata' - lvs marked white   *

VACCINIUM - Ericaceae
  delavayi / HH Sh / small / frs dark crimson / w China   69
  glauco-album / HH Sh / 4' / frs dark blue / Sikkim   42
  membranaceum / Sh / to 4½' / black frs / Mich. to Ore. & B. C.   69
  moupinense / Sh / dwarf / frs purplish-black / w China   46
  nummularia / HH Sh / small / fls rose-red to pinkish / Himalayas   69
  ovatum / HH Sh / 2-8' / frs black / California   46
  parviflorum - error fro V. parvifolium   *
  parvifolium / Sh / 6-12' / frs red / Alaska & southward   46
  vitis-idaea / Sh / 6" / frs red / northern hemisphere   42

VALERIANA - Valerianaceae
  celtica / R / 4-5" / brownish-yellow fls, aromatic / Alps of Eu.   33
  fonkii / HH R / mats / pale pink or lilac fls / Argentina   21
  moyanoi / HH R / flat rosettes / yellow fls / Argentina   21
  scouleri / P / 1-2' / white fls / California to Alaska   76
  sitchensis / P / 1-4' / white fls / Calif., Alaska, Montana   76
  supina / R / 4-6" / pink fls / e Alps   96

VALLOTA - Amaryllidaceae
  purpurea - see V. speciosa   41
  speciosa / Gh Bb / 2' / fls scarlet-red / South Africa   42

VANCOUVERIA - Berberidaceae
  chrysantha / R / 8-12" / soft yellow fls / Oregon, California   38
  hexandra / R / 10" / white fls / Washington to California   35
  planipetala / R / 9" / white fls / Oregon, California   35

VELTHEIMIA - Liliaceae
  bracteata / Gh Bb / ? / red-flecked yellow fls / South Africa   32
  capensis - in cultivation is V. viridifolia   41
  glauca / Gh Bb / 15" / white fls / Cape Province   36
  viridifolia / Gh Bb / 1½' / purple fls / South Africa   85

VERATRUM - Liliaceae
  album / P / 3-4' / yellowish-white fls / Europe, N. Africa   62
    " lobellianum - see V. lobelianum   54

VERATRUM, con.
californicum / P / 3-6' / greenish bell-shaped fls / w US   62
grandiflorum / P / 3-4½' / fls greenish-white / Japan   60
lobelianum / P / 2-5' / yellowish-green fls / Eurasia   54
nigrum / P / 3' / fls blackish-purple / s Europe, Asia   32
stamineum / P / 20-40" / white fls / Hokkaido, Honshu   60
viride / P / 2-5' / green fls / North America   62

VERBASCUM - Scrophulariaceae
acaule / R / 4" / bright yellow fls / Greece, in high mts.   92
   " 'Alba' - fls white   *
arcturus / HH P / 1-2' / yellow fls / Crete   92
banaticum / B / 20-40" / yellow fls / se Europe   92
blattaria / B / 1-4' / yellow fls / Europe   92
   "   f. albiflorum - the rarely white form   62
   "   alba - see V. b. forma albiflorum   *
bombyciferum / P / 4-6' / golden fls, felted lvs / Asia Minor   62
bugulifolium / P / 8-30" / yellowish fls / Turkey, Bulgaria   92
chaixii / P / 20-40" / yellow fls / s, c & e Europe   92
   " 'Album' - white fls   62
'Cotwold Gem' - see V. hybridum 'Cotwold Gem'   62
creticum / HH B / to 5' / yellowish fls / w Mediterranean region   92
dumulosum / R / 6-10" / fls bright yellow / Asia Minor   42
georgicum / B / to 5' / yellow fls / Turkey-in-Eu., Caucasus   92
graecum / B / to 5' / yellow fls, whitish lvs / s Balkan Penin.   92
heldreichii - see V. banaticum   92
hybridum 'Cotswold Gem' - 3-4', soft amber fls, purple centers   62
nigrum / P / 20-40" / fls yellow / Europe   92
   " 'Album' - white-flowered form   44
olympicum / B / 5-6' / golden fls / s Europe   95
pestalozzae / R / to 8" / yellow fls / Asia Minor   32
phoeniceum / P / 1-3' / violet fls / se & ec Europe   92
roripifolium / B / to 5' / metallic-bronze fls / s Bulgaria   92
thapsus / B / 1-6' / yellow fls / Europe   92
wiedmannianum / B / 3' / indigo-blue to violet fls / Asia Minor   32

VERBENA - Verbenaceae
bipinnatifida / P / 6-18" / fls lilac or purple / S. Dak. to Mexico 35
bonariensis / P gr as A / 4'+ / fls reddish-purple / Brazil   74
canadensis / P / 6-18" / rosy-purple fls / Okla., Kan., Colorado   76
hastata / P / 3-5' / violet fls / North America   62
peruviana / P gr as A / 4-6" / scarlet to pink fls / South America 90
rigida / P gr as A / 1½-2' / fls violet-purple / Argentina   42

VERNONIA - Compositae
noveboracensis / P / 6-7' / fls blue-purple / Mass. & Ohio to Ga.   71

VERONICA - Scrophulariaceae
alpina / R / 6" / fls blue / Eurasia   35
   " 'Alba' - white form, 6-8"   44
aphylla / R / procumbent / fls deep blue / c & n Europe   92
armena / R / low mound / fls azure-blue / Armenia, in mts.   (1)
austriaca / P / 10-20" / bright blue fls / e, ec & se Europe   92
balfouriana - see HEBE balfouriana   2
bellidioides / R / to 8" / fls lilac to violet-blue / Pyrenees   92
bidwellii - see PARAHEBE bidwellii   43
bombycina / HH R / neat tuffet / reddish fls; woolly lvs / Syria   33
bonarota - see PAEDEROTA bonarota   92

(1) - De WOLF in Baileya 4:4

VERONICA, con.
  catarractae - see PARAHEBE catarractae   46
  densiflora / R / to 6" / large pale blue fls / Altai Mts.   29
  densifolia - error for V. densiflora?   *
  epacridea - see HEBE epacridea   2
  forrestii / R / 6-15" / fls reddish / Yunnan   9
  fruticans / R / 6" / clear blue fls / nw Europe   35
  fruticulosa / R / 6" / veined pink fls / Europe, in mts.   38
  gentianoides / P / 1-1½' / fls light blue / Caucasus   42
  grandiflora / R / to 4" / blue-purple fls / w Aleutian Islands   (1)
  grandis v. holophylla - 3', glossy coriaceous lvs, blue fls, Japan   (2)
  X guthrieana - see HEBE X guthrieana   *
  holophylla - see V. grandis v. holophylla   (2)
  hookeriana - see PARAHEBE hookeriana   *
  incana / P / 1' / fls dark blue / Russia   42
     "   'Wendy' - lavender-blue fls   85
  longifolia / P / 2' / lilac-blue fls / n, e & c Europe   44
  lycopodioides - see HEBE lycopodioides   46
  macrantha - see HEBE macrantha   46
  nipponica / R / to 4" / fls pale blue-purple / Honshu   60
  nivea - see PARAHEBE hookeriana   *
  nummularia / R / procumbent / fls blue or pink / Pyrenees   92
  perfoliata - see HEBE perfoliata   *
  pirolaeformis / R / short / fls rose or pale violet / China   9
  prostrata / R / 2-8" / fls deep blue / Eurasia   44
     "   'Heavenly Blue' - sapphire-blue fls   44
     "   'Spode Blue' - clear pale china-blue fls   38
  pyrolaeformis - see V. pirolaeformis   9
  repens / R / 4" / fls pink / Corsica, Sardinia   92
  rupestris - see V. prostrata   42
     "   nana - see V. prostrata   *
  saturejoides / R / flat creeper / clear blue fls / Balkans   35
  schmidtiana / R / 4-10" / fls pale blue-purple / n Japan   60
  selleri - error for V. stelleri   *
  serpyllifolia / R / to 8" / fls white or pale blue / Europe   92
  spicata / P / 12-16" / blue-lilac fls / Europe   32
     "   'Nana' - 6", lavender-blue fls   35
     "   'Rosea' - fls purplish-pink   32
     "   'Wendy' - see V. incana 'Wendy'   87
  stelleri / R / 3-14" / blue fls / e Asia, se Alaska   (3)
  surculosa / R / 3" / white fls, purplish-eyed / Asia Minor   32
  turrilliana / R / to 16" / deep blue fls / e Balkan Penin.   92
  wormskioldii stelleri - see V. stelleri   (3)

VERONICASTRUM - Scrophulariaceae
  virginicum / P / to 6' / fls white or purplish / e North America   34

VESICARIA graeca - see ALYSSOIDES graeca   90
     "   utriculata - see ALYSSOIDES utriculata   90

VESTIA - Solanaceae
  lycioides / Gh Sh / 3' / fls pale yellow / Chile   20

VIBURNUM - Caprifoliaceae
  acerifolium / Sh / to 6' / frs red to blackish / e North America   46
  X carlcephalum - V. carlesii X macrocephalum   46

  (1) - WHITE, ed. - The Alaska-Yukon Wild Flowers Guide. 1974
  (2) - De WOLF in Baileya 4:4
  (3) - ANDERSON - Flora of Alaska. 1959

VIBURNUM, con.
```
  cassinoides / Sh / 6-10' / red, blue to black frs / e N. America         46
  dentatum / Sh / 10' / frs blue-black / e North America                   46
  ellipticum / Sh / 6'+ / fls whitish; frs blackish / Calif. to Wash.      69
  farreri / Sh / to 10' / frs red / n China                                46
  furcatum / Sh / 10'+ / frs red to black / Japan, Korea                   46
  lentago / Sh / 15'+ / frs blue-black / e North America                   46
  opulus / Sh / 10'+ / white fls; red frs / Eurasia                        46
      "    'Xanthocarpum' - golden yellow frs                              46
  plicatum 'Lanarth' - strong growth, less horizontal than type           46
  prunifolium / Sh / 18' / frs blue-black / e North America                46
  recognitum / Sh / 3-9' / the northern Arrowwood / ne N. America          34
  rhytidophyllum / Sh / red to black frs / c & w China                     46
  sieboldii / Sh / 15' / pink to blue-black frs / Japan                    46
  trilobum / Sh / 10'+ / red persistent frs / n North America              46
  wrightii / Sh / 6'+ / glistening red frs / Far East                      46
```

VICIA - Leguminosae
```
  crocea / P / 20-32" / fls bright orange-yellow / Caucasus, Iran         (1)
  onobrychoides / P / 2' / purple fls / s Europe                           45
  pyrenaica / R / to 1' / fls bright violet-purple / Spain                 91
  sylvatica / P / 2-5' / fls white, purple-veined / n, c & e Europe        91
  unijuga / R / 12'+ / brilliant blue fls / Siberia                        33
```

VINCETOXICUM - Asclepiadaceae
```
  hirundinaria / P / to 4', twining / fls white or yellow / Europe         92
  officinale - see T. hirundinaria                                         92
```

VIOLA - Violaceae
```
  adunca / R / low / violet to deep purple fls / w North America           35
  aetolica / R / 6-20" / yellow fls / Balkans                              91
  alba / R / 2-6" / fragrant white or violet fls / s Europe                91
  albanica - see V. magellensis                                           91
  alpina / R / to 4" / violet fls / ne Alps, Carpathians                   91
  appalachiensis / R / 2½" / fls pale to deep violet / West Virginia       83
  arborescens / R / 4-8" / fls whitish or pale violet / w Medit. reg.      91
  arenaria - see V. rupestris                                             21
      "    rosea - see V. rupestris 'Rosea'                                *
  'Arkwright's Ruby' - 6", deep ruby-crimson with black blotch            85
  arvensis / A / to 16" / fls cream, yellow, bluish-violet / Europe        91
  beckwithii / R / 3" / purple fls / w North America                       38
  bertolonii / R / to 1' / fls violet or yellow / Maritime Alps            91
      "    corsica - see V. corsica                                       91
  biflora / R / to 8" / yellow fls / Europe, in mts.                       91
  blanda / R / 2-4" / white fls, purple veins / e North America            12
  'Bowles Black' - see Viola tricolor 'E. A. Bowles'                      (2)
  brevistipulata / R / to 1' / yellow fls / n & c Japan, in high mts.      60
  calcarata / R / 2" / fls violet or yellow / Alps                         91
  canadensis / R / 1' / white & lavender fls / North America               35
  canina / R / 4-16" / fls blue / Europe                                   91
  chaerophylloides - see V. dissecta v. chaerophylloides                  60
  cenisia / R / 2" / fls bright violet / sw Alps                           91
  conspersa / R / 3½-6" / fls pale violet to whitish / e N. America        12
  cornuta / R / 8-12" / fragrant lilac or violet fls / Pyrenees            91
      "    'Alba' - white fls                                             35
      "    'Minor' - 2-3", clear blue fls, Pyrenees                       38
```

(1) - SHISHKIN & BOBROV - Flora of the USSR. Vol. 13 1972(trans.)
(2) - ALLAN - E. A. Bowles & his Garden. 1973

VIOLA, con.

```
corsica / R / 4-8" / violet fls / Corsica, Sardinia                     91
cotyledon ssp. lologensis - loose growth, fls white, deep blue, S. Am.21
crassa / R / to 5" / fls deep yellow / n Japan in alpine regions        60
cucullata / R / tufted / blue-violet fls, invasive / e & c N. Am.       34
    "     'Freckles' - see V. papilionacea 'Freckles'                  (1)
cuneata / R / 5" / white & purple fls / California, Oregon              76
cunninghamii / R / 6" / white fls / New Zealand                        78
curtisii - see V. tricolor ssp. curtisii                               91
dissecta v. chaerophylloides - finely dissected lvs; fls purple, Jap.  60
    "            "         f. eizanensis - purplish fls                 60
    "            "            "     'Alba' - white fls                  38
douglasii / R / 4" / light golden-yellow fls / California, Oregon       76
dubyana / R / 4" / violet fls / Italian Alps                           91
eizanensis - see V. dissecta v. chaerophylloides f. eizanensis         60
    "     'Alba' - see V. dissecta var. c. forma e. 'Alba'              *
elatior / P / to 20" / fls pale blue / c & e Europe                    91
elegantula / R / to 1' / fls violet & yellow / Albania, Jugoslavia     91
escondidaensis - South American, densely leafy stems                   21
eugeniae / R / compact / fls yellow or violet / Apennines              91
fimbriatula / R / small / violet-purple fls / e & c North America      71
glabella / R / 8" / yellow fls / Colorado                              33
gracilis / R / to 1' / fls violet or yellow / Balkans                  91
    "    'Alba' - white fls                                            95
    "    'Lord Nelson' - fls deeper in color                           62
grypoceris / R / to 1' / fls pale violet, inodorous / Japan            60
hallii / R / 4" / fls purple & cream / California, Oregon              35
hederacea / R / 2-3" / purple & white fls / Australia                  33
hirtipes / R / to 6" / fls pale rose-purple / Japan, in mts.           60
hispida / R / to 10" / fls violet or yellowish / nw France             91
japonica / R / 3" / fls purple / Japan, s Korea, in lowlands           60
jooii / R / 4-12" / fragrant reddish fls / Roumania                    91
kitaibeliana v. rafinesquii - A, 4"+, bluish-white fls, Eurasia        34
labradorica / R / 4-6" / lilac fls, purplish lvs / n N. America        62
    "     purpurea - characteristic of the species                     *
lanceolata / R / small / white fls / e North America                   34
langsdorffii / R / 2-9" / deep to light violet fls / Alaska            12
lobata / R / 4" / fls deep lemon-yellow / California, Oregon           76
lutea / R / 8"+ / fls parti-colored yellow & violet / w Europe         91
lyallii / R / 6" / white fls, purple veined / New Zealand              78
macedonica - see V. tricolor ssp. macedonica                          91
maculata / R / ? / golden yellow fls / Falklands                      21
magellensis / R / 2-4" / violet or pink fls / Greece                   91
mandschurica / R / ? / deep violet fls / Manchuria                    21
nigra 'Bowles Black' - see V. tricolor 'E. A. Bowles'                  *
nuttallii / R / 2-4" / deep lemon-yellow fls / c North America        12
    "     praemorsa - see V. praemorsa                                (2)
odorata / R / to 6" / fls dark violet or white / Europe               91
orbiculata / R / clump / yellow fls / B. C. to Ore. & Mont.           74
pallens / R / to 3½" / white fls / North America                      12
palmata / R / 3-5" / blue-violet fls / e & c United States            12
papilionacea / R / 3-6" / rich violet fls / ne United States          34
    "     'Freckles' - white fls, blue spotted                        (1)
pedata / R / 4-5" / deep & light purple fls / e North America         38
    " bicolor - is the first-named form above, hence the type         34
```

(1) - SCORGIE in Bull. Am. Rock Garden Soc. 11:2
(2) - BAKER in Brittonia 9:4

VIOLA, con.
```
  pedatifida / R / to 10" / fls soft reddish-violet / c North America    12
  pedunculata / R / 2-5" / orange-yellow fls / w & s California          76
  pensylvanica / R / 8-12" / yellow fls / e North America                34
  pinnata / R / 4" / fragrant pale violet fls / Alps                     91
  praemorsa / R / 3" / deep lemon-yellow fls / California to B. C.        12
  primulifolia / R / 3" / fls white / e North America                    73
  pubescens / R / 8-12" / lemon-yellow fls, striped purple / ne N. Am.    12
  pumilio / R / 2" / small white fls / Japan, on sunny hills             60
  reichenbachiana 'Rosea' - 6", pink-violet fls, Europe                   *
  rossii / R / to 10" / fls pale rose-purple / Far East, in mts.         60
  rostrata / R / 4-8" / pale lavender-violet fls / e North America       12
  rotundifolia / R / to 6" / deep lemon-yellow fls / e United States     12
  rupestris / R / 4" / fls reddish-violet to white / Europe              91
       'Rosea' - selection for pink fls                                   21
  sagittata / R / 4-6" / violet fls / e North America                    38
  saxatilis - see V. tricolor ssp. subalpina                             91
       "     aetolica - see V. aetolica                                   91
       "     macedonica - see V. tricolor v. macedonica                  91
  sempervirens / R / 8" / lemon-yellow fls / Calif. to Vancouver Is.     12
  septentrionalis / R / 6" / violet fls, varying lighter / e N. Am.      12
  sheltonii / R / 6" / lemon-yellow & brown fls / nw United States       12
  sororia / R / to 6" / violet or lavender fls / e North America         34
  stojanowii / R / 4" / fls yellow / s Bulgaria, n Greece                91
  striata / P / 1-2' / fls ivory-white or cream / N. Y. & Minn. to Ga.   12
  sylvestris rosea - see V. reichenbachiana 'Rosea'                      91
  tricolor / A / 8" / fls blue-violet / Europe                           42
       "  'Bowles Black' - see V. t. 'E. A. Bowles'                      (1)
       "  ssp. curtisii - P, to 6", fls variously-colored, w Europe      91
       "  'E. A. Bowles' - B, velvety blackish fls                      (1)
       "  ssp. macedonica - R, violet & yellow fls, Balkans              91
       "  ssp. subalpina - R, sometimes B, to 1', s & c Eu., in mts.     91
  variegata / R / 6" / pale violet fls / Siberia                         33
  verecunda v. yakusimana - R, 1", white fls, Kyushu, in high mts.       60
  volcanica / HH R / 3" rosette / small blue fls; fleshy lvs / S. Am.    21
  yakusimana - see V. verecunda v. yakusimana                            60
  yubariana / R / 2" / yellow fls / Hokkaido                             60
```

VISCARIA alpina - see LYCHNIS alpina   90
```
       "      "  'Alba' - see LYCHNIS alpina 'Alba'                       *
       "      atropurpurea - see LYCHNIS viscaria ssp. atropurpurea       90
       "      viscosa - see LYCHNIS viscaria                              90
       "         "  albiflora - see LYCHNIS viscaria 'Alba'               44
       "         "  atropurpurea - see LYCHNIS viscaria spp. atropurpurea 90
       "      vulgaris - see LYCHNIS viscaria                             90
```

VITTADINIA - Compositae
```
  australis / R / to 1' / white-rayed fls / Australia, New Zealand       32
```

WAHLENBERGIA - Campanulaceae
```
  albomarginata / R / 6" / fls blue to white / New Zealand               25
  consimilis / P / 8-30" / fls dark blue / Australia                     20
  dalmatica - see EDRAIANTHUS dalmaticus                                  *
  graminifolia - see EDRAIANTHUS graminifolius                           29
  hederacea / R / prostrate / light blue fls / Europe, England           38
  marginata / A or P / 15" / blue fls / New Zealand                      11
  pumilio / R / 2" / lavender fls / Balkans                              38
  pygmaea / HH R / ½" / large white or bluish fls / New Zealand           2
```

(1) - ALLAN - E. A. Bowles & his Garden. 1973

WAHLENBERGIA, con.
```
  saxicola / R / 3-4" / bright light blue fls / Tasmania          33
  tasmanica / R / 3" / fls sky-blue to white / Tasmania           25
```

WALDSTEINIA - Rosaceae
```
  sibirica - see W. ternata                                       60
  ternata / R / creeping / white fls / Siberia, Japan             60
```

WATSONIA - Iridaceae
```
  beatricis / HH C / 3' / pure white fls / Cape Province          84
  marginata / HH C / 3-4' / rose to lilac-pink fls / South Africa 84
  pillansii / HH C / 4' / orange-red fls / e Cape Province        84
  socium / HH C / 16-20" / reddish-gold fls / Natal               37
  wilmaniae / HH C / to 4' / rose- or lilac-purple fls / Cape Province 84
```

WELWITSCHIA - Welwitschiaceae
```
  bainesii - see W. mirabilis                                     32
  mirabilis - African desert plant of botanical interest          32
```

WERNERIA - Compositae
```
  nubigena / R / mats / white daisies, often pink-backed / S. Am. 21
```

WOODSIA - Polypodiaceae
```
  alpina / F / 2-6" / high mountain fern / England, Wales         50
  ilvensis / R / 2-6" / easily raised from spores / Gt. Britain, in mts 50
  mexicana / F / 3-7" / masses of sori / Chisos Mts., Mexico      (1)
  obtusa / R / 6-12" / gray-green fronds / North America          50
  polystichoides / F / 9" / tufted habit / Japan                  20
```

WULFENIA - Scrophulariaceae
```
  amherstiana / R / 4-8" / dull blue fls / Himalayas              32
  baldaccii / R / 8" / bright blue fls / n Albania                92
  carinthiaca / P / 12-18" / deep purple fls / e Europe, in mts.  35
     "       'Alba' - white fls                                    *
```

WYETHIA - Compositae
```
  helianthoides / P / 8-32" / white or creamy fls / c Oregon, Nevada  76
```

XERANTHEMUM - Compositae
```
  annuum / A / 1-2' / rosy-red fls / s Europe                     32
```

XEROPHYLLUM - Liliaceae
```
  asphodeloides / P / to 4½' / showy white fls / New Jersey to Ga. 34
  tenax / P / 2-5' / ivory fls / Rocky Mts. & west-ward           35
```

YUCCA - Liliaceae
```
  aloifolia / HH P / 12'+ / white fls / North Carolina to W. Indes 32
  filamentosa / Sh / 4-12' / white-threaded lvs / se United States 42
  glauca / P / 3-5' / greenish-white fls / South Dakota to N. Mexico 46
  rupicola / HH Sh / 20" / Twisted-leaf Yucca / c Texas           32
  schottii / HH Sh / to 12' / white fls / se Arizona, New Mexico  (2)
```

```
(1) - McDOUGALL & SPERRY - Plants of Big Bend Nat. Park.  1951
(2) - WEBBER - Yuccas of the South-west.  1953
```

ZANTEDESCHIA - Araceae
  aethiopica / HH Tu / to 3' / white dpathes / South Africa   84

ZAUSCHNERIA - Onagraceae
  arizonica / HH P / 2' / fls scarlet / Arizona   10
  californica / HH R / to 1' / scarlet fls / California, Mexico   38
      "   'Dublin' - selection for early-flowering   6
      "   v. latifolia - somewhat wider-leaved, more herbaceous   46
      "   "   'Alba' - white fls   *
  'Dublin' - see Z. californica 'Dublin'   6
  latifolia 'Alba' - see Z. californica v. latifolia 'Alba'   *

ZENOBIA - Ericaceae
  pulverulenta / Sh / 2-4' / white fls / North Carolina to Florida   46

ZEPHYRANTHES - Amaryllidaceae
  'Ajax' - HH Bb, creamy-sulphur fls, Z. citrina X candida   56
  atamasco / HH Bb / 10" / white & pink fls / Missouri to Florida   84
  candida / HH Bb / 4-8" / white fls, shaded green / Argentina, Uru.   56
  carinata / HH Bb / 1' / pink fls / West Indies   (1)
  citrina / HH Bb / 6" / golden yellow fls in autumn / West Indies?   56
  concolor / HH Bb / 14"+ / yellow fls / Mexico   (2)
  drummondii / Bb / ? / white fls / Texas, New Mexico   73
  grandiflora - see Z. carinata   32
  macrosiphon / HH Bb / 12" / bright red fls / Mexico   37
  verecunda / HH Bb / 8" / white fls / Mexico, in mts.   84

ZIGADENUS - Liliaceae
  elegans / P / to 3' / fls creamy-white / Alaska to Iowa   34
  fremontii / P / 12-16" / fls greenish-white / w North America   85
      "   v. minor - 4-8", fls white   59
  gramineus / P / 8-15" / pale yellow fls / c Canada   19
  venenosus / P / 1-2' / fls white / B.C. & Utah to Baja California   74

ZINNIA - Compositae
  elegans pumila - 1', the dwarf annual zinnia   89
  grandiflora / R / to 8" / yellow fls / Kansas to Texas   74

ZIZIA - Umbelliferae
  aperta - error for Z. aptera   *
  aptera / P / 1-2' / small yellow fls / North Dakota to Oklahoma   76
  aurea / P / to 3' / Golden Alexanders / e North America   34

ZYGOPHYLLUM - Zygophyllaceae
  atriplicoides / P / 3' / yellow fls / America   45
  fabago / HH P / 1-4' / yellow fls, coppery at base / Syria   `29